Middle School 3-2

중간고사 완벽대비

적중100

영어 기출 문제집

중3

천재 | 정사열

Best Collection

구성과 특징

교과서의 주요 학습 내용을 중심으로 학습 영역별 특성에 맞춰 단계별로 다양한 학습 기회를 제공하여
단원별 학습능력 평가는 물론 중간 및 기말고사 시험 등에 완벽하게 대비할 수 있도록 내용을 구성

Words & Expressions

Step1 Key Words 단원별 핵심 단어 설명 및 풀이
Key Expression 단원별 핵심 숙어 및 관용어 설명
Word Power 반대 또는 비슷한 뜻 단어 배우기
English Dictionary 영어로 배우는 영어 단어

Step2 실력평가 단원별 수시평가 대비 주관식, 객관식 문제풀이

Step3 서술형 대비 학업성취도 및 수행능력평가 대비 서술형 문제풀이

Conversation

Step1 핵심 의사소통 소통에 필요한 주요 표현 방법 요약
핵심 Check 기본적인 표현 방법 및 활용능력 확인

Step2 대화문 익히기 교과서 대화문 심층 분석 및 확인

Step3 교과서 확인학습 빈칸 채우기를 통한 문장 완성 능력 확인

Step4 기본평가 시험대비 기초 학습 능력 평가

Step5 실력평가 단원별 수시평가 대비 주관식, 객관식 문제풀이

Step6 서술형 대비 학업성취도 및 수행능력평가 대비 서술형 문제풀이

Grammar

Step1 주요 문법 단원별 주요 문법 사항과 예문을 알기 쉽게 설명
핵심 Check 기본 문법사항에 대한 이해 여부 확인

Step2 기본평가 시험대비 기초 학습 능력 평가

Step3 실력평가 단원별 수시평가 대비 주관식, 객관식 문제풀이

Step4 서술형 대비 학업성취도 및 수행능력평가 대비 서술형 문제풀이

Reading

Step1 구문 분석 단원별로 제시된 문장에 대한 구문별 분석과 내용 설명
확인문제 문장에 대한 기본적인 이해와 인지능력 확인

Step2 확인학습A 빈칸 채우기를 통한 문장 완성 능력 확인

Step3 확인학습B 제시된 우리말을 영어로 완성하여 작문 능력 키우기

Step4 실력평가 단원별 수시평가 대비 주관식, 객관식 문제풀이

Step5 서술형 대비 학업성취도 및 수행능력평가 대비 서술형 문제풀이
교과서 구석구석 교과서에 나오는 기타 문장까지 완벽 학습

Composition

|영역별 핵심문제|
단어 및 어휘, 대화문, 문법, 독해 등 각 영역별 기출문제의 출제 유형을 분석하여 실전에 대비하고 연습할 수 있도록 문제를 배열

|단원별 예상문제|
기출문제를 분석한 후 새로운 시험 출제 경향을 더하여 새롭게 출제될 수 있는 문제를 포함하여 시험에 완벽하게 대비할 수 있도록 준비

|서술형 실전 및 창의사고력 문제|
학교 시험에서 점차 늘어나는 서술형 시험에 집중 대비하고 고득점을 취득하는데 만전을 기하기 위한 학습 코너

|단원별 모의고사|
영역별, 단계별 학습을 모두 마친 후 실전 연습을 위한 모의고사

on the textbook

교과서 파헤치기

- 단어Test1~3 영어 단어 우리말 쓰기, 우리말을 영어 단어로 쓰기, 영영풀이에 해당하는 단어와 우리말 쓰기
- 대화문Test1~2 대화문 빈칸 완성 및 전체 대화문 쓰기
- 본문Test1~5 빈칸 완성, 우리말 쓰기, 문장 배열연습, 영어 작문하기 복습 등 단계별 반복 학습을 통해 교과서 지문에 대한 완벽한 습득
- 구석구석지문Test1~2 지문 빈칸 완성 및 전문 영어로 쓰기

이책의 차례 # Contents

Lesson 5

Pictures Speak a Thousand Words

 의사소통 기능

- 궁금증 표현하기
  I'm curious about that balloon.

- 정의하기
  It means you must not enter.

 언어 형식

- 가정법 과거
  I **would** be so happy **if** you **were** with me.

- 관계대명사 whose
  It was written in 1973 by a woman **whose** husband was far away.

Words & Expressions

Key Words

- □ **ad**(= advertisement)[æd] 명 광고
- □ **awesome**[ɔ́ːsəm] 형 근사한, 멋진, 엄청난, 어마어마한
- □ **backpack**[bǽkpæk] 명 배낭
- □ **balloon**[bəlúːn] 명 풍선
- □ **battery**[bǽtəri] 명 건전지
- □ **battle**[bǽtl] 명 전쟁, 전투
- □ **bee**[biː] 명 벌
- □ **board**[bɔːrd] 명 넓은 판, 판자
- □ **border**[bɔ́ːrdər] 명 국경, 경계
- □ **Braille**[breil] 명 점자
- □ **cell phone** 휴대 전화
- □ **chimney**[tʃímni] 명 굴뚝
- □ **close**[klous] 부 가까이, 근접하여
- □ **cross**[krɔːs] 동 건너다, 가로지르다
- □ **curious**[kjúəriəs] 형 호기심이 많은, 궁금한
- □ **dead**[ded] 형 죽은, 쓸모없는
- □ **discover**[diskʌ́vər] 동 발견하다
- □ **dot**[dɑt] 명 점
- □ **enemy**[énəmi] 명 적군, 적대자
- □ **exactly**[igzǽktli] 부 정확하게
- □ **expression**[ikspréʃən] 명 표현
- □ **foreign**[fɔ́ːrən] 형 외국의
- □ **gesture**[dʒéstʃər] 명 몸짓, 몸동작
- □ **ground**[graund] 명 땅, 지면
- □ **hidden**[hídn] 형 숨은, 숨겨진
- □ **hire**[haiər] 동 고용하다
- □ **hug**[hʌg] 명 포옹 동 포옹하다
- □ **hunter**[hʌ́ntər] 명 사냥꾼
- □ **husband**[hʌ́zbənd] 명 남편
- □ **ill**[il] 형 아픈, 병든

- □ **knock**[nɑk] 동 치다, 두드리다
- □ **Latin**[lǽtən] 명 라틴어 형 라틴어의
- □ **letter**[létər] 명 글자, 문자
- □ **light**[lait] 동 불을 붙이다, 불을 밝히다
- □ **loudly**[láudli] 부 큰 소리로, 시끄럽게
- □ **mean**[miːn] 동 의미하다
- □ **message**[mésidʒ] 명 메시지, 전갈, 전언
- □ **misunderstanding**[misəndərstǽndiŋ] 명 오해
- □ **oil**[ɔil] 명 기름
- □ **point**[pɔint] 동 가리키다, 지시하다
- □ **pond**[pɑnd] 명 연못
- □ **powerful**[páuərfəl] 형 강한, 강력한
- □ **prepare**[pripέər] 동 준비하다
- □ **product**[prɑ́dʌkt] 명 상품, 제품
- □ **pull**[pul] 동 끌다, 잡아당기다
- □ **rather**[rǽðər] 부 다소, 약간
- □ **reply**[riplái] 명 답장
- □ **ring**[riŋ] 명 반지
- □ **seat**[siːt] 명 좌석, 의석
- □ **seem**[siːm] 동 ~처럼 보이다
- □ **seriously**[síəriəsli] 부 진지하게, 심각하게
- □ **sign language** 수화
- □ **soldier**[sóuldʒər] 명 군인
- □ **son**[sʌn] 명 아들
- □ **system**[sístəm] 명 체계, 시스템
- □ **toward**[tɔːrd] 전 ~을 향하여
- □ **traffic**[trǽfik] 명 교통
- □ **translate**[trænsléit] 동 번역하다, 해석하다
- □ **vote**[vout] 동 투표하다, 선출하다
- □ **whether**[hwéðər] 접 ~이든지 아니든지

Key Expressions

- □ **at a price of** ~의 가격으로
- □ **be careful with** ~에 조심하다
- □ **be covered with** ~로 덮이다
- □ **be curious about** ~에 대하여 궁금해 하다
- □ **except for** ~을 제외하고
- □ **get over** 이겨내다, 극복하다
- □ **in good health** 건강하여
- □ **instead of** ~ 대신에
- □ **Let's see**. (= **Let me see**.) 글쎄., 어디 보자.

- □ **look after** ~을 돌보다
- □ **pick up** 집어 올리다, 차에 태우다
- □ **right away** 즉시, 당장
- □ **step back** 물러서다
- □ **the rich** (= **rich people**) 부자들
- □ **turn off** ~을 끄다
- □ **vote for** ~에 (찬성하는) 투표를 하다
- □ **wait for** ~을 기다리다
- □ **win many seats** 많은 의석을 확보하다

01 〈보기〉에서 알맞은 단어를 찾아 빈칸을 완성하시오. (한 단어를 추가하고 필요하면 변형하여 쓰시오.)

┌─ 보기 ─┐
except   look   wait   lot
└─────┘

(1) There are _____ great shoes in this store.

(2) We had to _____ him at the restaurant for twenty minutes.

(3) I am doing okay, and the weather is nice _____ the fine dust.

(4) My neighbor asked me to _____ her cat.

02 대화의 빈칸에 〈영영풀이〉에 해당하는 단어를 주어진 철자로 쓰시오.

┌─────────────────────────┐
G: What are these dots for? I'm curious about them.
B: Oh, they are _____. They are for blind people.
G: I see. Now I can guess what they mean.
└─────────────────────────┘

┌─────────────────────────┐
〈영영풀이〉 a system of printing for blind people, using raised patterns that they read by touching
└─────────────────────────┘

➡ _____

03 다음 우리말과 같은 표현이 되도록 문장의 빈칸을 채우시오.

(1) 그들은 또한 감시를 위해 경비원을 고용할 수도 있다.
➡ They can also _____ a security guard to keep watch.

(2) 이건 나와 지나 사이에 오해가 있었기 때문이었어.
➡ This was because there was a _____ between Jina and me.

(3) 그는 다소 별나지만 그의 소설 속의 메시지는 우리에게 매우 친근하다.
➡ He is _____ strange, but his novels' messages are very familiar to us.

04 영영풀이에 해당하는 단어를 〈보기〉에서 찾아 첫 번째 빈칸에 쓰고, 두 번째 빈칸에는 우리말 뜻을 쓰시오.

┌─ 보기 ─┐
oil   translate   ring   discover
└─────┘

(1) _____: a piece of jewelry in the form of a circle that you wear on a finger: _____

(2) _____: to find out something that you did not know before: _____

(3) _____: a thick liquid made from plants or animals that is used in cooking: _____

(4) _____: to change spoken or written words into another language: _____

05 다음 빈칸에 주어진 철자로 시작하는 알맞은 단어를 쓰시오.

(A) Koreans use more water than other f_____ countries with large populations.

(B) Human beings are the greatest h_____ and have always eaten meat.

(C) He must be a s_____ because he is wearing the uniform.

教科書

Conversation

① 궁금증 표현하기

> • I'm curious about that balloon. 나는 저 풍선이 궁금해.

■ 궁금증을 표현할 때는 curious(궁금한, 호기심이 많은), wonder(궁금하다), want to know(알고 싶다) 등의 표현을 이용하여 'I'm curious about ~.(나는 ~이 궁금해.)', 'I wonder ~.(나는 ~이 궁금하다.)' 라고 말한다. 또한 궁금한 내용을 알고 싶다는 의미를 'I would like to know ~', 'I want to know ~.', 'I don't know why ~.'라고 표현할 수도 있다.

■ 궁금함을 나타내는 'I'm curious'와 명사구를 같이 쓸 때는 'I'm curious about+명사구'이고, 명사절과 함께 쓸 때는 'I'm curious if/whether ~.' 또는 'I'm curious 의문사 (주어)+동사 ~.'이다. 'I wonder ~.'를 사용할 때의 어순은 'I wonder+의문사+주어+동사 ~.', 'I wonder+if/whether+주어+동사 ~.'이고, 명사(구)와 함께 나타낼 때는 'I wonder about+명사(구)'이다.

■ 궁금한 점에 대하여 알고 싶을 때는 'Can you tell me about ~?(~에 대하여 이야기해 줄 수 있니?)', 'I'm interested to know ~.(나는 ~을 아는 것에 관심 있어.)'와 같이 표현할 수 있고, 'Can I ~?', 'Can/Could you ~?' 등과 같이 요구/요청을 나타내는 조동사 표현을 사용하여 'Can I ask you ~?' 또는 'Can you tell me ~?'와 같이 궁금한 점에 대하여 물어볼 수 있다. 그 외에 궁금증을 나타낼 때는 'Do you know ~?' 등을 사용할 수도 있다.

궁금증 표현하기

• I am curious about ~. 나는 ~이 궁금하다.

• I'm curious if/whether 주어+동사 ~. 나는 ~가 궁금하다.

• I'm wondering + if/whether/의문사 주어+동사 ~. 나는 ~인지 궁금하다.

• I would like/want to know ~. 나는 ~이 알고 싶다.

• I'd be very interested to know ~. 나는 ~이 알고 싶다.

• Can you tell me about ~? ~에 대해 말해 줄 수 있니?

• I want to know 명사구/명사절 ~. 나는 ~을 알고 싶다.

핵심 Check

1. 다음 밑줄 친 부분 대신 바꿔 쓰기에 적절하지 않은 것은?

G: I'm curious about that robot. Why is it standing there?

B: It's a kind of ad. It tells people their batteries are very powerful.

① I'm wondering about that robot.

② Can I tell you about that robot?

③ I would like to know about that robot.

④ Can you tell me about that robot?

⑤ I'd be very interested to know about that robot.

② 정의하기

• **It means you must not enter.** 그것은 네가 들어가지 말아야 한다는 것을 의미해.

■ 'I'm curious ~.' 등으로 상대방이 궁금증을 표현하거나 의미를 물어보면 'This/It means ~.(그것은 ~을 의미한다.)' 또는 'It is ~.(그것은 ~이다.)' 등의 표현을 사용하여 상대방이 궁금해 하거나, 알고 싶어 하는 것의 의미나 정의를 설명하게 된다.

■ 정의를 말할 때는 'X means ~.(X는 ~을 의미한다.)' 또는 'The meaning of X is ~.(X의 의미는 ~이다.)'를 사용하고, 'X stands for ~.(X는 ~을 나타낸다.)'도 어떤 말이나 문자, 기호, 신호, 상징 등의 의미를 설명할 때 사용한다.

■ 보통 의미를 설명하거나 정의를 나타내는 말은 상대방이 궁금증을 표현하거나 설명을 요청할 때 그 대답으로 쓰인다. 설명을 요청할 때 쓰는 표현은 'What is X (exactly)?(X가 (정확하게) 무엇이니?)', 'What does that mean?(그것이 무슨 뜻입니까?)', 'What do you mean by X?(X가 무슨 뜻이니?)' 등이다.

■ 상대방에게 설명을 요청할 때는 'Could you explain the meaning of it?', 'Could you tell me more about them?' 등의 표현을 사용하거나, Could 대신 Would, Can, Will 등을 사용하기도 한다. 또한 'Do you mind if I ask you to explain ~?'이라고 말할 수도 있다.

정의하기

• This means ~. 이것은 ~을 의미한다.
• X stands for ~. X는 ~을 나디낸다.
• The meaning of this is ~. 이것의 의미는 ~이다.

설명 요청하기

• What is X exactly? X가 정확하게 무엇이니?
• What do you mean by X? X가 무슨 뜻이니?
• What is the meaning of that exactly? 정확하게 그게 무슨 뜻입니까?
• Could you explain what it means? 그게 무엇을 의미하는지 설명 좀 해주시겠습니까?
• What does that mean? 그것이 무슨 뜻입니까?

핵심 Check

2. 주어진 어휘를 이용하여 밑줄 친 우리말에 해당하는 영어 문장을 쓰시오.

B: If there's no enemy, they don't smoke at all, do they?

G: Yes, they do. Smoke from one chimney means "No enemy."

B: Now smoke is rising from three chimneys. What does that mean?

G: <u>그것은 적이 국경선 근처에 접근하고 있다는 것을 의미해.</u> (close, an enemy)

➡ _____

Conversation 교과서 대화문 익히기

Step Up – Real-life Scene

B: This painting has some hidden secrets in it.

G: Really? ❶I'm curious about them. Where are the secrets?

B: Find one yourself.

G: ❷Let's see. ... Oh, I see some letters here.

B: You found one! ❸It means "Jan van Eyck was here. 1434." It's Latin.

G: That's awesome! Any other secrets?

B: Okay. This dog tells us the man here was very rich.

G: I don't understand.

B: They had to spend lots of money ❹to buy a dog of that kind at that time.

G: I see. Only ❺the rich could have that kind of dog, right?

B: Exactly. Pictures speak a thousand words, you know.

B: 이 그림은 그 안에 숨겨진 비밀이 몇 개 있어.

G: 정말? 난 그것들이 궁금해. 그 비밀들은 어디에 있니?

B: 너 스스로 하나 찾아봐.

G: 어디 보자. … 오, 여기 글자들이 몇 개 보여.

B: 너 하나 찾았구나! 그것은 "Jan van Eyck가 여기 있었다. 1434."를 의미해. 그것은 라틴어야.

G: 멋지다! 다른 비밀들은?

B: 좋아. 이 개는 여기 있는 이 남자가 매우 부자였다는 것을 우리에게 말해 주지.

G: 나는 이해가 안 돼.

B: 당시에 저런 종류의 개를 사려면 많은 돈을 써야 했어.

G: 알겠다. 단지 부자들만 저런 종류의 개를 살 수 있었어, 맞지?

B: 정확해. 알다시피, 그림이 천 마디 말을 하지.

❶ 궁금증을 나타내는 표현으로 '~가 궁금해'로 해석한다.
❷ '글쎄.. 어디 보자.'의 의미로 'Let me see.'와 같은 의미로 사용된다.
❸ 상대방이 궁금증을 표현하거나 의미를 물어보면 'This/It means ~.(그것은 ~을 의미한다.)' 또는 'It is ~.(그것은 ~이다.)' 등의 표현을 사용해서 상대방이 궁금해 하거나 알고 싶어 하는 것의 의미나 정의를 설명하는 표현이다.
❹ 부정사의 부사적 용법 중 '목적'으로 '~하기 위해'로 해석한다.
❺ 'the+형용사'는 '복수명사'로 '~한 사람들'의 의미이다.

Check(√) True or False

(1) The girl found one secret in the painting.   T ☐ F ☐

(2) The man in the picture wasn't very rich.   T ☐ F ☐

 ### Start Off – Listen & Talk A 1

B: What are the soldiers doing with the five chimneys on TV?

G: They are sending messages to the king ❶by using the chimneys.

B: Really? I'm curious about the system. Can you tell me more?

G: Well, do you see the two ❷smoking chimneys?

B: Yes. What do ❸they mean?

G: ❸They mean ❹they just saw an enemy.

B: TV에서 병사들이 5개의 굴뚝으로 무엇을 하고 있니?

G: 그들은 그 굴뚝을 이용하여 왕에게 메시지를 보내고 있어.

B: 정말? 난 그 체계가 궁금해. 좀 더 말해 줄 수 있어?

G: 음, 연기 나는 굴뚝 두 개가 보이지?

B: 그래. 그것들은 무엇을 의미하니?

G: 그것들은 그들이 방금 적을 봤다는 것을 의미해.

❶ 'by+ing'는 '~함으로써'로 해석한다.
❷ 'smoking'은 현재분사로 '연기 나는'의 의미이다.
❸ 'the two smoking chimneys'를 가리킨다.
❹ 'the soldiers'를 가리키는 대명사다.

Check(√) True or False

(3) The soldiers are sending messages to the king by using the chimneys.   T ☐ F ☐

(4) The boy wants to know about the system.   T ☐ F ☐

Get Ready 2

(1) G: I'm curious about that robot. Why is it standing there?
B: It's a kind of ad. ❶It tells people their batteries are very powerful.

(2) G: What's this? I'm curious about it.
B: It's a traffic sign. ❷It means "Do not enter."
G: Oh, I see.

(3) G: ❸What are these dots for? I'm curious about them.
B: Oh, they are Braille. They are for blind people.
G: I see. Now I can guess what they mean.

(4) G: I'm curious about that balloon. Why is it hanging there?
B: Oh, that. It's an ad. ❹It says the product is very powerful.

❶ people 뒤에 목적어를 이끄는 접속사 that이 생략되어 있다.
❷ '그것은 ~을 의미하다'라는 뜻으로 정의를 나타내는 표현이다.
❸ 'What ~ for?'는 '~은 무엇을 위한 것이니?'라는 의미이다.
❹ says 뒤에 목적어를 이끄는 접속사 that이 생략되어 있다.

Start Off – Listen & Talk A 2

B: If there's no enemy, they don't smoke at all, ❶do they?
G: Yes, they do. ❷Smoke from one chimney means "No enemy."
B: Now smoke is rising from three chimneys. What does that mean?
G: It means an enemy is coming ❸close to the border.

❶ 앞 문장이 일반동사 부정문일 때 사용하는 부가의문문으로 '그렇지?'의 의미로 사용된다.
❷ 주어가 단수명사 'Smoke'이므로 동사는 단수 'means'이다.
❸ 이 문장에서 'close'는 부사로 '가까이'란 의미이다.

Start Off – Listen & Talk B

B: Now the enemy is crossing the border in the dark. What are the soldiers going to do ❶to send messages? I'm curious about that.
G: They will ❷light four chimneys.

B: ❸When they light all five of the chimneys, what does that mean?
G: ❹It means the battle has started.

❶ 부정사의 부사적 용법 중 '목적'으로 '메시지를 보내기 위해'라고 해석한다.
❷ 여기서 'light'는 동사로 '불을 붙이다'의 의미이다.
❸ 'when'이 이끄는 문장은 시간의 부사절로 '~할 때'로 해석한다.
❹ 동사 'means'와 주어 'the battle' 사이에는 목적어를 이끄는 접속사 'that'이 생략되어 있다.

Start Off – Speak Up

B: I'm curious about sign language.
G: ❶Are you? ❷Let me show you one expression. Look.
B: What does it mean?
G: It means "Hello."

❶ Are you curious about sign language?를 줄여 쓴 표현이다.
❷ 'let(사역동사)+목적어+동사원형' 형태로 'Let me show ~'는 '내가 …에게 ~을 보여줄게'로 해석한다.

Express Yourself A

1. W: What does this woman's gesture mean? I'm curious about it.
M: ❶I think it means "Jump into the pond."
W: Why do you think so?
M: The boy has lots of bees on his head. And the woman is pointing at the pond.

2. W: This woman doesn't want a dollar. So what does her gesture mean?
M: It means she wants a chicken.
W: Then the boy should bring a chicken ❷to get the fruit, right?
M: I think so.

3. W: What does this man's gesture mean? I'm curious about it.
M: It means "Turn it off."
W: Really? ❸What makes you think so?
M: ❹The other hunter there is coming close to an animal.
W: Oh, I see.

❶ 상대방이 궁금해 하는 것의 의미나 정의를 설명하는 표현이다.
❷ 부정사의 부사적 용법 중 '목적'으로 '과일을 얻기 위해'라고 해석한다.
❸ 여기서 make는 사역동사로 '목적어+목적보어(동사원형)' 형태를 취한다. 그리고 '왜 그렇게 생각하니?'의 뜻으로 'Why do you think so?'와 같은 표현이다.
❹ 'The other+단수명사' 형태로 '나머지 사냥꾼 한 명'을 나타낸다.

다음 우리말과 일치하도록 빈칸에 알맞은 말을 쓰시오.

Get Ready 2

(1) G: I'm _____ _____ that robot. Why _____ _____
  standing there?
  B: It's _____ _____ _____ ad. It _____ people their
  _____ are very _____.

(2) G: What's this? I'_____ _____ _____ it.
  B: It's a _____ _____. It _____ "Do not _____."
  G: Oh, I see.

(3) G: What are these _____ _____? I'_____ _____
  _____ them.
  B: Oh, they are _____. They are for _____ people.
  G: I see. Now I can _____ what they _____.

(4) G: I'm _____ about that _____. Why is it _____ there?
  B: Oh, that. It's an _____. It says the _____ is very _____.

Start Off – Listen & Talk A

1. B: What are the _____ doing with the five _____ on TV?
  G: They are sending _____ to the king _____ _____ the
  _____.
  B: Really? I'_____ _____ _____ the _____. Can you tell
  me more?
  G: Well, do you see the two _____ _____?
  B: Yes. _____ do they _____?
  G: They mean they just saw an _____.

2. B: If there's no _____, they don't _____ _____ _____,
  _____ they?
  G: Yes, they do. _____ from one _____ means "No enemy."
  B: Now smoke is _____ from three chimneys. _____ _____
  that _____?
  G: _____ _____ an enemy is coming _____ to the _____.

Start Off B

B: Now the enemy _____ _____ the _____ in the _____.
  What are the _____ _____ _____ _____ to send
  _____? I'm curious _____ that.
G: They will _____ four _____.
B: When they _____ all five of the _____, what does that mean?
G: _____ _____ the _____ has started.

14 Lesson 5. Pictures Speak a Thousand Words

해석

(1) G: 나는 저 로봇에 대해 알고 싶어. 그건 왜 저기에 서 있는 거니?
  B: 그건 일종의 광고야. 그것은 그들의 건전지가 매우 강력하다는 것을 사람들에게 말하고 있어.

(2) G: 이것은 뭐지? 난 그게 궁금해.
  B: 그것은 교통 표지판이야. 그것은 "들어오지 마시오."를 의미해.
  G: 오, 알겠어.

(3) G: 이 점들은 무엇을 위한 거니? 난 그것들에 대해 알고 싶어.
  B: 오, 그것들은 점자야. 그것들은 시각장애인을 위한 것이야.
  G: 알겠어. 이제 그것들이 무엇을 의미하는지 추측할 수 있어.

(4) G: 나는 저 풍선이 궁금해. 그건 왜 저기에 매달려 있니?
  B: 오, 저것. 그건 광고야. 그것은 그 상품이 매우 강력하다는 것을 말하고 있어.

1. B: TV에서 병사들이 5개의 굴뚝으로 무엇을 하고 있니?
  G: 그들은 그 굴뚝을 이용하여 왕에게 메시지를 보내고 있어.
  B: 정말? 난 그 체계가 궁금해. 좀 더 말해 줄 수 있어?
  G: 음, 연기 나는 굴뚝 두 개가 보이지?
  B: 그래. 그것들은 무엇을 의미하니?
  G: 그것들은 그들이 방금 적을 봤다는 것을 의미해.

2. B: 만약 적이 없다면, 그들은 연기를 전혀 피우지 않아, 그렇지?
  G: 아니, 연기를 피워. 굴뚝 한 곳에서 연기가 나오면 "적이 없음"을 의미해.
  B: 이제 연기가 굴뚝 세 개에서 올라가고 있어. 그것은 무엇을 의미하니?
  G: 그것은 적이 국경 가까이 접근하고 있음을 의미해.

B: 이제 적이 어둠 속에서 국경을 침입하고 있어. 메시지를 보내기 위해서 병사들은 무슨 일을 할까? 나는 그것이 궁금해.
G: 그들은 굴뚝 4개에 불을 붙일 거야.
B: 그들이 5개 굴뚝 모두에 불을 붙였을 때, 그것은 무엇을 의미하니?
G: 그것은 전투가 시작되었음을 의미해.

Start Off – Speak Up

B: I'_____ _____ _____ sign _____.
G: Are you? _____ me _____ you one _____. Look.
B: _____ does it _____?
G: _____ _____ "Hello."

Step Up– Real-life Scene

B: This painting has some _____ _____ in it.
G: Really? I'm _____ _____ them. Where are the _____?
B: Find one _____.
G: _____ _____. ... Oh, I see some _____ here.
B: You found _____! It _____ "Jan van Eyck was here. 1434." It's _____.
G: That's _____! _____ _____ secrets?
B: Okay. This dog _____ us the man here was very _____.
G: I don't _____.
B: They had to _____ _____ _____ money _____ _____ a dog of that _____ at that time.
G: I see. Only _____ _____ could have _____ _____ of dog, right?
B: _____. Pictures _____ _____ _____ words, you know.

Express Yourself A

1. W: What does this woman's _____ mean? I'm _____ it.
   M: I think _____ _____ "Jump into the _____."
   W: _____ do you _____ _____?
   M: The boy has _____ _____ bees on his head. And the woman is _____ at the _____.

2. W: This woman doesn't want a dollar. _____ what does her _____ _____?
   M: _____ _____ she wants a _____.
   W: Then the boy _____ _____ a chicken _____ _____ the fruit, _____?
   M: _____ _____ _____.

3. W: _____ does this man's _____ _____? I'm curious about it.
   M: It means "_____ _____ _____."
   W: Really? _____ _____ you think so?
   M: _____ _____ _____ there is coming _____ to an animal.
   W: Oh, I _____.

해석

B: 난 수화가 궁금해.
G: 그러니? 내가 표현 하나를 알려줄게. 봐.
B: 그것은 무엇을 의미하니?
G: 그것은 "안녕하세요."를 의미해.

B: 이 그림은 그 안에 숨겨진 비밀이 몇 개 있어.
G: 정말? 난 그것들이 궁금해. 그 비밀들은 어디에 있니?
B: 너 스스로 하나 찾아봐.
G: 어디 보자. ⋯ 오, 여기 글자들이 몇 개 보여.
B: 너 하나 찾았구나! 그것은 "Jan van Eyck가 여기 있었다. 1434."를 의미해. 그것은 라틴어야.
G: 멋지다! 다른 비밀들은?
B: 좋아. 이 개는 여기 있는 이 남자가 매우 부자였다는 것을 우리에게 말해주지.
G: 나는 이해가 안 돼.
B: 당시에 저런 종류의 개를 사려면 많은 돈을 써야 했어.
G: 알겠다. 단지 부자들만 저런 종류의 개를 살 수 있었어, 맞지?
B: 정확해. 알다시피, 그림이 천 마디 말을 하지.

1. W: 이 여자의 몸짓은 무엇을 의미하니? 난 그것이 궁금해.
   M: 내 생각에 그것은 "연못으로 뛰어들어."를 의미해.
   W: 왜 그렇게 생각하니?
   M: 그 소년은 머리 위에 **많은** 벌이 있어. 그리고 그 여자**는** 연못을 가리키고 있어.
2. W: 이 여자는 1달러를 원하지 않아. 그렇다면 그녀의 몸짓은 무엇을 의미하니?
   M: 그것은 그녀가 닭 한 마리를 원한다는 것을 의미해.
   W: 그럼 그 소년은 과일을 얻기 위해 닭을 한 마리 가져와야 하는구나, 맞지?
   M: 난 그렇게 생각해.
3. W: 이 남자의 몸짓은 무엇을 의미하니? 난 그것이 궁금해.
   M: 그것은 "그것을 쏴."를 의미해.
   W: 정말? 왜 그렇게 생각하니?
   M: 거기 있는 나머지 다른 사냥꾼이 어떤 동물 가까이 접근하고 있어.
   W: 오, 알겠어.

Conversation 시험대비 기본평가

01 우리말에 맞도록 주어진 단어를 활용하여 빈칸을 채우시오.

> 그것은 네가 들어가지 말아야 한다는 것을 의미해. (mean)

➡ _____ _____ you must _____ _____.

02 다음 대화의 빈칸에 들어갈 말로 <u>어색한</u> 것은?

> G: What are these dots for? _____
> B: Oh, they are Braille. They are for blind people.
> G: I see. Now I can guess what they mean.

① I'm curious about them.
② I would like to know about them.
③ I'd be very interested to know about them.
④ Let me show you one expression
⑤ Can you tell me about them?

03 다음 대화의 빈칸에 들어갈 말로 적절한 것은?

> A: What does your name mean? I'm curious about it.
> B: _____
> A: That's beautiful.

① I know whose name it is. It's Hyeja's.
② What does it mean?   ③ It means "bright girl."
④ What does this letter mean?   ⑤ I don't care about it.

04 다음 대화의 밑줄 친 말의 의도로 알맞은 것은?

> G: <u>I'm curious about that balloon.</u> Why is it hanging there?
> B: Oh, that. It's an ad.

① 관심 표현하기   ② 충고 구하기
③ 가능성 묻기   ④ 유감 표현하기
⑤ 궁금증 표현하기

[01~02] 다음 대화를 읽고 물음에 답하시오.

W: What does this man's gcsture (a)mean? I'm curious about (b)it.
M: It means "(c)Turn it off."
W: Really? _____(A)_____
M: (d)Other hunter there is coming (e)close to an animal.
W: Oh, I see.

01 위 대화의 빈칸 (A)에 들어갈 말로 알맞은 것을 모두 고르시오.

① How do you think so?
② What do you think about it?
③ What makes you think so?
④ Do you think I should turn it off?
⑤ Why do you think so?

[서답형]
02 위 대화의 (a)~(e)에서 어법상 틀린 곳을 찾아 바르게 고치시오. (1개)

➡ 틀린 것: _____
➡ 고치기: _____ ➡ _____

[03~04] 다음 대화를 읽고 물음에 답하시오.

B: Now the enemy is crossing the border in the dark. What are the soldiers going to do to send messages? _____(A)_____
G: They will light four chimneys.
B: When they light all five of the chimneys, _____(B)_____?
G: It means the battle has started.

03 위 대화의 빈칸 (A)에 들어갈 말로 알맞은 것은?

① I'm curious about who the soldiers are.
② Can you tell me how to light chimneys?

③ Do you think they should light chimneys?
④ I'm curious about that.
⑤ Can you tell me about the messages?

04 위 대화의 흐름상 빈칸 (B)에 들어갈 알맞은 표현은?

① why did you say so
② what does that mean
③ do you think so
④ why not
⑤ do you mean the battle has started

[05~06] 다음 대화를 읽고 물음에 답하시오.

B: What are the soldiers doing with the five chimneys on TV?
G: They are sending (a)messages to the king by using the chimneys.
B: Really? I'm (b)curious about the system. Can you tell me more?
G: Well, do you see the two (c)smoking chimneys?
B: Yes. What do they mean?
G: They mean they just (d)saw an enemy.
B: If there's no enemy, they don't smoke at all, do they?
G: (A)Yes, they do. Smoke from one chimney means "(e)An enemy."
B: Now smoke is rising from three chimneys. What does that mean?
G: It means an enemy is coming close to the border.

05 위 대화의 흐름상 어휘의 쓰임이 어색한 것은?

① (a)　② (b)　③ (c)　④ (d)　⑤ (e)

06 위 대화의 밑줄 친 (A)의 우리말을 바르게 옮긴 것은?

① 응, 적이 와.　　　② 아니, 적이 오지 않아.

③ 응, 연기를 피워.　　④ 아니, 연기를 피워.

⑤ 응, 연기를 피우지 않아.

서답형

07 다음 대화의 빈칸에 들어갈 단어를 주어진 영영풀이를 보고 '복수형'으로 쓰시오.

> G: I'm curious about that robot. Why is it standing there?
> B: It's a kind of ad. It tells people their _____ are very powerful.

> <영영풀이> an object that provides electricity for things such as radios, toys, or cars

➡ _____

[08~09] 다음 대화를 읽고 물음에 답하시오.

> G: What are these dots _____(a)_____?
> _____(A)_____ them.
> B: Oh, they are Braille. They are _____(b)_____ blind people.
> G: I see. Now I can guess what they mean.
>
> G: _____(A)_____ that balloon. Why is it hanging there?
> B: Oh, that. It's an ad. It says the product is very powerful.

08 위 대화의 빈칸 (A)에 공통으로 들어갈 말로 어색한 것은?

① I'm curious about

② I'm surprised about

③ I'd like to know about

④ I wonder about

⑤ I want to know about

09 위 대화의 빈칸 (a)와 (b)에 공통으로 들어갈 단어를 쓰시오.

➡ _____

[10~11] 다음 대화를 읽고 물음에 답하시오.

> B: This painting has some hidden secrets in (a)it.
> G: Really? I'm curious about them. Where are the secrets?
> B: Find one yourself. (A)
> G: Let's see. ... Oh, I see some letters here.
> B: You found one! (B) It means "Jan van Eyck was here. 1434." It's Latin.
> G: That's awesome! Any other secrets?
> B: Okay. (C)
> G: I don't understand. (D)
> B: They had to spend lots of money to buy a dog of that kind at that time.
> G: I see. (E) Only the rich could have that kind of dog, right?
> B: Exactly. Pictures speak a thousand words, you know.

10 위 대화의 (A)~(E) 중 주어진 문장이 들어갈 위치로 알맞은 것은?

> This dog tells us the man here was very rich.

① (A)　② (B)　③ (C)　④ (D)　⑤ (E)

11 밑줄 친 (a)가 가리키는 것을 영어로 쓰시오.

➡ _____

[01~02] 다음 대화를 읽고 물음에 답하시오.

B: This painting has some hidden secrets in it.
G: Really? _____(A)_____ Where are the secrets?
B: Find one yourself.
G: Let's see. ... Oh, I see some letters here.
B: You found one! ____(B)____ "Jan van Eyck was here. 1434." It's Latin.
G: That's awesome! Any other secrets?
B: Okay. This dog tells us the man here was very rich.
G: I don't understand.
B: They had to spend lots of money to buy a dog of that kind at that time.
G: I see. Only the rich could have that kind of dog, right?
B: Exactly. Pictures speak a thousand words, you know.

01 위 대화를 읽고 다음 물음에 영어로 답하시오.

Q: What do the letters the girl found mean?

➡ _____

02 위 대화의 빈칸 (A)와 (B)에 들어갈 말을 〈조건〉에 맞게 영어로 쓰시오.

┌─── 조건 ────┐
(A) • 궁금증을 표현하는 말을 쓸 것.
    • '대명사'와 'curious'를 사용할 것.
(B) • 상대방이 알고 싶어 하는 것의 의미나 정의를 표현하는 말을 2단어로 쓸 것..
└──────────┘

➡ (A) _____
  (B) _____

03 다음 대화의 밑줄 친 우리말 해석에 맞게 주어진 〈조건〉에 맞게 영어로 쓰시오.

W: What does this woman's gesture mean? I'm curious about it.
M: I think it means "Jump into the pond."
W: 왜 그렇게 생각하니?
M: The boy has lots of bees on his head. And the woman is pointing at the pond.

┌─── 조건 ────┐
• 'make', 'think'를 이용할 것
└──────────┘

➡ _____

[04~05] 다음 대화를 읽고 물음에 답하시오.

B: What are the soldiers doing with the five chimneys on TV?
G: (a)그들은 그 굴뚝을 이용하여 왕에게 메시지를 보내고 있어.
B: Really? I'm curious about the system. Can you tell me more?
G: Well, do you see the two smoking chimneys?
B: Yes. What do they mean?
G: _____(A)_____

04 위 대화의 흐름상 빈칸 (A)에 주어진 어구를 알맞은 순서로 배열하시오.

(saw / they / mean / just / an enemy / they)

➡ _____

05 위 대화의 (a)의 우리말을 주어진 〈조건〉에 맞게 영작하시오.

┌─── 조건 ────┐
• '진행형'과 'by ~ing'를 이용할 것.
└──────────┘

➡ _____

Grammar

1 가정법 과거

• I **would** be so happy if you **were** with me. 당신이 나와 함께 있다면 난 정말 행복할 거예요.

■ 형태: If+주어+동사 과거형, 주어+조동사 과거형(would/should/could/might)+동사원형
  의미: 만약 …한다면 ~할 텐데(현재 사실과 반대되는 상상이나 가정)

■ 가정법 문장이라는 표시로 과거 동사를 사용할 뿐 의미상 과거를 나타내지 않고, 현재 말하는 사람의 느낌이나 감정을 표현한다.

  • If I **had** a car, I **could** give you a ride home. 만일 내가 차가 있다면, 너를 집까지 태워 줄 텐데.

    = As I **don't have** a car, I **can't give** you a ride home.
      나는 차를 가지고 있지 않아서, 너를 집까지 태워줄 수 없다.

■ if절에 쓰이는 be동사의 과거형은 'were'를 사용하지만, 구어체에서는 주어가 'I' 또는 3인칭 단수인 경우 'was'를 쓰기도 한다.

  • If I **were[was]** rich, I **would** help all the children in need.
    내가 부자라면, 도움이 필요한 모든 어린이들을 도와줄 텐데.

■ 가정법 과거 문장을 현재시제의 직설법으로 바꿀 수 있다.

  • If he **knew** the answer, he **would** be very glad. 그가 정답을 안다면, 그는 매우 기쁠 텐데.

    = As he **doesn't know** the answer, he **is not** very glad. 그는 정답을 모르기 때문에, 그는 별로 기쁘지 않다.

■ if는 if절의 동사가 'were' 또는 'had'일 때 생략될 수 있으며, 이때는 주어와 동사가 도치된다.

  • If my family **were** at home, I **would** tell them everything about my school life.
    만일 가족들이 집에 있다면, 나는 그들에게 내 학교생활에 관한 모든 것을 말할 텐데.

    = **Were** my family at home, I **would** tell them everything about my school life.

  • If Tom **had** a sister, he **could** play with her all day long.
    만일 Tom이 여동생이 있다면, 그는 하루 종일 그녀와 놀 수 있을 텐데.

    = **Had** Tom a sister, he **could** play with her all day long

 핵심 Check

1. 다음 괄호 안에서 알맞은 것을 고르시오.

  (1) If I (am / were) a fish, I would swim in the pond.

  (2) She (will / would) be very happy if she won the lottery.

② 관계대명사 whose

• It was written in 1973 by a woman **whose** husband was far away.
그것은 남편이 멀리 떨어져 살았던 한 여자에 의해 1973년에 쓰여졌다.

■ 형태: 선행사+whose+명사
의미: ~인, ~의

■ 소유격을 대신하고 두 문장을 이어주는 접속사 역할을 하는 관계대명사이다.

  • My brother has a girl friend. + He likes **her cat**.
    → My brother has a girl friend **whose cat** he likes.
      나의 남동생은 그녀의 고양이를 그가 좋아하는 여자 친구가 있다.

■ 선행사가 사물인 경우 'of which'를 쓰기도 한다.

  • I have a bag. + **Its handle** is made of bamboo.
    → I have a bag **whose handle** is made of bamboo. 나는 손잡이가 대나무로 만들어진 가방을 가지고 있다.
  • I have a bag. + The handle **of it** is made of bamboo.
    → I have a bag the handle **of which** is made of bamboo.
    → I have a bag **of which** the handle is made of bamboo.

■ 소유격 관계대명사 다음의 동사는 소유격 관계대명사가 갖고 있는 명사의 수를 따른다.

  • I know a small girl whose **parents are** tall. 나는 부모님이 키가 큰 작은 소녀를 알고 있다.

■ 소유격과 한정사(a, an, the, this, that, some, any 등)는 함께 쓸 수 없으므로 소유격 관계사 다음에 한정사를 쓰지 않는다.

  • I have a dog whose the tail is long. (×)
    → I have a dog **whose** tail is long. 또는 I have a dog **of which** the tail is long.

핵심 Check

2. 다음 괄호 안에서 알맞은 것을 고르시오.

  (1) He has a sister (of which / whose) eyes are brown.
  (2) The house (of which / whose) windows are very big is my father's.
  (3) I have a friend whose brothers (enjoy / enjoys) skateboarding.

01 다음 우리말에 맞게 괄호 안에 주어진 단어를 이용하여 문장을 완성하시오.

(1) 내가 오리라면, 물속에서 수영할 수 있을 텐데. (if, be)

➡ _____, I could swim in the water.

(2) 날개를 가졌다면 너는 뭘 하겠니? (what, do)

➡ _____ if you had wings?

(3) Bubu는 그의 개가 인형을 가지고 다니는 소년이야. (be, carry)

➡ Bubu is the boy _____.

(4) Lala는 그녀의 개가 핫도그를 원하는 소녀야. (want, hot dog)

➡ Lala is the girl _____.

02 다음 문장에서 어법상 어색한 부분을 바르게 고쳐 쓰시오.

(1) If I had wings, I will fly in the sky.

➡ _____

(2) What would you do if you are a fish?

➡ _____

(3) Koko is the boy of which the bag is on a big cat.

➡ _____

(4) The girl who cat is dancing is Didi.

➡ _____

03 다음 〈보기〉의 문장을 참고하여 빈칸을 완성하시오.

┌─ 보기 ├─

As she doesn't know the result, she is not happy.

= If she knew the result, she would be happy.

(1) As I don't have a lot of money, I can't travel around the world.

= _____

(2) As I am not tall, I can't be a basketball player.

= _____

01 다음 두 문장을 한 문장으로 고칠 때 빈칸에 알맞은 말은?

> • The movie attracted 10 million viewers.
> • The director of the movie won the Academy award.
>   → The movie _____ the director won the Academy award attracted 10 million viewers.

① who   ② whose   ③ which
④ of which   ⑤ what

 02 다음 빈칸에 들어갈 알맞은 것은?

> I have a ring _____ owner is unknown.

① whose   ② who   ③ that
④ of which   ⑤ whom

시답형

03 관계대명사를 이용하여 두 문장을 한 문장으로 바꿔 쓰시오.

> • There was a queen.
> • Her daughter was cursed by an evil fairy.

➡ _____

_____

04 다음 중 어법상 올바른 문장을 고르시오.

① If I were him, I would buy the bag.
② If I had a car, I could drove her home.
③ Were I rich, I can help all of you.
④ She would be very happy if she wins the prize.
⑤ If your mom knew you passed the test, she will be very surprised.

 05 다음 문장의 뜻이 나머지 넷과 다른 것은?

① If I were in good physical condition, I could work out with you.
② Were I in good physical condition, I could work out with you.
③ With good physical condition, I can work out with you.
④ As I am not in good physical condition, I can't work out with you.
⑤ Because I am not in good physical condition, I can't work out with you.

06 빈칸에 공통으로 들어갈 말은? (대 · 소문자 무시)

> • If I _____ you, I would save some money for the future.
> • _____ I you, I would save some money for the future.

① am   ② were   ③ had
④ had been   ⑤ weren't

서답형

07 다음 괄호 안에 주어진 단어들을 바르게 배열하여 문장을 완성하시오.

> Miso (a girl, jumping, dog, is, whose, rope, is).

➡ _____

서답형

08 다음 두 문장을 가정법을 이용하여 한 문장으로 쓰시오.

> • I don't have a lot of money.
> • I can't buy that car.

➡ _____

_____

09 다음 문장과 같은 뜻을 가진 문장을 <u>모두</u> 고르시오.

> As we don't have enough time, we can't stay longer.

① If we didn't have enough time, we couldn't stay longer.

② If we have enough time, we can stay longer.

③ If we had enough time, we could stay longer.

④ Without enough time, we could stay longer.

⑤ With enough time, we could stay longer.

10 다음 문장에서 어법상 <u>어색한</u> 것을 바르게 고쳐 다시 쓰시오.

(1) If I have a monkey, I could play with it.

➡ _____

_____

(2) The boys whose mom is a lawyer lives next door.

➡ _____

_____

 중요

11 다음 중 어법상 <u>어색한</u> 문장을 고르시오.

① If he were here, he could help us.

② If I were a cheetah, I could run faster than you.

③ If I were not tired, I could go swimming.

④ If my brother were tall, he could play basketball better.

⑤ I lent it to you if I had the book.

12 다음 괄호 안에서 알맞은 말을 고르시오.

(1) If I were a millionaire, I (built / would build) a castle.

(2) I would call him if I (knew / had known) his phone number.

(3) I have a friend, (who / whose) family is from Germany.

(4) This is the student (who / whose) came from France.

(5) We need to help animals in Australia (which / whose) lives are in danger.

13 다음 우리말을 영어로 바르게 옳긴 것은?

> 내가 날개를 가졌다면, 내 친구를 만나러 부산으로 날아갈 텐데.

① If I have wings, I will fly to Busan to meet my friend.

② If I have wings, I would fly to Busan to meet my friend.

③ If I had wings, I will fly to Busan to meet my friend.

④ If I had wings, I would fly to Busan to meet my friend.

⑤ If I had had wings, I would fly to Busan to meet my friend.

14 주어진 어휘를 이용하여 다음 우리말을 영어로 쓰시오.

> 내가 새라면, 나는 산 너머로 날아갈 텐데. (a bird, fly, over)

➡ _____

서답형

15 다음 괄호 안에 주어진 단어들을 바르게 배열하여 문장을 완성하시오.

> The animal (begins, with z, whose, is, a zebra, name).

➡ _____

_____

16 다음 우리말을 바르게 영작한 것은?

> 내 아들이 더 열심히 공부하면 나는 행복할 텐데.

① I will be happier if my son studied harder.
② I am happier if my son studied harder.
③ I would be happier if my son studies harder.
④ I would be happier if my son studied harder.
⑤ I would be happier if my son has studied harder.

17 다음 두 문장을 한 문장으로 바르게 옮긴 것은?

> • A girl is preparing for the audition.
> • Her dream is to be a movie star.

① A girl is preparing for the audition whose dream is to be a movie star.
② A girl is preparing for the audition who dream is to be a movie star.
③ A girl is preparing for the audition her dream is to be a movie star.
④ A girl whose dream is to be a movie star is preparing for the audition.
⑤ A girl of which the dream is to be a movie star is preparing for the audition.

중요

18 빈칸에 들어갈 말을 순서대로 바르게 연결한 것은?

> • I like the candies _____ taste like apples.
> • I like the fresh baked bread _____ smell is so sweet.

① whose   – whose
② whose   – which
③ of which – which
④ which   – of which
⑤ which   – whose

서답형

19 주어진 어휘를 이용하여 다음 우리말을 영어로 쓰시오.

> 내가 대통령을 만난다면, 그와 악수를 할 텐데.
> (the President, shake)

➡ _____

_____

서답형

20 대화의 빈칸에 공통으로 들어갈 단어를 쓰시오.

(1) A: What _____ you do if you were a fish?
   B: If I were a fish, I _____ swim in the pond.
(2) A: What would you do if you _____ a duck?
   B: If I _____ a duck, I could swim in the water.

서답형

21 다음 두 문장이 같은 뜻이 되도록 빈칸에 알맞은 말을 쓰시오.

> If she worked with him, she would be very disappointed with him.
> = As _____,
>   she _____.

01 관계대명사를 이용하여 두 문장을 한 문장으로 쓰시오.

(1) • I have a friend.
    • His brother enjoys skateboarding.
    ➡ _____
    _____

(2) • The boy is my brother.
    • He is dancing on the floor.
    ➡ _____
    _____

(3) • He wants to ride a bike.
    • I bought it yesterday.
    ➡ _____
    _____

(4) • Do you like the house?
    • Its roof looks like a hat.
    ➡ _____
    _____

(5) • The boy is Jeje.
    • His cat is spinning a hula hoop.
    ➡ _____
    _____

02 다음 우리말을 주어진 어휘를 이용하여 영어로 옮기시오.

(1) 내가 강한 팔을 가졌다면, 나는 나무에 오를 수
    있을 텐데. (strong, climb)
    ➡ _____
    _____

(2) 내가 긴 코를 가졌다면, 나는 샤워하기 위해 그
    것을 쓸 수 있을 텐데. (nose, shower)
    ➡ _____
    _____

(3) 내가 아름다운 목소리를 가졌다면, 나는 나무에
    서 노래할 거야. (voice, on the tree)
    ➡ _____
    _____

03 주어진 문장을 가정법 문장으로 다시 쓰시오.

(1) As I am not an English teacher, I don't
    play word games every day.
    ➡ _____
    _____

(2) As I am not on the moon, I can't jump
    much higher.
    ➡ _____
    _____

04 잘못된 부분을 바르게 고쳐 문장을 다시 쓰시오.

(1) Did he rich, he could travel to Europe.
    ➡ _____
    _____

(2) The boy whose is talking to Mary is my
    cousin.
    ➡ _____
    _____

(3) He lent me the book of which I want to
    read.
    ➡ _____
    _____

(4) I stayed at the house which walls are
    white.
    ➡ _____
    _____

(5) If I were you, I took a swimming
    lesson.
    ➡ _____
    _____

05 다음 그림을 보고 빈칸에 알맞은 말을 써 넣으시오.

(1)

| If I were the boy, I _____ |
| the fruit to the monkey right away. |

(2)

| If I were the boy, I _____ . |

(3)

| If I were the girl, I _____ |
| out of the water right away. |

06 다음 주어진 우리말에 맞게 빈칸에 들어갈 단어를 각각 쓰시오.

내가 만일 BTS 멤버라면, 나는 가난한 어린이들을 위해 춤추고 노래할 수 있을 텐데.
→ If I _____ a member of BTS, I
_____ _____ _____ _____
for poor children.

07 주어진 문장이 같은 뜻이 되도록 빈칸에 알맞은 말을 쓰시오.

(1) If he knew her, he would talk to her.
➡ As he doesn't know her, _____
_____ .

(2) If he were at home, I would tell him the truth.
➡ _____ , I would tell him the truth.

08 주어진 〈보기〉를 참고하여 두 문장을 하나의 문장으로 쓰시오.

┤ 보기 ├
The boy doesn't understand her gesture.
The woman doesn't want his money.
→ The boy whose money the woman doesn't want doesn't understand her gesture.

(1) The boy doesn't understand the man's gesture. His cell phone is ringing loudly.
➡ _____

(2) The girl doesn't understand the man's gesture. Her feet are in the water.
➡ _____
_____

(3) The boy doesn't understand her gesture. The woman is pulling his hand.
➡ _____
_____

(4) The boy doesn't understand its gesture. The monkey is pulling his bag.
➡ _____
_____

A Picture Letter from a Mother of Three

Speaking to family members or friends in a foreign country is rather
동명사 주어
easy and simple today. But before the days of phones and the Internet,
시대
it was not that easy. People just sent a letter and waited for a reply for
= Speaking to family members or friends in a foreign country
weeks. And it was a lot harder if they couldn't read or write.
비교급을 강조하는 부사: a lot. much. far. still. even(훨씬)
This letter shows how people got over these difficulties. It was
관계부사 = the way, the way how(×)
written in 1973 by a woman whose husband was far away. She lived
소유격 관계대명사
in Sicily, an Italian island, while her husband worked in Germany. At
Sicily와 an Italian island는 동격
the time, more than 5% of the people in Italy could not read or write,
= over   illiterate: 글을 (읽거나 쓸 줄) 모르는, 문맹의
and she was one of them. This letter was discovered by Sicilian writer
→ 능동태: Sicilian writer Gesualdo Bufalino discovered this letter.
Gesualdo Bufalino.

Here's how he translated the pictures into words.
~가 여기 있다
My dear love, I miss you so much, and I reach my arms out toward
My dear love: 부부간의 호칭(여보, 당신)   reach ~ out: (손 등을) 내밀다, 뻗다
you, together with our three kids. We are all in good health except for
be in good health: 건강 상태가 좋다
the little one. He's a little sick, but not seriously.
= kid   = he's not seriously sick.

foreign 외국의

rather 다소, 약간

wait for ~을 기다리다

reply 답장

get over 이겨내다, 극복하다

husband 남편

discover 발견하다

translate 번역하다, 해석하다

toward ~을 향하여

in good health 건강하여

except for ~을 제외하고

seriously 진지하게, 심각하게

확인문제

● 다음 문장이 본문의 내용과 일치하면 T, 일치하지 않으면 F를 쓰시오.

1 It is rather easy and simple today to speak to family members or friends in a foreign
   country. ☐

2 Before the days of phones and the Internet, people just sent a letter and waited for a
   reply for a few days. ☐

3 Speaking to family members or friends in a foreign country was a lot harder if
   people couldn't read or write. ☐

4 In 1973, more than 5% of the people in the world could not read or write ☐

5 Gesualdo Bufalino was a Sicilian writer. ☐

6 Gesualdo Bufalino translated words into the pictures. ☐

I already sent you a letter, but there was no reply, so I am sad about it.

there was no reply(편지를 보냈는데 답장이 없는 것)

If I got a letter from you, I would be very happy. Your mother fell ill,

가정법 과거 → 직설법: As I don't get a letter from you, I'm not very happy.   *= became ill*

and I'm going to visit her in the hospital with some money and food. I'll

go there with our middle son while the oldest looks after the youngest.

while: ~하는 동안에(접속사)   *= the oldest kid*   *= the youngest kid*

I had two workers prepare our field and plant seeds for 150,000

사역동사 had로 목적어 다음에 동사원형(prepare, plant)을 쓴다.   *~의 비용으로*

lire. I voted for the DC. The PCI lost so many seats that it almost

너무 …해서 ~하다

seems dead. But whether one or the other wins, it's the same. Nothing

seem+형용사: ~해 보인다   *whether ~ or: ~이든지 아니든지*

changes for us poor people. We worked yesterday, and we will work

again tomorrow.

We picked lots of olives from our olive trees this year. I hired a man

whose sons are good workers. He knocked the olives down, and his

소유격 관계대명사   *knock ~ down: ~을 두드려 떨어뜨리다*

two sons helped him, picking them up from the ground. I paid him

'주우면서'라는 의미로 동시 동작을 표현

27,000 lire for the work. I spent 12,000 more for the olive press. I got

pay A B for C: A에게 C에 대한 대가로 B를 지불하다

enough oil to fill a large pot and a small one. I can sell it at a price of

enough … to ~: ~할 만큼 충분한 …   *= pot*   *~의 가격으로*

1,300 lire a liter.

~당, ~에

My love, my heart thinks of you as Christmas is coming. I would be

so happy if you were with me. We all miss you so much. I'm sending

가정법 과거. → 직설법: As you are not with me, I'm not so happy.

you a big hug from me and our three little kids. Goodbye, dear love.

My heart is yours, joined to you as our two rings are.

과거분사(분사구문)   *as: ~하듯이, ~하는 것처럼*   *are 뒤에 'joined'가 생략되었음.*

단어	뜻
ill	아픈, 병든
look after	~을 돌보다
prepare	준비하다
vote	투표하다, 선출하다
seat	의석
seem	~처럼 보이다
dead	죽은, 쓸모없는
whether	~이든지 아니든지
lots of	많은
hire	고용하다
knock	치다, 두드리다
ground	땅, 지면
oil	기름
at a price of	~의 가격으로
hug	포옹; 포옹하다
ring	반지

확인문제

● 다음 문장이 본문의 내용과 일치하면 T, 일치하지 않으면 F를 쓰시오.

1 The writer already sent her husband a letter, but there was no reply. ☐

2 The writer visited her mother-in-law in the hospital with some money and food. ☐

3 The writer got two workers to prepare their field and to plant seeds for 150,000 lire. ☐

4 The writer spent 27,000 lire for the olive press. ☐

5 The writer would be so happy if her husband were with her. ☐

6 The writer's husband is sending the writer and their three little kids a big hug. ☐

● 우리말을 참고하여 빈칸에 알맞은 말을 쓰시오.

1 _____ _____ _____ from a Mother of Three

2 _____ to family members or friends in a foreign country _____ _____ easy and simple today.

3 But before the days of phones and the Internet, it was not _____ _____.

4 People just sent a letter and _____ _____ a reply _____ _____.

5 And it was a lot harder if they _____ _____ _____.

6 This letter shows how people _____ _____ these difficulties.

7 It was written in 1973 by a woman _____ husband was _____ _____.

8 She lived in Sicily, an Italian island, while her husband worked _____ _____.

9 At the time, _____ _____ _____ of the people in Italy could not read or write, and she was _____ _____ _____.

10 This letter _____ _____ _____ Sicilian writer Gesualdo Bufalino.

11 Here's how he _____ the pictures _____ words.

12 My dear love, I miss you so much, and I _____ my arms _____ toward you, together with our three kids.

13 We are _____ _____ _____ _____ except for the little _____.

14 He's a little sick, but _____ _____.

15 I already sent you a letter, but _____ _____ _____ _____, so I am sad about it.

16 If I _____ a letter from you, I _____ _____ very happy.

1	세 아이의 엄마가 보낸 그림 편지
2	오늘날 외국에 있는 가족이나 친구와 대화하는 것은 다소 쉽고 간단하다.
3	하지만 전화와 인터넷 시대 이전에는 그것이 그렇게 쉽지 않았다.
4	사람들은 단지 편지를 보내고 답장을 몇 주 동안 기다렸다.
5	그리고 그들이 읽거나 쓸 수 없었다면 그건 훨씬 더 힘들었다.
6	이 편지는 사람들이 이런 어려움을 어떻게 극복했는지 보여준다.
7	그것은 남편이 멀리 떨어져 살았던 한 여자에 의해 1973년에 쓰여졌다.
8	그녀의 남편은 독일에서 일한 반면, 그녀는 이탈리아의 섬인 시실리에서 살았다.
9	그 당시에는 5% 이상의 이탈리아 사람들이 읽거나 쓸 수 없었고, 그녀도 그들 중 한 명이었다.
10	이 편지는 시실리의 작가 Gesualdo Bufalino가 발견하였다.
11	그가 그림들을 어떻게 글로 번역했는지는 다음과 같다.
12	사랑하는 여보, 난 당신이 정말 그립고, 우리 세 아이와 함께 당신을 향해 내 팔을 쭉 뻗고 있어요.
13	막내를 제외하고는 우리 모두 건강해요.
14	그 아이는 약간 아프지만 심각하진 않아요.
15	난 당신에게 이미 편지를 보냈지만, 답장이 없어서 그것 때문에 나는 슬퍼요.
16	당신에게서 편지를 받는다면, 나는 정말 행복할 거예요.

17 Your mother ___ _____, and I'm going to visit her in the hospital with some money and food.

18 I'll go there with our middle son _____ the oldest _____ _____ the youngest.

19 I _____ two workers _____ our field and _____ seeds for 150,000 lire.

20 I _____ _____ the DC.

21 The PCI lost _____ many seats _____ it almost seems dead.

22 But _____ _____ _____ _____ _____ wins, it's the same.

23 _____ _____ for us poor people.

24 We worked yesterday, and we _____ _____ _____ tomorrow.

25 We _____ lots of olives _____ our olive trees this year.

26 I _____ a man _____ sons are good workers.

27 He _____ the olives _____, and his two sons helped him, _____ them _____ from the ground.

28 I _____ him 27,000 lire _____ the work.

29 I _____ 12,000 more _____ the olive press.

30 I got _____ oil _____ _____ a large pot and a small _____.

31 I can sell it _____ _____ _____ _____ 1,300 lire a liter.

32 My love, my heart thinks of you _____ Christmas is coming.

33 I _____ _____ so happy if you _____ with me.

34 We all _____ you so much.

35 I'm sending you _____ _____ _____ from me and our three little kids.

36 Goodbye, _____.

37 My heart is yours, _____ to you _____ our two rings are.

---

17 당신의 어머니께서는 병이 드셨고, 나는 약간의 돈과 음식을 가지고 병원에 있는 어머니를 방문할 예정이에요.

18 큰애가 막내를 돌보는 동안 둘째와 함께 그곳에 갈 거예요.

19 나는 150,000리라에 두 일꾼을 시켜 우리 밭을 준비하고 씨앗을 심게 했어요.

20 나는 DC에 투표했어요.

21 PCI는 매우 많은 의석을 잃어서 거의 죽은 것처럼 보여요.

22 하지만 이쪽이 이기건 저쪽이 이기건, 상황은 똑같아요.

23 우리 가난한 사람들에게는 아무것도 바뀌지 않지요.

24 우리는 어제도 일했고, 내일도 다시 일할 거예요.

25 우리는 올해 올리브나무에서 올리브를 많이 땄어요.

26 나는 아들들이 훌륭한 일꾼인 한 남자를 고용했어요.

27 그가 올리브를 쳐서 떨어뜨리면 그의 두 아들이 땅에서 올리브를 주우면서 그를 도왔어요.

28 나는 그 일을 위해 그에게 27,000리라를 지급했어요.

29 올리브 압착을 위해 12,000리라를 더 썼어요.

30 나는 큰 항아리 하나와 작은 항아리 하나를 채울 만큼 충분한 기름을 얻었어요.

31 리터당 1,300리라의 가격으로 팔 수 있을 것 같아요.

32 여보, 크리스마스가 다가오면서 내 마음은 당신을 떠올려요.

33 당신이 나와 함께 있다면 난 정말 행복할 거예요.

34 우리는 모두 당신을 매우 많이 그리워해요.

35 나와 우리 세 아이의 큰 포옹을 보내요.

36 잘 있어요, 여보.

37 내 마음은 당신의 것이에요, 우리들의 두 반지처럼 당신과 연결된 채로요.

● 우리말을 참고하여 본문을 영작하시오.

1 세 아이의 엄마가 보낸 그림 편지
➡ _____

2 오늘날 외국에 있는 가족이나 친구와 대화하는 것은 다소 쉽고 간단하다.
➡ _____

3 하지만 전화와 인터넷 시대 이전에는 그것이 그렇게 쉽지 않았다.
➡ _____

4 사람들은 단지 편지를 보내고 답장을 몇 주 동안 기다렸다.
➡ _____

5 그리고 그들이 읽거나 쓸 수 없었다면 그건 훨씬 더 힘들었다.
➡ _____

6 이 편지는 사람들이 이런 어려움을 어떻게 극복했는지 보여 준다.
➡ _____

7 그것은 남편이 멀리 떨어져 살았던 한 여자에 의해 1973년에 쓰여졌다.
➡ _____

8 그녀의 남편은 독일에서 일한 반면, 그녀는 이탈리아의 섬인 시실리에서 살았다.
➡ _____

9 그 당시에는 5% 이상의 이탈리아 사람들이 읽거나 쓸 수 없었고, 그녀도 그들 중 한 명이었다.
➡ _____

10 이 편지는 시실리의 작가 Gesualdo Bufalino가 발견하였다.
➡ _____

11 그가 그림들을 어떻게 글로 번역했는지는 다음과 같다.
➡ _____

12 사랑하는 여보, 난 당신이 정말 그립고, 우리 세 아이와 함께 당신을 향해 내 팔을 쭉 뻗고 있어요.
➡ _____

13 막내를 제외하고는 우리 모두 건강해요.
➡ _____

14 그 아이는 약간 아프지만 심각하진 않아요.
➡ _____

15 난 당신에게 이미 편지를 보냈지만, 답장이 없어서 그것 때문에 나는 슬퍼요.
➡ _____

16 당신에게서 편지를 받는다면, 나는 정말 행복할 거예요.
➡ _____

17 당신의 어머니께서는 병이 드셨고, 나는 약간의 돈과 음식을 가지고 병원에 있는 어머니를 방문할 예정이에요.
➡ _____

18 큰애가 막내를 돌보는 동안 둘째와 함께 그곳에 갈 거예요.
➡ _____

19 나는 150,000리라에 두 일꾼을 시켜 우리 밭을 준비하고 씨앗을 심게 했어요.
➡ _____

20 나는 DC에 투표했어요.
➡ _____

21 PCI는 매우 많은 의석을 잃어서 거의 죽은 것처럼 보여요.
➡ _____

22 하지만 이쪽이 이기건 저쪽이 이기건, 상황은 똑같아요.
➡ _____

23 우리 가난한 사람들에게는 아무 것도 바뀌지 않지요.
➡ _____

24 우리는 어제도 일했고, 내일도 다시 일할 거예요.
➡ _____

25 우리는 올해 올리브나무에서 올리브를 많이 땄어요.
➡ _____

26 나는 아들들이 훌륭한 일꾼인 한 남자를 고용했어요.
➡ _____

27 그가 올리브를 쳐서 떨어뜨리면 그의 두 아들이 땅에서 올리브를 주우면서 그를 도왔어요.
➡ _____

28 나는 그 일을 위해 그에게 27,000리라를 지급했어요.
➡ _____

29 올리브 압착을 위해 12,000리라를 더 썼어요.
➡ _____

30 나는 큰 항아리 하나와 작은 항아리 하나를 채울 만큼 충분한 기름을 얻었어요.
➡ _____

31 리터당 1,300리라의 가격으로 팔 수 있을 것 같아요.
➡ _____

32 여보, 크리스마스가 다가오면서 내 마음은 당신을 떠올려요.
➡ _____

33 당신이 나와 함께 있다면 난 정말 행복할 거예요.
➡ _____

34 우리는 모두 당신을 매우 많이 그리워해요.
➡ _____

35 나와 우리 세 아이의 큰 포옹을 보내요.
➡ _____

36 잘 있어요, 여보.
➡ _____

37 내 마음은 당신의 것이에요, 우리들의 두 반지처럼 당신과 연결된 채로요.
➡ _____

[01~03] 다음 글을 읽고 물음에 답하시오.

> ⓐSpeaking to family members or friends in a foreign country is rather easy and simple today. But before the days of phones and the Internet, it was not that easy. People just sent a letter and waited for a reply for weeks. And it was a lot harder if they couldn't read or write.

01 위 글의 밑줄 친 ⓐSpeaking과 문법적 쓰임이 같은 것을 모두 고르시오.

① They were speaking in low voices.
② He went out without speaking to me.
③ Generally speaking, the more you pay, the more you get.
④ He is good at speaking English.
⑤ Be quiet! He hasn't finished speaking.

02 위 글의 제목으로 알맞은 것을 고르시오.

① How to Communicate with Family Members Who Couldn't Read or Write
② The Advantage of Phones and the Internet
③ The Development of the International Mail Service
④ The Difficulty of Speaking to People Abroad in Old Days
⑤ The Hard Lives of People Who Couldn't Read or Write

03 Which question CANNOT be answered after reading the passage?

① Today, is it difficult to speak to family members or friends in a foreign country?
② Before the days of phones and the Internet, was it easy to speak to family members or friends in a foreign country?
③ Before the days of phones and the Internet, how did people speak to people in a foreign country?
④ How long did it take to receive a reply after sending a letter to people in a foreign country?
⑤ How did people who couldn't read or write speak to people in a foreign country?

[04~06] 다음 글을 읽고 물음에 답하시오.

> We picked lots of olives from our olive trees this year. I ___ⓐ___ a man whose sons are good workers. He knocked the olives down, and his two sons helped him, picking them up from the ground. I paid him 27,000 lire for ⓑthe work. I spent 12,000 more for the olive press. I got enough oil to fill a large pot and a small one. I can sell it at a price of 1,300 lire ⓒa liter.

서답형
04 주어진 영영풀이를 참고하여 빈칸 ⓐ에 철자 h로 시작하는 단어를 쓰시오.

employed

➡ _____

서답형
05 위 글의 밑줄 친 ⓑthe work가 가리키는 것을 우리말로 쓰시오.

➡ _____
_____

06 위 글의 밑줄 친 ⓒa와 바꿔 쓸 수 있는 말을 쓰시오.

➡ _____

[07~09] 다음 글을 읽고 물음에 답하시오.

This letter shows how people got over these difficulties. (①) She lived in Sicily, an Italian island, while her husband worked in Germany. (②) At the time, more than 5% of the people in Italy could not read or write, and she was one of them. (③) This letter was discovered ___ⓐ___ Sicilian writer Gesualdo Bufalino. (④)

Here's how he translated the pictures ___ⓑ___ words. (⑤)

07 위 글의 빈칸 ⓐ와 ⓑ에 들어갈 전치사가 바르게 짝지어진 것은?

	ⓐ	ⓑ		ⓐ	ⓑ
①	for	to	②	by	into
③	in	to	④	for	into
⑤	by	on			

08 위 글의 흐름으로 보아, 주어진 문장이 들어가기에 가장 적절한 곳은?

> It was written in 1973 by a woman whose husband was far away.

①   ②   ③   ④   ⑤

09 According to the passage, which is NOT true?

① A woman whose husband worked in Germany wrote this letter in 1973.

② She lived in Sicily, an Italian island, and she was illiterate.

③ At the time, over 5% of the Italians could not read or write.

④ Sicilian writer Gesualdo Bufalino discovered this letter.

⑤ Gesualdo Bufalino translated her words into pictures.

[10~12] 다음 글을 읽고 물음에 답하시오.

I had two workers ___ⓐ___ our field and plant seeds for (A)150,000 lire. I voted for the DC. (B)The PCI lost ___ⓑ___ many seats ___ⓒ___ it almost seems dead. But whether one or the other wins, it's the same. Nothing changes for us poor people. We worked yesterday, and we will work again tomorrow.

10 위 글의 빈칸 ⓐ에 들어갈 알맞은 말을 고르시오.

① prepare   ② to prepare

③ prepared   ④ to have prepared

⑤ had prepared

11 문장 (B)가 다음과 같은 뜻이 되도록, 빈칸 ⓑ와 ⓒ에 들어갈 알맞은 말을 쓰시오.

> The PCI lost so many seats as to seem almost dead.

➡ ⓑ _____ ⓒ _____

12 위 글의 밑줄 친 (A)150,000을 영어로 읽는 법을 쓰시오.

➡ _____

[13~14] 다음 글을 읽고 물음에 답하시오.

My dear love, I miss you so much, and I reach my arms out toward you, together with our three kids. We are all in good health except for the little one. He's a little sick, but not seriously.

13 다음 중 위 글의 내용을 나타내는 그림 편지를 고르시오.

서답형

14 위 글의 내용을 다음과 같이 정리하고자 한다. 빈칸 (A)와 (B)에 들어갈 알맞은 단어를 쓰시오.

> A woman (A)_____ her husband who was far away and wrote a letter showing how she and their (B)_____ _____ were getting along.

[15~17] 다음 글을 읽고 물음에 답하시오.

> I'm sending you a big hug from me and our three little kids. Goodbye, dear love. My heart is yours, ⓐ to you as our two rings (A)are.

서답형

15 위 글의 빈칸 ⓐ에 join을 알맞은 형태로 쓰시오.

➡ _____

16 다음 중 위 글의 내용을 나타내는 그림 편지를 고르시오.

서답형

17 위 글의 밑줄 친 (A)are 뒤에 생략된 말을 쓰시오.

➡ _____

[18~20] 다음 글을 읽고 물음에 답하시오.

> I already sent you a letter, but there was no reply, so I am sad about it. ⓐIf I got a letter from you, I would be very happy. Your mother fell ill, and I'm going to visit her in the hospital with some money and food. I'll go there with our middle son while the oldest ⓑlooks after the youngest.

서답형

18 위 글의 밑줄 친 ⓐ를 직설법 문장으로 고치시오.

➡ _____
또는 _____

19 위 글의 밑줄 친 ⓑlooks after와 바꿔 쓸 수 있는 말을 모두 고르시오.

① takes care of   ② takes after
③ cares for   ④ looks for
⑤ asks after

서답형

20 Why does the writer say that it is the same whether the DC or the PCI wins? Fill in the blanks (A)~(C) with suitable words.

> Because (A)_____ changes for poor people and they (B)_____ yesterday, and they (C)_____ _____ again tomorrow.

[21~23] 다음 글을 읽고 물음에 답하시오.

My dear love, I ⓐmiss you so much, and I reach my arms out toward you, together with our three kids. We are all in good health except for the little one. He's a little sick, but not seriously.

I already sent you a letter, but there was no reply, so I am sad about ⓑit. ⓒ당신에게서 편지를 받는다면, 나는 정말 행복할 거예요. Your mother fell ill, and I'm going to visit her in the hospital with some money and food. I'll go there with our middle son while the oldest looks after the youngest.

21 위 글의 밑줄 친 ⓐmiss와 같은 의미로 쓰인 것을 고르시오.

① The bullet did miss her by about six inches.
② I will miss her when she leaves.
③ You must not miss meals when you're training.
④ The sale prices were too good to miss.
⑤ She didn't want to miss a good party last night.

서답형

22 위 글의 밑줄 친 ⓑit이 가리키는 것을 본문에서 찾아 쓰시오.

➡ _____

서답형

23 위 글의 밑줄 친 ⓒ의 우리말에 맞게 주어진 어휘를 이용하여 12 단어로 영작하시오.

got, from, very happy

➡ _____

[24~26] 다음 글을 읽고 물음에 답하시오.

We picked lots of olives from our olive trees this year. I hired a man whose sons are good workers. He knocked the olives down, and his two sons helped him, picking them up from the ground. I paid him 27,000 lire ___ⓐ___ the work. I spent 12,000 more for the olive press. I got enough oil to fill a large pot and a small one. I can sell it ___ⓑ___ a price of 1,300 lire ⓒa liter.

24 위 글의 빈칸 ⓐ와 ⓑ에 들어갈 전치사가 바르게 짝지어진 것은?

　　　ⓐ　ⓑ　　　　　　ⓐ　ⓑ
① for – to　　　② in – by
③ in – at　　　④ for – at
⑤ on – by

25 위 글의 밑줄 친 ⓒa와 같은 의미로 쓰인 것을 모두 고르시오.

① There's a Mrs. Green to see you.
② They cost 7 dollars a kilo.
③ A lion is a dangerous animal.
④ I can type 50 words a minute.
⑤ There's a visitor for you.

26 위 글을 읽고 알 수 없는 것을 고르시오.

① Did they pick lots of olives from their olive trees this year?
② Whom did the writer hire?
③ How much did the writer pay the worker?
④ How much oil did the writer get?
⑤ How much did the writer earn by selling the olive oil?

[01~03] 다음 글을 읽고 물음에 답하시오.

ⓐ이 편지는 사람들이 이런 어려움을 어떻게 극복
했는지 보여 준다. It was written in 1973 by a
woman whose husband was far away. She
lived in Sicily, an Italian island, while her
husband worked in Germany. At the time,
more than 5% of the people in Italy could not
read or write, and she was one of them. ⓑ
This letter was discovered by Sicilian writer
Gesualdo Bufalino.

Here's how he translated the pictures into
words.

01 위 글의 밑줄 친 ⓐ의 우리말에 맞게 주어진 어휘를 알맞게
배열하시오.

> these difficulties / people / how / this
> letter / shows / got over

➡ _____

_____

02 위 글의 밑줄 친 ⓑ를 능동태로 고치시오.

➡ _____

_____

03 To whom did the woman write the letter? Fill in the
blanks (A) and (B) with suitable words.

> She wrote it to (A)_____ _____
> who worked (B)_____ _____ .

[04~06] 다음 글을 읽고 물음에 답하시오.

My dear love, I miss you so much, and I ⓐ
reach my arms out toward you, together with

our three kids. ⓑ우리 모두 건강해요 except
for the little ⓒone. He's a little sick, but not
seriously.

04 위 글의 밑줄 친 ⓐ와 바꿔 쓸 수 있는 단어를 철자 s로 시
작하여 쓰시오.

➡ _____

05 위 글의 밑줄 친 ⓑ의 우리말에 맞게 6단어로 영작하시오.

➡ _____

06 위 글의 밑줄 친 ⓒone이 가리키는 것을 본문에서 찾아 쓰
시오.

➡ _____

[07~09] 다음 글을 읽고 물음에 답하시오.

We picked lots of olives from our olive trees
this year. I hired a man whose sons are good
workers. He knocked the olives down, and
his two sons helped him, picking ⓐthem up
from the ground. I paid him ___(A)___ lire for
the work. I spent ___(B)___ more for the olive
press. I got enough oil to fill a large pot and
a small one. I can sell it at a price of ___(C)___
lire a liter.

07 다음 그림을 참조하여 위 글의 빈칸 (A)~(C)에 들어갈 알맞
은 숫자를 쓰시오.

➡ (A) _____ (B) _____ (C) _____

08 위 글의 밑줄 친 ⓐthem이 가리키는 것을 본문에서 찾아 쓰시오.

➡ _____

09 How much did the writer spend picking the olives and pressing them? Answer in English in a full sentence. (4 words)

➡ _____

[10~12] 다음 글을 읽고 물음에 답하시오.

ⓐI already sent you a letter, but there was no reply, so I am sad about it. ⓑIf I got a letter from you, I will be very happy. Your mother fell ill, and I'm going to visit her in the hospital with some money and food. I'll go there with our middle son while the oldest looks after the youngest.

10 위 글의 밑줄 친 ⓐ를 3형식 문장으로 고치시오.

➡ _____

11 위 글의 밑줄 친 ⓑ에서 어법상 틀린 부분을 찾아 고치시오.

_____ ➡ _____

12 Why is she going to the hospital and with what will she go there? Fill in the blanks (A) and (B) with suitable words.

Because her mother-in-law (A)_____
_____ and is in the hospital, she is
going to the hospital with (B)_____
_____ _____ _____ .

[13~14] 다음 글을 읽고 물음에 답하시오.

(A)I had two workers prepare our field and plant seeds ___ⓐ___ 150,000 lire. I voted ___ⓑ___ the DC. The PCI lost so many seats that it almost seems dead. But whether one or the other wins, it's the same. Nothing changes for us poor people. We worked yesterday, and we will work again tomorrow.

13 위 글의 빈칸 ⓐ와 ⓑ에 공통으로 들어갈 알맞은 전치사를 쓰시오.

➡ _____

14 위 글의 밑줄 친 (A)를 got을 사용하여 고칠 때, 빈칸에 들어갈 알맞은 말을 쓰시오.

➡ I got two workers _____ our field

[15~16] 다음 글을 읽고 물음에 답하시오.

My love, my heart thinks of you ___ⓐ___ Christmas is coming. (A)I would be so happy if you were with me. We all miss you so much.

I'm sending you a big hug from me and our three little kids. Goodbye, dear love. My heart is yours, joined to you ___ⓑ___ our two rings are.

15 위 글의 빈칸 ⓐ와 ⓑ에 공통으로 들어갈 알맞은 말을 쓰시오.

➡ _____

16 위 글의 밑줄 친 (A)를 직설법 문장으로 고치시오.

➡ _____
또는 _____

해석

Express Yourself C1

The boy whose head is covered with bees doesn't understand the woman's
<u>소유격 관계대명사</u>　　　　　　　　　　　　<u>don't(×)</u>

gesture. I think it means "Jump into the pond." If I were the boy, I would jump
　　　　　= the woman's gesture　　　　　　　= Were I

into the pond right away.
　　　　　= right now = at once = immediately

구문해설 • be covered with: ~로 덮이다 • gesture: 몸짓 • right away: 즉시, 당장

머리가 벌로 덮인 소년은 그 여자의 몸짓을 이해하지 못합니다. 제 생각에 그것은 "연못으로 뛰어들어."를 의미합니다. 제가 그 소년이라면, 저는 당장 연못으로 뛰어들겠습니다.

Project Do it Yourself

"Climb up the mountain."

If I had soldiers to lead, I would use kites to send my messages. For example,
가정법 과거형으로 if절에 과거동사를, 주절에는 '조동사 과거형+동사원형'을 사용한다.

I would fly a kite whose face looks like a mountain to make the soldiers climb
　　　　　　　소유격 관계대명사　　look like+명사: ~처럼 보이다　　　사역동사+목적어+동사원형

up the mountain.

구문해설 • kite: 연

"산 위로 올라가라"
내가 병사를 지휘한다면, 나는 나의 메시지를 보내기 위해 연을 사용하겠다. 예를 들어, 나는 병사들이 산 위로 올라가게 하려고 앞면이 산처럼 보이는 연을 날리겠다.

Link to the World

Hangeul was created by King Sejong. At first, many people didn't want to
　　　　　　　수동태

use this new writing system. However, King Sejong tried hard to help people
　　　　　　　　　　　　　　　　　　　　　　　　　　~하기 위해서

use Hangeul. Thanks to him, we can express anything with Hangeul now. If
목적보어(= to use)

we didn't know Hangeul, we could not express ourselves easily.
　가정법 과거　　　　　　　　　조동사의 과거+동사원형　　재귀대명사(주어 = 목적어)

구문해설 • writing system: 문자 체계 • thanks to: ~ 덕택에
• express ourselves: 자기 자신을 표현하다

한글은 세종대왕에 의해 창제되었다. 처음에는 많은 사람이 이 새로운 문자 체계를 사용하는 것을 원하지 않았다. 하지만, 세종대왕은 사람들이 한글을 사용하도록 돕기 위해 열심히 노력했다. 그분 덕택에, 우리는 지금 한글로 무엇이든 표현할 수 있다. 우리가 한글을 모른다면, 우리 자신을 쉽게 표현할 수 없을 것이다.

Words & Expressions

01 다음 주어진 두 단어의 관계가 같도록 빈칸에 알맞은 단어를 쓰시오.

> hire – employ : embrace – _____

02 다음 문장의 빈칸 (a)와 (b)에 들어갈 단어가 바르게 짝지어진 것은?

> • Do you have your own way to ___(a)___ the cold?
> • This is why it is important to ___(b)___ respectable politicians.

① break down – reject
② get over – vote for
③ stand up for – accept
④ pick up – vote for
⑤ get over – compete

[03~04] 다음 영영풀이에 해당하는 것을 고르시오.

03

> the man that a woman is married to

① son　　　　　② hunter
③ manager　　　④ reporter
⑤ husband

04

> a position as a member of a committee, court, etc.

① seat　　　　　② permission
③ reply　　　　　④ figure
⑤ vote

05 다음 대화의 빈칸에 들어갈 말을 〈영영풀이〉를 참고하여 주어진 철자로 시작하여 쓰시오.

> B: I'm curious about sign language.
> G: Are you? Let me show you one e_____. Look.
> B: What does it mean?
> G: It means "Hello."

> 〈영영풀이〉 a group of words that has a special meaning

➡ _____

06 다음 밑줄 친 부분의 뜻이 잘못된 것은?

① The little boy seemed very hungry. (~하게 보였다)
② The woman was so surprised to see the dead insects by the window. (죽은)
③ Whether or not you come to the party, you must call him. (~인지 아닌지)
④ I was asked to prepare a report for our next meeting. (준비하다)
⑤ He knocked me on the head. (쳤다)

Conversation

07 다음 대화의 흐름상 단어의 쓰임이 어색한 부분을 찾아 바르게 고치시오. (1개)

> B: Now the enemy is crossing the (a)board in the dark. What are the soldiers going to do to send (b)messages? I'm curious about that.
> G: They will (c)light four chimneys.
> B: When they light all five of the (d)chimneys, what does that mean?
> G: It means the (e)battle has started.

_____ ➡ _____

[08~09] 다음 대화를 읽고 물음에 답하시오.

> B: This painting has some hidden secrets in it.
> G: Really? I'm curious about them. Where are the secrets?
> B: Find one yourself.
> G: Let's see. ... Oh, I see some letters here.
> B: You found one! It means "Jan van Eyck was here. 1434." It's Latin.
> G: That's awesome! Any other secrets?
> B: Okay. This dog tells us the man here was very rich.
> G: I don't understand.
> B: They had to spend lots of money to buy a dog of that kind at that time.
> G: I see. Only the rich could have that kind of dog, right?
> B: Exactly. Pictures speak a thousand words, you know.

08 위 대화를 읽고 답할 수 없는 질문은?

① What does the painting have?
② What do the letters the girl found mean?
③ Are the letters the girl found English?
④ What kind of a dog did people at that time like to raise?
⑤ What makes people think the man in the picture was very rich?

09 위 대화의 제목으로 가장 적절한 것은?

① How to Hide the Secrets in the Painting
② Can You Read Jan van Eyck's Painting?
③ Different Hobbies in Different Times
④ Can You Appreciate the Painting Correctly?
⑤ Jan van Eyck's Genius for Drawing the Painting

10 다음 대화를 순서에 맞게 바르게 배열한 것은?

> (A) I see. Now I can guess what they mean.
> (B) Oh, they are Braille. They are for blind people.
> (C) What are these dots for? I'm curious about them.

① (A) – (B) – (C)
② (B) – (A) – (C)
③ (C) – (B) – (A)
④ (A) – (C) – (B)
⑤ (C) – (A) – (B)

11 다음 짝지어진 대화 중 어색한 것은?

① A: What does his gesture mean? I'm curious about it.
　 B: It means "Step back from the pond."
② A: What would you do if you were a fish?
　 B: If I were a fish, I would swim in the pond.
③ A: What would you do if you had a beautiful voice?
　 B: If I had a beautiful voice, I would sing on the tree.
④ A: This woman doesn't want a dollar. So what does her gesture mean?
　 B: It means she wants a chicken.
⑤ A: I'm curious about sign language.
　 B: Let me show you one expression. Look. What does it mean?

12 주어진 문장과 같은 뜻이 되도록 바꾼 것 중 올바르지 <u>않은</u> 것을 고르시오.

① As the bag is expensive, I can't buy it.
   = If the bag were cheap, I could buy it.

② As I don't have a car, I can't give you a ride to school.
   = If I had a car, I could give you a ride to school.

③ As he doesn't know how to open the door, he can't enter the house.
   = If he knew how to open the door, he could enter the house.

④ If I had a bike, I would ride it to school.
   = As I have no bike, I don't ride it to school.

⑤ If he were good at dancing, he could take part in the contest.
   = As he is not poor at dancing, he can't take part in the contest.

13 다음 주어진 문장과 같은 의미의 문장을 가정법을 이용하여 쓰시오.

(1) As I know the singer, I can shake hands with him.
   = If _____
   _____.

(2) As he is not smart, he doesn't prepare for the game in advance.
   = If _____
   _____.

14 다음 빈칸에 들어갈 말이 <u>다른</u> 하나를 고르시오.

① I have speakers _____ sound loud.

② The girl _____ shirt is red is Emma's sister.

③ That is the shop _____ owner is not kind.

④ I know a boy _____ parents are both teachers.

⑤ My partner is the man _____ mother used to be an announcer.

15 다음 ⓐ~ⓔ 중 어법상 어색한 것을 찾아 바르게 고치시오.

Hangeul ⓐ<u>was created</u> by King Sejong. At first, many people didn't want ⓑ<u>to use</u> this new writing system. However, King Sejong tried hard ⓒ<u>to help</u> people use Hangeul. Thanks to him, we can express anything with Hangeul now. If we ⓓ<u>don't</u> know Hangeul, we could not express ⓔ<u>ourselves</u> easily.

_____ ➡ _____

16 다음 중 밑줄 친 부분의 쓰임이 나머지 넷과 <u>다른</u> 것은?

① Look at the car <u>whose</u> color is gold.

② I climbed the mountain <u>whose</u> top was covered with snow.

③ I'm not sure <u>whose</u> bag this is.

④ This is the backpack <u>whose</u> owner is unknown.

⑤ The girl <u>whose</u> dog has died is crying.

17 다음 중 어법상 <u>어색한</u> 문장의 개수로 알맞은 것은?

a. If I felt better, I could go shopping.
b. Were she you, she would never do that.
c. If I have more time, I could do it better.
d. If I were you, I won't go there.
e. If I knew her, I will introduce her to you.

① 1개   ② 2개   ③ 3개   ④ 4개   ⑤ 5개

18 우리말과 같은 뜻이 되도록 빈칸에 알맞은 말을 쓰시오.

> 그 소년이 키가 더 크다면, 그 장면을 볼 수 있을 텐데.
> → The boy _____ the scene if he _____ .

19 다음 우리말을 주어진 어휘를 이용하여 영어로 옮기시오.

(1) 내가 병사들을 지휘한다면, 나는 나의 메시지를 보내기 위해 연을 사용하겠다.

➡ If I had soldiers to lead, I _____ _____ . (kites, messages)

(2) 나는 앞면이 산처럼 보이는 연을 날리겠다.

➡ I would fly a kite _____ _____ . (face, look like)

(3) 가방이 과일로 가득한 소년은 원숭이를 보는 중이다.

➡ The boy _____ is looking at the monkey. (full of, fruit)

Reading

[20~22] 다음 글을 읽고 물음에 답하시오.

> This letter shows how people ①got over these difficulties. It was written in 1973 by a woman ②whose husband was far away. She lived in Sicily, an Italian island, while her husband worked in Germany. At the time, ③ more than 5% of ④the people in Italy could not read or write, and she was one of ⓐthem. This letter was discovered by Sicilian writer Gesualdo Bufalino.
>
> Here's ⑤how he translated the pictures into words.

20 위 글의 밑줄 친 ①~⑤와 바꿔 쓸 수 있는 말로 옳지 <u>않은</u> 것을 고르시오.

① overcame   ② of which
③ over   ④ the Italians
⑤ the way

21 위 글의 밑줄 친 ⓐthem이 가리키는 것을 영어로 쓰시오.

➡ _____
_____

22 위 글의 뒤에 올 내용으로 가장 알맞은 것을 고르시오.

① Gesualdo Bufalino가 시실리 여인의 그림 편지를 발견한 상황
② 이탈리아 사람들의 높은 문맹율
③ Gesualdo Bufalino가 그림 편지들을 글로 번역한 내용
④ 여인의 남편이 보낸 답장의 내용
⑤ Gesualdo Bufalino가 시실리 여인의 말을 그림 편지로 옮겨준 내용

[23~25] 다음 글을 읽고 물음에 답하시오.

> My dear love, I miss you so much, and I reach my arms out toward you, together with our three kids. We are all in good health except for the little ⓐone. He's a little sick, but not seriously.
>
> I already sent you a letter, but there was no reply, so I am sad about it. If I got a ⓑletter from you, I would be very happy. Your mother fell ill, and I'm going to visit her in the hospital with some money and food. I'll go there with our middle son while the oldest looks after the youngest.

23 위 글의 밑줄 친 ⓐone과 문법적 쓰임이 같은 것을 고르시오.

① Do you want one biscuit or two?
② I saw her one afternoon last week.
③ They all went off in one direction.
④ One must observe the rules.
⑤ I have many bags, and this one is my favorite.

24 위 글의 밑줄 친 ⓑletter와 바꿔 쓸 수 있는 말을 본문에서 찾아 쓰시오.

➡ _____

25 According to the passage, which is NOT true?

① The writer misses her husband so much.
② The writer's little kid is a little sick.
③ The writer is sending a letter to her husband for the first time.
④ The writer's mother-in-law fell ill and is in the hospital now.
⑤ The writer's oldest kid will look after the youngest while their mom goes to visit their grandmother in the hospital.

[26~27] 다음 글을 읽고 물음에 답하시오.

We picked lots of olives from our olive trees this year. (①) He knocked the olives down, and his two sons helped him, ⓐ땅에서 그것들을 주우면서. (②) I paid him 27,000 lire for the work. (③) I spent 12,000 more for the olive press. (④) I got enough oil to fill a large pot and a small one. (⑤) I can sell it at a price of 1,300 lire a liter.

26 위 글의 흐름으로 보아, 주어진 문장이 들어가기에 가장 적절한 곳은?

I hired a man whose sons are good workers.

① ② ③ ④ ⑤

27 위 글의 밑줄 친 ⓐ의 우리말에 맞게 주어진 어휘를 이용하여 6 단어로 영작하시오.

picking, ground

➡ _____

[28~29] 다음 글을 읽고 물음에 답하시오.

The boy whose backpack the monkey is pulling doesn't understand its gesture. I think (A)it means "Give the fruit to me." If I ___ⓐ___ the boy, I would give the fruit to the monkey right away.

28 위 글의 빈칸 ⓐ에 be를 알맞은 형태로 쓰시오.

➡ _____

29 위 글의 밑줄 친 (A)it이 가리키는 것을 본문에서 찾아 쓰시오.

➡ _____

01 출제율 90%

다음 짝지어진 단어의 관계가 같도록 주어진 철자로 시작하는 단어를 쓰시오.

> ill – healthy : dead – a_____

02 출제율 95%

다음 영영풀이에 해당하는 단어는?

> to make something ready for use

① prefer   ② prepare
③ vote   ④ translate
⑤ encourage

03 출제율 90%

다음 대화를 읽고 빈칸에 들어갈 말을 〈조건〉에 맞게 쓰시오.

┤ 조건 ├
• 'It means'와 enter를 사용하여 정의를 나타내는 표현을 쓸 것.

> G: What's this? I'm curious about it.
> B: It's a traffic sign. _____
> G: Oh, I see.

➡ _____
_____

[04~05] 다음 대화를 읽고 물음에 답하시오.

> B: What are the soldiers doing with the five chimneys on TV?
>
> (A) Really? I'm curious about the system. Can you tell me more?
> (B) Well, do you see the two smoking chimneys?
> (C) They are sending messages to the king by using the chimneys.

(D) Yes. What do they mean?

G: They mean they just saw an enemy.

04 출제율 100%

위 대화의 (A)~(D)를 순서대로 배열하시오.

➡ _____

05 출제율 95%

위 대화를 읽고 다음 질문에 영어로 답하시오. (be for를 이용하시오)

> Q: What do you think the chimneys are for?

➡ _____

06 출제율 90%

다음 대화의 빈칸 (A)에 들어갈 말로 알맞은 것은?

> B: If there's no enemy, they don't smoke at all, do they?
> G: _____(A)_____ Smoke from one chimney means "No enemy."
> B: Now smoke is rising from three chimneys. What does that mean?
> G: It means an enemy is coming close to the border.

① No, they don't.
② Yes, they don't.
③ Yes, they do.
④ No, they do.
⑤ Yes, they are.

다음 대화에서 주어진 문장이 들어갈 위치로 알맞은 것은?

> B: This painting has some hidden secrets in it.
>
> G: Really? I'm curious about them. Where are the secrets?
>
> B: Find one yourself. (A)
>
> G: Let's see. ... Oh, I see some letters here.
>
> B: You found one! (B) It's Latin.
>
> G: That's awesome! (C) Any other secrets?
>
> B: Okay. This dog tells us the man here was very rich.
>
> G: (D) I don't understand.
>
> B: They had to spend lots of money to buy a dog of that kind at that time.
>
> G: I see. (E) Only the rich could have that kind of dog, right?
>
> B: Exactly. Pictures speak a thousand words, you know.

> It means "Jan van Eyck was here. 1434."

① (A) ② (B) ③ (C) ④ (D) ⑤ (E)

08 다음 대화의 빈칸 (A)에 들어갈 말로 알맞은 것은?

> W: What does this woman's gesture mean? I'm curious about it.
>
> M: _____ (A)
>
> W: Why do you think so?
>
> M: The boy has lots of bees on his head. And the woman is pointing at the pond.

① It means "You're welcome."

② It means "History repeats itself."

③ It means she wants a chicken.

④ I think it means "Jump into the pond."

⑤ It means "Turn it off."

09 다음 짝지어진 대화 중 어색한 것은?

① A: What does its gesture mean? I'm curious about it.
   B: It means "Give the fruit to me."

② A: What would you do if you had strong arms?
   B: If I had strong arms, I could climb trees.

③ A: Do you know what this means?
   B: Sure.

④ A: Do you know what this means?
   B: No, I don't. What does it mean?

⑤ A: This house is famous for having thousands of secrets in it.
   B: Really? It means you must find the secrets.

10 다음 대화의 빈칸에 들어갈 말로 알맞은 것은?

> W: This woman doesn't want a dollar. So what does her gesture mean?
>
> M: _____
>
> W: Then the boy should bring a chicken to get the fruit, right?
>
> M: I think so.

① It means you must not ride a bike here.

② It means you must be careful with the animals.

③ It means she wants a chicken.

④ It means you must drive slowly here.

⑤ It means the battle has started.

11 다음 ①~⑤ 중 어법상 어색한 것은?

> The house ①which doors ②are painted ③red ④is ⑤my grandfather's.

✏ 출제율 90%

12 'whose'를 사용하여 〈보기〉와 같이 두 문장을 한 문장으로 연결하시오.

┌─ 보기 ─┐

Tom easily found the store.
+ Its address was on the Internet.
→ Tom easily found the store whose address was on the Internet.

(1) Is there any student?
+ His name was not called.

➡ _____
_____

(2) Mike is the boy.
+ His hair is very short.

➡ _____
_____

(3) The house is my uncle's.
+ Its windows are very big.

➡ _____
_____

(4) My sister is the girl.
+ Her cat is eating a fish.

➡ _____
_____

(5) Do you know the old man?
+ His shoes are red and blue.

➡ _____
_____

✏ 출제율 95%

13 잘못된 부분을 바르게 고쳐 문장을 다시 쓰시오.

(1) I know a boy who mother grows bananas.

➡ _____

(2) The boy of which dog is barking is my cousin.

➡ _____

(3) The girl whose hat is covered with flowers are a great dancer.

➡ _____
_____

(4) You were with me, I could show you my painting.

➡ _____
_____

(5) If I were a fish, I can swim in the water.

➡ _____
_____

[14~16] 다음 글을 읽고 물음에 답하시오.

Speaking to family members or friends in a foreign country is rather easy and simple today. But before the days of phones and the Internet, ⓐit was not ⓑthat easy. People just sent a letter and waited for a reply for weeks. And ⓒit was ⓓa lot harder if they couldn't read or write.

✏ 출제율 95%

14 위 글의 밑줄 친 ⓐit과 ⓒit이 공통으로 가리키는 것을 본문에서 찾아 쓰시오.

➡ _____
_____

✏ 출제율 100%

15 아래 〈보기〉에서 위 글의 밑줄 친 ⓑthat과 문법적 쓰임이 같은 것의 개수를 고르시오.

┌─ 보기 ─┐

① I can't walk that far.
② Can you see that dog?
③ I know that you are busy.
④ This book is mine and that one is yours.
⑤ Are you sure she's that young?

① 1개   ② 2개   ③ 3개   ④ 4개   ⑤ 5개

16 위 글의 밑줄 친 ⓐa lot과 바꿔 쓸 수 없는 말을 고르시오.

① much ② even ③ still
④ rather ⑤ far

[17~19] 다음 글을 읽고 물음에 답하시오.

My dear love, I miss you so much, and ⓐI reach my arms out toward you, together with our three kid s. (①) He's a little sick, but not seriously. (②)

I already sent you a letter, but there was no reply, so I am sad about it. (③) If I got a letter from you, I would be very happy. (④) Your mother fell ill, and I'm going to visit her in the hospital with some money and food. (⑤) I'll go there with our middle son while the oldest looks after the youngest.

17 위 글의 흐름으로 보아, 주어진 문장이 들어가기에 가장 적절한 곳은?

> We are all in good health except for the little one.

① ② ③ ④ ⑤

18 위 글의 밑줄 친 ⓐ를 다음과 같이 바꿔 쓸 때 빈칸에 들어갈 알맞은 단어를 쓰시오.

➡ I reach _____ my arms toward you

19 위 글을 읽고 알 수 없는 것을 고르시오.

① How many kids were there in the writer's family?
② Was the oldest kid sick?

③ Why was there no reply from her husband?
④ With whom will the writer visit the hospital?
⑤ Who will look after her youngest son while she goes to the hospital?

[20~21] 다음 글을 읽고 물음에 답하시오.

ⓐThe boy whose head is covered with bees don't understand the woman's gesture. I think it means "Jump into the pond." If I were the boy, I would jump into the pond ⓑright away.

20 위 글의 밑줄 친 ⓐ에서 어법상 틀린 부분을 찾아 고치시오.

_____ ➡ _____

21 위 글의 밑줄 친 ⓑright away와 바꿔 쓸 수 있는 말을 모두 고르시오.

① hesitatingly ② right now
③ at once ④ gradually
⑤ immediately

01 다음 대화의 우리말에 맞게 주어진 단어를 알맞은 순서로 배열하시오.

> G: I'm curious about that robot. Why is it standing there?
>
> B: It's a kind of ad. 그것은 그들의 건전지가 매우 강력하다는 것을 사람들에게 말하고 있어.

(their / it / people / tells / batteries / powerful / are / very)

➡ _____

[02~03] 다음 대화를 읽고 물음에 답하시오.

> B: This painting has some hidden secrets in it.
> G: Really? I'm curious about them. Where are the secrets?
> B: Find one yourself.
> G: Let's see. ... Oh, I see some letters here.
> B: You found one! It means "Jan van Eyck was here. 1434." It's Latin.
> G: That's awesome! Any other secrets?
> B: Okay. This dog tells us the man here was very rich.
> G: I don't understand.
> B: They had to spend lots of money to buy a dog of that kind at that time.
> G: I see. Only the rich could have that kind of dog, right?
> B: Exactly. _____, you know.

02 위 대화의 흐름상 빈칸은 글의 주제문에 해당한다. 〈조건〉에 맞게 쓰시오.

> ┤ 조건 ├
> • 'pictures'와 'a thousand'를 이용하시오.

➡ _____

03 위 대화를 읽고 요약문을 완성하시오.

> The boy and the girl are talking about the _____ of Jan van Eyck's painting. The girl finds some _____ letters. It _____ "Jan van Eyck was here. 1434." The boy tells her about the dog. Only _____ could have that kind of dog at that time, so the man in the picture was very _____.

04 다음 글에서 어법상 틀린 곳의 기호를 쓰고 바르게 고치시오.

> Hangeul ㉠created by King Sejong. At first, many people didn't want to use this new writing system. However, King Sejong tried hard to help people ㉡using Hangeul. ㉢Thanks to him, we can express ㉣anything with Hangeul now. If we didn't know Hangeul, we ㉤can't express ourselves easily.

➡ (1) _____ (2) _____
　 (3) _____

05 다음 문장을 가정법을 이용하여 같은 의미의 문장으로 바꾸어 쓰시오.

(1) As I have some money, I can buy the new shoes.

➡ _____

_____

(2) As Suji is not here, I can't tell her the story.

➡ _____

_____

06 괄호 안에 주어진 표현을 사용하여 밑줄 친 우리말을 영어로 완성하시오.

(1) (the alarm clock)
A: I was late for school again today. I don't want to be late anymore.
B: 내가 너라면, 자명종을 맞춰 놓겠어.
➡ _____

(2) (by hand)
A: I can't finish my report. My computer is broken.
B: 내가 너라면, 그것을 손으로 쓰겠어.
➡ _____

(3) (search)
A: The music in the movie is so touching. I want to know the name of the song.
B: 내가 너라면, 인터넷에서 그것을 검색해 볼 텐데.
➡ _____

[07~08] 다음 글을 읽고 물음에 답하시오.

We picked lots of olives from our olive trees this year. I hired a man whose sons are good workers. ⓐHe knocked the olives down, and his two sons helped him, picking up them from the ground. I paid him 27,000 lire for the work. I spent 12,000 more for the olive press. I got enough oil to fill a large pot and a small one. I can sell ⓑit at a price of 1,300 lire a liter.

07 위 글의 밑줄 친 ⓐ에서 어법상 틀린 부분을 찾아 고치시오.

_____ ➡ _____

08 위 글의 밑줄 친 ⓑit이 가리키는 것을 영어로 쓰시오.

➡ _____

[09~11] 다음 글을 읽고 물음에 답하시오.

Speaking to family members or friends in a foreign country (A)[is / are] rather easy and simple today. But before the days of phones and the Internet, it was not that easy. People just sent a letter and waited for a reply for weeks. And (a)그들이 읽거나 쓸 수 없었다면 그건 훨씬 더 힘들었다.

This letter shows how people got over these difficulties. It was written in 1973 by a woman ___ⓐ___ husband was far away. She lived in Sicily, an Italian island, (B)[during / while] her husband worked in Germany. At the time, more than 5% of the people in Italy could not read or write, and she was one of them. This letter was discovered by Sicilian writer Gesualdo Bufalino.

Here's (C)[how / what] he translated the pictures into words.

09 Fill in the blank ⓐ with a suitable word.

➡ _____

10 위 글의 괄호 (A)~(C)에서 어법상 알맞은 낱말을 골라 쓰시오.

➡ (A) _____ (B) _____ (C) _____

11 위 글의 밑줄 친 (a)의 우리말에 맞게 주어진 어휘를 이용하여 11 단어로 영작하시오.

a lot

➡ _____

창의사고력 서술형 문제

01 주어진 〈보기〉와 같이 표지판에 관한 의미를 묻고 답을 하시오.

be careful with the animals

SPEED 30
drive slowly here

not ride a bike here

| 보기 |
| A: What does this sign mean? |
| B: It means you must be careful with the animals. |

(1) _____

(2) _____

02 가정법 과거를 이용하여, 친구에게 충고하는 말을 써 보시오.

(1) If I were you, _____.

(2) Were I you, _____.

(3) If I were in your position, _____.

(4) If I were in your shoes, _____.

03 다음 내용과 대화를 바탕으로 기자의 방송 내용을 완성하시오.

The girl's bag is in the pond. The girl is trying to pick up her bag, but she seems to be in danger.
A: What does the man's gesture mean? I'm curious about it.
B: It means "Step back from the pond."

The girl whose bag is (A)_____ doesn't understand the man's (B)_____. I think it means "(C)_____." If I were the girl, I would step back from the pond.

단원별 모의고사

01 다음 단어에 대한 영어 설명이 <u>어색한</u> 것은?

① hidden: not easy to find
② reply: an answer to a letter
③ rather: in some degree
④ ill: in a way that is bad or dangerous enough to make you worried
⑤ toward: in the direction of

02 다음 짝지어진 단어의 관계가 같도록 빈칸에 알맞은 말을 쓰시오.

curious – inquisitive : boundary – _____

03 다음 영영풀이에 해당하는 단어를 고르시오.

the surface of the Earth

① disease ② hospital ③ ill
④ ground ⑤ health

04 다음 중 짝지어진 대화가 <u>어색한</u> 것은?

① A: What does that mean?
  B: It means an enemy is coming close to the border.
② A: What does this man's gesture mean? I'm curious about it.
  B: It means "Turn it off."
③ A: I'm curious about sign language.
  B: Are you? Let me show you one expression. Look.
④ A: What does her name mean? I'm curious about it.
  B: It means "bright girl."
⑤ A: What does this letter mean?
  B: This letter was written in blue ink.

05 빈칸에 들어갈 말로 알맞은 것은?

B: Now the enemy is crossing the border in the dark. What are the soldiers going to do to send messages? I'm curious about that.
G: _____
B: When they light all five of the chimneys, what does that mean?
G: It means the battle has started.

① Can you tell me more?
② They will light four chimneys.
③ They're curious about that, too.
④ They mean they just saw an enemy.
⑤ It means you must not enter.

06 대화의 흐름상 빈칸에 들어갈 말을 본문에서 찾아 쓰시오. (2 단어)

B: If there's no enemy, they don't smoke at all, do they?
G: Yes, they do. Smoke from one chimney means "_____."
B: Now smoke is rising from three chimneys. What does that mean?
G: It means an enemy is coming close to the border.

➡ _____

07 다음 대화의 빈칸에 들어갈 말로 알맞은 것은?

G: What are these dots for? I'm curious _____ them.
B: Oh, they are Braille. They are for blind people.

① about ② from ③ with
④ for ⑤ to

[08~09] 다음 대화를 읽고 물음에 답하시오.

> B: This painting has _____(A)_____ in it.
> G: Really? I'm curious about them. Where are the secrets?
> B: Find one yourself.
> G: Let's see. ... Oh, I see some letters here.
> B: You found one! It means "Jan van Eyck was here. 1434." It's Latin.
> G: That's awesome! Any other secrets?
> B: Okay. This dog tells us the man here was very rich.
> G: I don't understand.
> B: They had to spend lots of money to buy a dog of that kind at that time.
> G: I see. Only the rich could have that kind of dog, right?
> B: Exactly. Pictures speak a thousand words, you know.

08 위 대화의 빈칸 (A)에 들어갈 말로 알맞은 것은?

① some values
② several disappointing facts
③ some hidden secrets
④ wide gap between the rich and poor
⑤ some obvious facts

09 Why do people think the man in the picture was very rich?

➡ _____

_____

10 봉수대 신호에 관한 다음 대화의 빈칸 (A)~(C)에 들어갈 말을 〈보기〉에서 찾아 쓰시오.

> B: What are the soldiers doing with the five chimneys on TV?
> G: They are sending messages to the king by using the chimneys.
> B: Really? I'm curious about the system. Can you tell me more?
> G: Well, do you see the two smoking chimneys?
> B: Yes. What do they mean?
> G: _____(A)_____
> B: If there's no enemy, they don't smoke at all, do they?
> G: Yes, they do. Smoke from one chimney means "No enemy."
> B: Now smoke is rising from three chimneys. What does that mean?
> G: It means an enemy is coming close to the border.
> B: _____(B)_____ What are the soldiers going to do to send messages? I'm curious about that.
> G: They will light four chimneys.
> B: When they light all five of the chimneys, what does that mean?
> G: _____(C)_____

> ┤ 보기 ├
> • It means the battle has started.
> • They mean they just saw an enemy.
> • Now the enemy is crossing the border in the dark.

➡ (A) _____
(B) _____
(C) _____

11 빈칸 (A)에 들어갈 말로 알맞은 것은?

> W: What does this man's gesture mean?
> _____(A)_____
> M: It means "Turn it off."
> W: Really? What makes you think so?
> M: The other hunter there is coming close to an animal.
> W: Oh, I see.

① It means " History repeats itself."
② I'm curious about it.
③ I'm curious about sign language.
④ I'm curious about the system.
⑤ I'm curious about that balloon.

12 다음 중 빈칸에 들어갈 단어가 <u>다른</u> 것은?

① If she _____ in Seoul now, she could see the parade.
② If it _____ not for your beautiful voice, people wouldn't listen to your song.
③ If you _____ on a desert island, what would you do first?
④ We couldn't live for a day if there _____ no water in the world.
⑤ I would fight bad guys if I _____ super powers.

13 다음 두 문장을 한 문장으로 바르게 옮긴 것은?

• The man is good at playing soccer.
• His son is a world-famous soccer player.

① The man is good at playing soccer whose son is a world-famous soccer player.
② The man whose son is a world-famous soccer player is good at playing soccer.
③ The man whose son is good at playing soccer is a world-famous soccer player.
④ The man his son is a world-famous soccer player is good at playing soccer.
⑤ The man is good at playing soccer his son is a world-famous soccer player.

14 다음 우리말을 영어로 바르게 옮긴 것은?

네가 좋아하는 아이돌이 너와 사랑에 빠지면, 너는 어떻게 하겠니?

① If your favorite idol star falls in love with you, what would you do?
② If your favorite idol star fell in love with you, what would you do?
③ If your favorite idol star fell in love with you, what will you do?
④ If your favorite idol star fell in love with you, what you would do?
⑤ If your favorite idol star were fallen in love with you, what would you do?

15 다음 우리말과 일치하도록 주어진 단어를 알맞게 배열하시오.

나는 직업이 소방관인 오빠가 있다.
(have, job, is, a, I, brother, a, fire fighter, whose)

➡ _____

16 다음 문장에서 밑줄 친 우리말을 영어로 옮기시오.

(1) <u>내가 신이라면</u>, I would help poor children.
➡ _____
(2) <u>내가 과거로 여행한다면</u>, I would tell people to protect our environment more.
➡ _____

[17~19] 다음 글을 읽고 물음에 답하시오.

Speaking to family members or friends in a foreign country is rather easy and simple today. But before the days of phones and the Internet, it was not that easy. People just sent a letter and waited for a reply for weeks. And it was a lot harder if they couldn't read or write.

This letter shows how people got over ⓐ <u>these difficulties</u>. It was written in 1973 by a woman whose husband was far away. She lived in Sicily, an Italian island, while her husband worked in Germany. At the time, more than 5% of the people in Italy could not read or write, and she was one of them. This letter was discovered by Sicilian writer Gesualdo Bufalino.

ⓑHere's the way how he translated the pictures into words.

17 위 글의 주제로 알맞은 것을 고르시오.

① the easy way to speak to people in a foreign country
② the difficulties that illiterate people experienced in the past
③ the high illiteracy rate of Italy in the past
④ a picture letter from a woman who couldn't read or write to her husband in a foreign country
⑤ the letter from Gesualdo Bufalino to a Sicilian woman

18 What do the underlined ⓐthese difficulties mean? Fill in the blanks (A) and (B) with suitable words.

> They mean the difficulties that people, especially the illiterate, experienced while trying to speak to family members or friends in (A)_____ _____ _____ before the days of (B)_____ _____ _____ _____.

19 위 글의 밑줄 친 ⓑ에서 어법상 틀린 부분을 찾아 고치시오.

_____ ➡ _____

[20~22] 다음 글을 읽고 물음에 답하시오.

We picked lots of olives from our olive trees this year. I hired a man whose sons are good workers. He knocked the olives down, and his two sons helped him, ⓐpicking them up from the ground. I paid him ⓑ27,000 lire for the work. I spent ⓒ12,000 more for the olive press. I got enough oil to fill a large pot and a small one. I can sell it at a price of ⓓ1,300 lire a liter.

20 아래 〈보기〉에서 위 글의 밑줄 친 ⓐpicking과 문법적 쓰임이 다른 것의 개수를 고르시오.

┤ 보기 ├
① I like to study, listening to pop music.
② They supported him, saying that he was right.
③ I punished him for being dishonest.
④ He extended his hand, smiling brightly.
⑤ My dream is traveling in Europe.

① 1개   ② 2개   ③ 3개   ④ 4개   ⑤ 5개

21 위 글의 밑줄 친 ⓑ27,000, ⓒ12,000, ⓓ1,300을 영어로 읽는 법을 쓰시오.

➡ ⓑ _____
　 ⓒ _____
　 ⓓ _____

22 According to the passage, which is NOT true?

① The writer employed a man whose sons are good workers.
② The worker's two sons helped him pick the olives up from the ground.

③ The writer paid the worker 27,000 lire for the work.

④ The writer spent 12,000 lire for the olive press.

⑤ The writer can sell the olive oil at a price of 1,300 lire a liter.

25 다음 문장에서 위 글의 내용과 <u>다른</u> 부분을 찾아서 고치시오.

> The writer will visit her husband's mother with her oldest son.

➡ _____ ➡ _____

[23~25] 다음 글을 읽고 물음에 답하시오.

> My dear love, I miss you so much, and I reach my arms out toward you, together with our three kids. We are all _____ⓐ_____ good health except for the little one. He's a little sick, but not seriously.
>
> I already sent you (A)_____ _____, but there was no reply, so I am sad about it. If I got a letter from you, I would be very happy. Your mother fell ill, and I'm going to visit her in (B)_____ _____ with some money and food. I'll go there with our middle son while the oldest looks _____ⓑ_____ the youngest.

23 위 글의 빈칸 ⓐ와 ⓑ에 들어갈 전치사가 바르게 짝지어진 것은?

      ⓐ   ⓑ   ⓐ   ⓑ
① on – for   ② in – for
③ in – after   ④ on – to
⑤ for – after

24 다음 그림을 참조하여 위 글의 빈칸 (A)와 (B)에 들어갈 알맞은 말을 쓰시오.

➡ (A) _____ (B) _____

[26~27] 다음 글을 읽고 물음에 답하시오.

> We picked lots of olives from our olive trees this year. I hired a man whose sons are good workers. He knocked the olives down, and his two sons helped him, picking them up from the ground. I paid him 27,000 lire for the work. I spent 12,000 more for the olive press. I got enough oil ⓐ<u>to fill</u> a large pot and a small ⓑ<u>one</u>. I can sell it at a price of 1,300 lire a liter.

26 아래 <보기>에서 위 글의 밑줄 친 ⓐto fill과 to부정사의 용법이 같은 것의 개수를 고르시오.

> ┤ 보기 ├
> ① It's time for you to go to bed.
> ② He went to the library to borrow books.
> ③ I have a pet to play with.
> ④ She has a special way to cook rice.
> ⑤ It is very good to get up early in the morning.

① 1개   ② 2개   ③ 3개   ④ 4개   ⑤ 5개

27 위 글의 밑줄 친 ⓑone이 가리키는 것을 본문에서 찾아 쓰시오.

➡ _____

MEMO

Lesson 6

We Are All Makers

의사소통 기능

- 선호에 대해 묻기
  Which do you prefer, pandas or cats?

- 싫어하는 것 표현하기
  I hate holding things in my hands.

언어 형식

- the + 비교급, the +비교급
  The more books we share, the more we learn.

- It ... that 강조구문
  It is this filtered water that you can drink.

教科書

Words & Expressions

Key Words

- □ **3D print** 3차원 인쇄를 하다
- □ **actually** [ǽktʃuəli] 倶 사실, 실제로
- □ **artistic** [ɑːrtístik] 謄 예술적인
- □ **artwork** [ɑ́ːrtwərk] 몡 예술품, 공예품
- □ **available** [əvéiləbl] 謄 이용할 수 있는
- □ **battery life** 건전지 수명
- □ **beat** [biːt] 宕 물리치다
- □ **bookstore** [búkstɔr] 몡 서점
- □ **check** [tʃek] 宕 확인하다
- □ **cheerful** [tʃíərfəl] 謄 유쾌한, 기분 좋은
- □ **cloth** [klɔːθ] 몡 천, 옷감
- □ **collect** [kəlékt] 宕 모으다
- □ **colorful** [kʌ́lərfəl] 謄 화려한
- □ **company** [kʌ́mpəni] 몡 회사
- □ **connect** [kənékt] 宕 연결하다
- □ **cute** [kjuːt] 謄 귀여운
- □ **disease** [dizíːz] 몡 질병, 질환
- □ **display** [displéi] 몡 전시, 진열 宕 전시하다, 진열하다
- □ **drinkable** [dríŋkəbl] 謄 마실 수 있는
- □ **enter** [éntər] 宕 입력하다
- □ **facial** [féiʃəl] 謄 얼굴의
- □ **far** [fɑːr] 謄 먼
- □ **figure** [fígjər] 몡 (사람, 동물의) 상, 모양, 숫자
- □ **filter** [fíltər] 宕 ~을 거르다, 여과하다 몡 여과 장치
- □ **full moon** 보름달
- □ **impossible** [impɑ́səbl] 謄 불가능한
- □ **information** [ìnfərméiʃən] 몡 정보
- □ **jar** [dʒɑːr] 몡 항아리, 병
- □ **leave** [liːv] 宕 남겨 두다
- □ **length** [leŋkθ] 몡 길이
- □ **lovely** [lʌ́vli] 謄 사랑스러운, 아름다운
- □ **necessary** [nésəsèri] 謄 필요한
- □ **object** [ɑ́bdʒikt] 몡 물체
- □ **plant** [plænt] 宕 심다
- □ **possible** [pɑ́səbl] 謄 가능한 (↔ impossible 불가능한)
- □ **potter** [pɑ́tər] 몡 도공, 옹기장이, 도예가
- □ **pour** [pɔːr] 宕 붓다, 따르다
- □ **prefer** [prifɔ́ːr] 宕 선호하다, 더 좋아하다
- □ **print** [print] 宕 인쇄하다, 출판하다
- □ **produce** [prədjúːs] 宕 생산하다, 산출하다
- □ **proud** [praud] 謄 자랑으로 여기는
- □ **provide** [prəváid] 宕 제공하다
- □ **public** [pʌ́blik] 謄 공공의, 공중의
- □ **publisher** [pʌ́bliʃər] 몡 출판업자, 출판사
- □ **register** [rédʒistər] 宕 등록하다
- □ **relax** [rilǽks] 宕 (마음의) 긴장을 풀다
- □ **report** [ripɔ́ːrt] 宕 알리다, 보고하다
- □ **round** [raund] 謄 둥근
- □ **seed** [siːd] 몡 씨앗
- □ **shoulder bag** 어깨에 메는 가방
- □ **tear** [tiər] 宕 ~을 찢다, 뜯어내다(**tear–tore–torn**)
- □ **tiny** [táini] 謄 아주 작은
- □ **tired** [taiərd] 謄 지친
- □ **traditional** [trədíʃnl] 謄 전통적인
- □ **weight** [weit] 몡 무게, 중량
- □ **wonderful** [wʌ́ndərfəl] 謄 훌륭한

Key Expressions

- □ **both A and B** A와 B 둘 다
- □ **by hand** 손으로
- □ **find out** 알아내다
- □ **give away** 남에게 주다, 나누어 주다
- □ **hold ~ in hands** ~을 양손에 들다
- □ **How about -ing ~?** ~하는 것이 어떠니?
- □ **I can't wait for it!** 몹시 기다려진다!
- □ **not ~ anymore** 더 이상 ~ 않다
- □ **pick up** 집어들다
- □ **take a bath** 목욕하다
- □ **take a shower** 샤워하다
- □ **tear out** 찢다
- □ **think of ... as ~** …을 ~으로 생각하다
  (= regard ... as ~, look upon ... as ~)
- □ **this way** 이렇듯, 이런 식으로
- □ **Why don't we ~?** ~하는 게 어때?

Word Power

※ 서로 비슷한 뜻을 가진 어휘

☐ **actually** 사실, 실제로 – **really** 정말로
☐ **beat** 물리치다 – **defeat** 패배시키다, 물리치다
☐ **disease** 질병, 질환 – **illness** 질병
☐ **provide** 제공하다 – **furnish** 제공하다

☐ **artwork** 예술품, 공예품 – **craft** 공예품
☐ **company** 회사 – **corporation** 기업
☐ **proud** 자랑으로 여기는 – **boastful** 자랑하는
☐ **relax** (마음의) 긴장을 풀다 – **rest** 쉬다

※ 서로 반대의 뜻을 가진 어휘

☐ **beat** 물리치다 ↔ **surrender** 굴복하다
☐ **possible** 가능한 ↔ **impossible** 불가능한
☐ **public** 공공의 ↔ **private** 사적인

☐ **connect** 연결하다 ↔ **disconnect** 끊다
☐ **necessary** 필요한 ↔ **unnecessary** 불필요한
☐ **tiny** 아주 작은 ↔ **giant** 거대한

※ 명사 – 형용사

☐ **art** 예술 – **artistic** 예술적인
☐ **color** 색 – **colorful** 화려한
☐ **information** 정보 – **informative** 유용한 정보를 주는
☐ **love** 사랑 – **lovely** 사랑스러운, 아름다운
☐ **pride** 자랑 – **proud** 자랑으로 여기는

☐ **cheer** 환호성, 생기 – **cheerful** 유쾌한, 기분 좋은
☐ **face** 얼굴 – **facial** 얼굴의
☐ **length** 길이 – **long** 긴
☐ **necessity** 필요 – **necessary** 필요한
☐ **tradition** 전통 – **traditional** 전통적인

※ 동사 – 명사

☐ **collect** 모으다 – **collection** 수집
☐ **inform** 알려주다 – **information** 정보
☐ **produce** 생산하다 – **production** 생산
☐ **register** 등록하다 – **registration** 등록

☐ **connect** 연결하다 – **connection** 연결
☐ **prefer** 선호하다 – **preference** 선호
☐ **publish** 출판하다 – **publisher** 출판업자
☐ **weigh** 무게가 나가다 – **weight** 무게, 중량

English Dictionary

☐ **bookstore** 서점
→ a store that sells books
책을 파는 상점

☐ **drinkable** 마실 수 있는
→ clean and safe to drink
깨끗하고 마시기에 안전한

☐ **filter** ~을 거르다, 여과하다
→ to remove unwanted substances from liquids or gases 액체나 기체에서 원치 않는 물질을 제거하다

☐ **leave** 남겨 두다
→ to put something somewhere, especially in a place where it will stay
어떤 것을 어떤 장소 특히 그것이 머무를 장소에 두다

☐ **pour** 붓다, 따르다
→ to make a liquid flow out of a container
용기 밖으로 액체가 흘러가도록 만들다

☐ **public** 공공의, 공중의
→ relating to people in general
일반 대중과 관련된

☐ **publisher** 출판업자, 출판사
→ a person or company that prints books
책을 출판하는 사람 또는 회사

☐ **register** 등록하다
→ to put someone's or something's name on an official list 공식적인 명단에 누군가 또는 무엇인가의 이름을 올리다

☐ **tear** 찢다, 뜯어내다
→ to pull apart or to pull pieces off
잡아 찢거나 작은 조각으로 뜯어내다

☐ **tiny** 아주 작은
→ extremely small
매우 작은

서답형

01 다음 문장의 빈칸에 〈영어 설명〉에 해당하는 단어를 쓰시오.

Most curtains are made of _____.
〈영어 설명〉 material used for making things such as clothes

02 다음 빈칸에 공통으로 들어갈 말로 가장 적절한 것은?

• He made a bronze _____ of a horse.
• The _____ is lower than the OECD average of $6,741.

① character   ② letter
③ figure   ④ product
⑤ statue

[03~04] 다음 설명에 해당하는 단어를 고르시오.

03

to put someone's or something's name on an official list

① permit   ② hug
③ collect   ④ relax
⑤ register

04 〈중요〉

to remove unwanted substances from liquids or gases

① filter   ② print
③ prepare   ④ prefer
⑤ pour

서답형

05 다음 우리말에 맞게 주어진 단어를 이용하여 쓰시오.

그는 모든 음식을 가난한 사람들에게 나누어 주었다. (give)

➡ He _____ all the food to the poor.

06 〈중요〉 다음 빈칸에 들어갈 말이 알맞게 짝지어진 것은?

(A) He stayed in the hospital because he had a serious _____.
(B) She _____ her mom as her friend.

① illness – leaves
② secret – allows
③ project – hides
④ disease – thinks of
⑤ information – proves

07 다음 짝지어진 단어 중 성격이 <u>다른</u> 하나는?

① art – artistic   ② face – facial
③ color – colorful   ④ love – lovely
⑤ collect – collection

08 〈중요〉 다음 빈칸에 공통으로 알맞은 것은?

• _____: relating to all the people in a country
• e.g. When we are outside, we have to use _____ restrooms.

① private   ② public
③ possible   ④ drinkable
⑤ human

⭐중요
01 〈보기〉에서 알맞은 단어를 찾아 빈칸을 완성하시오. (필요하면 변형하여 쓰시오.)

┌─ 보기 ─┐
necessary   report   tear   drink
└─────────┘

(1) Is this water _____?

(2) He was the first reporter to _____ the big story.

(3) Food and water are _____ for humans to live.

(4) My cat _____ the pages of the book yesterday.

02 다음 대화의 빈칸에 〈영영풀이〉에 해당하는 단어를 쓰시오.

A: Which do you _____, working with a plan or working without a plan?

B: I _____ working without a plan.

<영영풀이> to like someone or something more than another person or thing

➡ _____

⭐중요
03 다음 우리말과 같은 표현이 되도록 문장의 빈칸을 채우시오. (철자가 주어진 것은 그 철자로 시작하는 단어를 쓸 것.)

(1) 그들의 밝은 미소와 유쾌한 춤이 많은 사람들에게 에너지를 주었습니다.
    ➡ Their bright smiles and c_____ dance gave many people energy.

(2) 믿기 힘들겠지만, 그것은 실제로 케이크입니다!
    ➡ It may be hard to believe, but it is a_____ a cake!

(3) 또 다른 장점은 그것들이 학생과 선생님 둘 다 보호한다는 것입니다.
    ➡ Another benefit is that they protect _____ students and teachers.

(4) 전자책은 종이책이 절대로 제공할 수 없는 다른 많은 서비스도 제공할 수 있다.
    ➡ E-books can also p_____ many other services paperback books can never p_____.

04 다음 영영풀이에 해당하는 단어를 〈보기〉에서 찾아 첫 번째 빈칸에 쓰고, 두 번째 빈칸에는 우리말 뜻을 쓰시오.

┌─ 보기 ─┐
bookstore   leave   pour
└─────────┘

(1) _____ : a store that sells books: _____

(2) _____ : to put something somewhere, especially in a place where it will stay:
    _____

(3) _____ : to make a liquid flow out of a container: _____

🏠난이도
05 두 문장의 뜻이 같도록 빈칸에 알맞은 말을 쓰시오.

• He worked for this company from the very beginning, so everyone regarded him as the real boss.

= He worked for this company from the very beginning, so everyone _____ him _____ the real boss.

➡ _____

Conryersation

① 선호에 대해 묻기

> • **Which do you prefer, pandas or cats?** 너는 판다와 고양이 중에서 어떤 것을 더 좋아하니?

■ A와 B 둘 중에 어떤 것을 더 좋아하는지 상대방의 선호를 물을 때는 'prefer(더 좋아하다)'를 사용하여 'Which do you prefer, A or B?(너는 A와 B 중에서 어느 것을 더 좋아하니?)' 또는 'Do you prefer A or B?(너는 A를 더 좋아하니, B를 더 좋아하니?)'라고 표현한다. which는 정해진 범주 내에서 특정 대상의 선호도를 물을 때 사용하는 표현이다.

■ '더 좋아하다'에 해당하는 'like better'를 사용하여 'Which do you like better[more], A or B?' 또는 'Which one do you like better, A or B?'의 형태로 나타낼 수 있고, Which가 뒤에 오는 명사를 수식하는 의문형용사로 쓰이는 경우에는 'which+명사'로 쓰일 수 있으므로 'Which 명사+do you prefer, A or B?'라고 할 수도 있다.

■ prefer로 자신이 좋아하는 것을 나타낼 때는 전치사 to를 사용하여 'prefer A to B(B보다는 A를 더 좋아한다)'의 형태로 선호를 표현한다. 이는 'like A better than B'에 해당한다. 어떤 것을 더 좋아한다는 것은 상대적인 선택이므로, 다른 하나를 좋아할 수도 싫어할 수도 있다. 두 가지를 모두 좋아하지만 어느 하나를 더 좋아한다면, 'I like both, but I like … better.'나 'I like both, but I prefer ….'처럼 말한다.

선호에 대해 묻기

- Do you prefer A or B?
- Do you like A better than B?
- Which do you like better, A or B?
- Do you prefer A to B?
- Which do you prefer, A or B?

선호를 표현할 때

- I prefer A (to B).
- I like A better (than B).

핵심 Check

1. 다음 밑줄 친 우리말에 맞게 영작하시오.

   G: 너는 회화 작품(paper drawings)과 나무 블록으로 만든 모형 중에서 어떤 것을 더 좋아하니?

   B: I prefer wood block figures.

   G: Me, too. Let's go to look at some of them.

   ➡ _____

② 싫어하는 것 표현하기

> • I hate holding things in my hands. 나는 손에 물건을 드는 것을 몹시 싫어해.

■ 자신이 좋아하는 것을 나타내는 말은 like, love, prefer 등을 사용하여 나타내지만, 싫어하는 것은 hate, dislike 등을 사용한다. 'I hate ~.(나는 ~하기를 싫어한다.)'는 자신이 하기 싫어하는 것을 강하게 표현하는 말이다.

■ '~를 싫어하다'라는 의미로 'hate' 뒤에 싫어하는 일을 나타내는 명사/동명사/to부정사를 사용하여 'hate+명사', 'hate+-ing', 'hate+to부정사' 형태로 나타내거나, 'hate+목적어(사람)+-ing', 'hate+목적어(사람)+for+명사'의 형태로 '~가 …하는 것을 싫어하다'의 의미로 사용하기도 한다.

■ 싫어하는 것을 나타낼 때는 hate, dislike 등을 사용하지만, 'don't like', 'don't love', 'don't want to ~' 등으로 자신이 좋아하지 않는 것, 즉 싫어하는 것을 표현할 수 있다. 싫어하는 정도가 매우 강할 때는 '~을 참을 수 없다'는 뜻으로 'can't stand', 'can't bear'를 쓰기도 한다. 'detest'는 '몹시 싫어하다, 혐오하다'의 뜻이다.

싫어하는 것 표현하기

- I hate 명사/-ing /to ~.
- I don't like 명사/-ing/to ~.
- I dislike ~.
- I don't want to ~.
- I can't stand ~.
- I can't bear ~.

핵심 Check

2. 다음 대화의 내용으로 보아, 빈칸에 들어가기에 적절하지 <u>않은</u> 것은?

B: Why don't we make a bag with old jeans?

G: Great! What kind of bag are we going to make?

B: Which do you prefer, a shoulder bag or a hand bag?

G: I prefer a shoulder bag. Actually, _____

B: Okay. Let's make a shoulder bag together.

① I don't want to hold things in my hands.

② I hate holding things in my hands.

③ I don't like to hold things in my hands.

④ I can stand holding things in my hands.

⑤ I dislike holding things in my hands.

Step Up - Real-life Scene

Minji: Seho, the book club day is just one week away.

Seho: Right, Minji. ❶I'm proud that we've collected so many interesting books ❷to give away.

Minji: Now, let's prepare some gifts for visitors. Do you have ❸any good ideas?

Seho: ❹How about making bookmarks?

Minji: Great idea! Let's write cheerful messages on them, too.

Seho: Okay. ❺Which do you prefer, making the bookmarks or writing the messages?

Minji: Actually, ❻I hate writing. I'd like to make the bookmarks.

Seho: No problem. I'll write the cheerful messages.

Minji: ❼I'm sure they will love our bookmarks.

민지: 세호야, 독서 동아리의 날이 겨우 한 주 남았어.
세호: 맞아, 민지야. 나는 우리가 나눠줄 재미있는 책을 많이 모아서 자랑스러워.
민지: 이제, 방문객들에게 줄 선물을 준비하자. 좋은 생각 있어?
세호: 책갈피를 만드는 게 어떨까?
민지: 좋은 생각이야! 거기에 기분 좋은 메시지도 쓰자.
세호: 그래. 너는 책갈피 만들기와 메시지 쓰기 중에서 어떤 것을 더 좋아하니?
민지: 사실, 나는 글쓰기를 몹시 싫어해. 나는 책갈피를 만들고 싶어.
세호: 문제없어. 내가 기분 좋은 메시지를 쓸게.
민지: 틀림없이 사람들이 우리가 만든 책갈피를 좋아할 거야.

❶ I'm proud that+주어+동사 ∼: ∼을 자랑스러워하다
❷ books를 수식하는 형용사 용법으로 '나누어줄'로 해석한다.
❸ '약간의, 어떤'의 의미로 의문문에서는 any를 사용한다.
❹ 'How about+동명사/명사?'는 '∼하는 게 어때?'라는 제안을 하는 표현이다.
❺ 상대방의 선호를 물을 때는 'prefer(더 좋아하다)'를 사용하여 'Which do you prefer, A or B?(너는 A와 B 중에서 어느 것을 더 좋아하니?)' 또는 'Do you prefer A or B?'로 표현한다. 이때 A와 B는 문법적으로 병렬 관계가 되어야 한다.
❻ 'I hate ∼(나는 ∼하는 것을 싫어한다)'는 자신이 하기 싫어하는 것을 강하게 표현하는 말이다.
❼ 'I'm sure (that)+주어+동사 ∼'는 '∼할 것을 확신해. 틀림없이 ∼할 거야'라는 확신을 나타내는 표현이다.

Check(√) True or False

(1) Minji and Seho are preparing for the book club day. T ☐ F ☐

(2) Minji hates making the bookmarks. T ☐ F ☐

 Start Off - Listen & Talk A 1

G: ❶Why don't we make something with jean pockets?

B: Great! What shall we make?

G: Which do you prefer, a pocket board or a cell phone holder?

B: I prefer a cell phone holder. It'll be easier ❷to make. And I hate ❸ spending too much time making things.

G: Okay. Let's make a cute cell phone holder together.

G: 청바지 주머니로 뭔가 만들어 보는 게 어떨까?
B: 좋아! 뭘 만들까?
G: 너는 주머니를 붙인 판과 휴대 전화 주머니 중에서 어떤 것을 더 좋아하니?
B: 나는 휴대 전화 주머니가 더 좋아. 만들기가 더 쉬울 거야. 그리고 나는 뭔가를 만드는 데 시간을 너무 많이 들이는 걸 몹시 싫어해.
G: 좋아. 귀여운 휴대 전화 주머니를 함께 만들자.

❶ 'Why don't we+동사원형?'은 '∼하는 게 어때?'라는 제안을 하는 표현으로 'How about+동명사/명사?'로 바꾸어 쓸 수 있다.
❷ 형용사 easier를 수식하는 부사적 용법으로 '만들기에'로 해석한다.
❸ 'spend+시간+-ing' 형태로 '∼하는 데 시간을 보내다'라는 의미이다.

Check(√) True or False

(3) The girl wants to make something with a cell phone holder. T ☐ F ☐

(4) The boy wants to make a cell phone holder. T ☐ F ☐

Get Ready 2

(1) G: ❶Which do you like better, cloth dolls or digital artwork?

B: I like digital artwork better. Actually, I don't like dolls much.

(2) G: Which do you prefer, paper drawings or wood block figures?

B: I prefer wood block figures.

G: Me, too. ❷Let's go to look at some of them.

(3) G: Which do you prefer, folding paper or making clothes?

B: I prefer folding paper. It's fun and a great way ❸to relax.

❶ 상대방에게 선호를 묻는 표현이다.
❷ 'Let's+동사원형'은 '~하자'는 제안을 하는 표현이다.
❸ 명사 'way'를 수식하는 형용사 용법이다.

 Start Off - Listen & Talk A 2

B: Why don't we make a bag with old jeans?

G: Great! ❶What kind of bag are we going to make?

B: Which do you prefer, a shoulder bag or a hand bag?

G: I prefer a shoulder bag. Actually, ❷I hate holding things in my hands.

B: Okay. Let's make a shoulder bag together.

❶ 'kind'는 명사로 '종류'라는 뜻이다.
❷ 'hate+동명사'로 싫어하는 것을 표현한다.

 Start Off - Listen & Talk B

G: Junha, what are you doing with jeans?

B: I'm ❶making a pencil case for you.

G: That's great! What ❷are you going to draw on it?

B: Which do you prefer, pandas or cats?

G: I prefer cats. They're lovely.

B: Okay. Let me draw a lovely cat on this pencil case.

G: Thanks! ❸I can't wait for it!

❶ 'make+직접목적어+for+간접목적어' 형태로 '~에게 …을 만들어 주다'라는 뜻이다.
❷ 'be going to+동사원형'은 '~할 예정이다'라는 의미이다.
❸ 'I can't wait for+명사/동명사'는 '~이 몹시 기다려져'라는 의미로 기대를 나타내는 표현이다.

 Start Off - Speak Up

A: Can I join your book-making project?

B: Sure. ❶Which do you prefer, paper books or digital books?

A: ❷I prefer digital books. Actually, I hate ❸ making paper books.

B: Okay. Let me introduce you to the digital book team.

❶ 'Which do you prefer, A or B?'는 상대방의 선호를 묻는 표현으로 A와 B는 병렬구조가 되어야 한다.
❷ 'I prefer digital books' 뒤에는 'to paper books'가 생략되어 있다.
❸ hate는 to부정사와 동명사를 목적어로 받을 수 있다.

 Start Off - Your Turn

A: Which do you prefer, ❶taking the bus or taking the subway?

B: I prefer taking the subway. ❷Actually, I hate taking the bus.

❶ 상대방이 선호를 묻는 표현으로 'Which do you prefer, A or B?' 구문으로 A와 B는 병렬구조가 되어야 한다. 즉, 'taking ~ or taking ...' 형태가 같아야 한다.
❷ 'actually'는 말하는 내용을 강조할 때 사용하는 표현이다.

 Express Yourself A

1. G: Which do you prefer, ❶flying kites or flying drones?

B: I prefer flying kites.

G: Why is that?

B: I hate working with machines.

2. B: Which do you prefer, making masks or making food art?

G: I like ❷both, but ❸it is making food art that I prefer.

B: Why is that?

G: ❹I love making something delicious.

❶ 상대방의 선호를 묻는 표현으로 'Which do you prefer, A or B?' 구문으로 A와 B는 병렬구조가 되어야 한다.
❷ 'both'는 'making masks and making food art'를 가리킨다.
❸ 'it ~ that ...' 강조구문으로 prefer의 목적어를 강조하는 문장이다.
❹ 자신이 좋아하는 것을 나타내는 말로 'like, love, prefer' 등을 사용하여 나타낸다.

● 다음 우리말과 일치하도록 빈칸에 알맞은 말을 쓰시오.

Get Ready 2

(1) G: _____ do you like _____, _____ dolls or digital _____?

B: I like digital artwork _____. _____, I don't like dolls much.

(2) G: _____ _____ _____ _____, paper _____ or _____ block figures?

B: I _____ wood block _____.

G: Me, too. _____ go to look at _____ _____ _____.

(3) G: _____ do you _____, _____ paper or making _____?

B: I prefer _____ _____. It's fun and a great way _____ _____.

Start Off - Listen & Talk A

1. G: _____ _____ _____ make something with jean _____?

B: Great! _____ _____ _____ make?

G: _____ do you prefer, a pocket _____ or a cell phone _____?

B: I _____ a cell phone _____. It'll be easier _____ _____. And I hate _____ too much time _____ things.

G: Okay. _____ make a cute cell phone holder _____.

2. B: _____ _____ _____ make a bag with old jeans?

G: Great! _____ _____ of bag are we going _____ _____?

B: Which do you _____, a shoulder bag or a hand bag?

G: I prefer a shoulder bag. Actually, I _____ _____ things _____ my hands.

B: Okay. _____ _____ a shoulder bag together.

Start Off - Listen & Talk B

G: Junha, what are you doing _____ _____?

B: I'm making a pencil case _____ you.

G: That's great! What are you going to _____ on it?

B: _____ _____ _____ _____, pandas or cats?

G: I _____ cats. They're _____.

B: Okay. Let me _____ a lovely cat on this pencil case.

G: Thanks! _____ _____ _____ _____ it!

(1) G: 너는 헝겊 인형과 디지털 예술품 중에서 어떤 것을 더 좋아하니?

B: 나는 디지털 예술품이 더 좋아. 사실, 나는 인형을 별로 좋아하지 않아.

(2) G: 너는 회화 작품과 나무 블록으로 만든 모형 중에서 어떤 것을 더 좋아하니?

B: 나는 나무 블록으로 만든 모형이 더 좋아.

G: 나도 그래. 그것 중에서 몇 개를 보러 가자.

(3) G: 너는 종이접기와 옷 만들기 중에서 어떤 것을 더 좋아하니?

B: 나는 종이접기가 더 좋아. 재미있고 긴장을 풀 수 있는 좋은 방법이야.

1. G: 청바지 주머니로 뭔가 만들어 보는 게 어떨까?

B: 좋아! 뭘 만들까?

G: 너는 주머니를 붙인 판과 휴대 전화 주머니 중에서 어떤 것을 더 좋아하니?

B: 나는 휴대 전화 주머니가 더 좋아. 만들기가 더 쉬울 거야. 그리고 나는 뭔가를 만드는 데 시간을 너무 많이 들이는 걸 몹시 싫어해.

G: 좋아. 귀여운 휴대 전화 주머니를 함께 만들자.

2. B: 우리 낡은 청바지로 가방을 하나 만드는 게 어떨까?

G: 좋아! 어떤 종류의 가방을 만들 건데?

B: 너는 어깨에 메는 가방과 손에 드는 가방 중에서 어떤 것을 더 좋아하니?

G: 나는 어깨에 메는 가방이 더 좋아. 사실, 나는 손에 물건을 드는 것을 몹시 싫어해.

B: 좋아. 어깨에 메는 가방을 함께 만들자.

G: 준하야, 청바지로 뭐 해?

B: 너에게 줄 필통을 만들고 있어.

G: 멋지다! 그 위에 뭘 그릴 거야?

B: 너는 판다랑 고양이 중에서 어떤 것을 더 좋아하니?

G: 나는 고양이를 더 좋아해. 고양이는 사랑스러워.

B: 좋아. 내가 이 필통 위에 사랑스러운 고양이를 그려 줄게.

G: 고마워! 몹시 기다려진다!

Start Off - Speak Up

A: Can I join your book-making project?

B: _____. _____ do you _____, paper books _____ digital books?

A: I _____ digital books. Actually, I hate _____ paper books.

B: Okay. Let me _____ you _____ the digital book team.

Start Off - Your Turn

A: _____ do you prefer, _____ the bus or _____ the subway?

B: I _____ _____ the subway. Actually, I _____ _____ the bus.

Step Up - Real-life Scene

Minji: Seho, the book club day is just one week _____.

Seho: Right, Minji. I'm _____ _____ we've _____ so many _____ books _____ _____ _____.

Minji: Now, let's _____ some gifts for visitors. Do you have _____ good ideas?

Seho: How about _____ bookmarks?

Minji: Great idea! _____ write cheerful messages on them, too.

Seho: Okay. _____ do you _____, making the bookmarks or _____ the messages?

Minji: Actually, I hate _____. I'd like to make the bookmarks.

Seho: _____ _____. I'll write the _____ _____.

Minji: I'm _____ they will love our _____.

Express Yourself A

1. G: Which do you prefer, _____ kites or _____ _____?

   B: I prefer _____ kites.

   G: Why is that?

   B: I hate _____ with _____.

2. B: _____ do you prefer, _____ masks or _____ food art?

   G: I like _____, but _____ is making food art _____ I _____.

   B: Why is that?

   G: I love making _____ _____.

해석

A: 너희 책 만들기 프로젝트에 내가 함께 해도 될까?
B: 물론이지. 너는 종이책과 전자책 중에서 어떤 것을 더 좋아하니?
A: 나는 전자책을 더 좋아해. 사실, 나는 종이책 만들기를 몹시 싫어해.
B: 알았어. 전자책 팀에 너를 소개할게.

A: 너는 버스 타기와 지하철 타기 중에서 어떤 것을 더 좋아하니?
B: 나는 지하철 타기를 더 좋아해. 사실, 나는 버스 타기를 몹시 싫어해.

민지: 세호야, 독서 동아리의 날이 겨우 한 주 남았어.
세호: 맞아, 민지야. 나는 우리가 나눠 줄 재미있는 책을 많이 모아서 자랑스러워.
민지: 이제, 방문객들에게 줄 선물을 준비하자. 좋은 생각 있어?
세호: 책갈피를 만드는 게 어떨까?
민지: 좋은 생각이야! 거기에 기분 좋은 메시지도 쓰자.
세호: 그래. 너는 책갈피 만들기와 메시지 쓰기 중에서 어떤 것을 더 좋아하니?
민지: 사실, 나는 글쓰기를 몹시 싫어해. 나는 책갈피를 만들고 싶어.
세호: 문제없어. 내가 기분 좋은 메시지를 쓸게.
민지: 틀림없이 사람들이 우리가 만든 책갈피를 좋아할 거야.

1. G: 너는 연날리기와 드론 날리기 중에서 어떤 것을 더 좋아하니?
   B: 나는 연날리기를 더 좋아해.
   G: 왜 그런데?
   B: 나는 기계를 작동하는 것을 몹시 싫어해.
2. B: 너는 가면 만들기와 푸드 아트 만들기 중에서 어떤 것을 더 좋아하니?
   G: 나는 둘 다 좋지만, 내가 더 좋아하는 것은 푸드 아트 만들기야.
   B: 왜 그런데?
   G: 나는 맛있는 것을 만들기를 좋아해.

01 다음 대화의 빈칸에 들어갈 말로 알맞은 것은?

> A: Can I join your book-making project?
> B: Sure. Which do you prefer, paper books or digital books?
> A: I prefer digital books. Actually, _____
> B: Okay. Let me introduce you to the digital book team.

① I'm curious about making paper books.

② I would like to know how to make bookmarks.

③ I prefer working with numbers and texts.

④ I hate making paper books.

⑤ Actually, I hate working on a team.

02 다음 대화의 빈칸에 들어갈 말로 적절한 것은?

> B: Which do you prefer, making masks or making food art?
> G: I like both, but it is making food art that I prefer.
> B: Why is that?
> G: _____

① I hate working with machines.

② I love making something delicious.

③ I prefer working alone.

④ I love working with pictures and music.

⑤ I hate making food art.

03 다음 대화의 밑줄 친 말의 의도로 알맞은 것은?

> G: Which do you prefer, taking the bus or taking the subway?
> B: I prefer taking the subway. Actually, I hate taking the bus.

① 관심 표현하기   ② 선호에 대해 묻기

③ 요청하기   ④ 유감 표현하기

⑤ 싫어하는 것 표현하기

[01~02] 다음 대화를 읽고 물음에 답하시오.

G: Junha, what are you doing with jeans?

B: I'm making a pencil case for you.

G: That's great! What are you going to draw on it?

B: _____(A)_____

G: I prefer cats. They're lovely.

B: Okay. (B)Let me to draw a lovely cat on this pencil case.

G: Thanks! I can't wait for it!

01 위 대화의 빈칸 (A)에 들어갈 말로 어색한 것은?

① Which do you prefer, pandas or cats?

② Do you prefer pandas or cats?

③ Which do you like better, pandas or cats?

④ Why do you like pandas better than cats?

⑤ Which do you like more, pandas or cats?

서답형

02 위 대화의 밑줄 친 (B)에서 어법상 어색한 부분을 찾아 고치시오.

_____ ➡ _____

[03~04] 다음 대화를 읽고 물음에 답하시오.

B: _____(A)_____ a bag with old jeans?

G: Great! What kind of bag are we going to make?

B: Which do you prefer, a shoulder bag or a hand bag?

G: I prefer a shoulder bag. _____(B)_____

B: Okay. Let's make a shoulder bag together.

03 위 대화의 빈칸 (A)에 들어갈 말로 알맞지 않은 것은?

① What about making

② Why don't we make

③ How do we make

④ How about making

⑤ Shall we make

04 위 대화의 흐름상 (B)에 들어갈 알맞은 표현은?

① Actually, I hate making photo books.

② Actually, I hate holding things in my hands.

③ Actually, I hate working with a plan.

④ Actually, I hate writing.

⑤ Actually, I hate taking a bus.

[05~07] 다음 대화를 읽고 물음에 답하시오.

Minji: Seho, (A)독서 동아리의 날이 겨우 한 주 남았어.

Seho: Right, Minji. I'm (a)proud that we've collected so many interesting books to (b)give away.

Minji: Now, let's _____(B)_____ some gifts for visitors. Do you have any good ideas?

Seho: (c)How about making bookmarks?

Minji: Great idea! Let's write cheerful messages on them, too.

Seho: Okay. Which do you (d)prefer, making the bookmarks or writing the messages?

Minji: Actually, I (e)love writing. I'd like to make the bookmarks.

Seho: No problem. I'll write the cheerful messages.

Minji: I'm sure they will love our bookmarks.

서답형

05 위 대화의 우리말 (A)에 맞게 주어진 단어를 알맞게 배열하시오.

> (one / the / club / is / just / book / week / away / day)

➡ _____

서답형

06 위 대화의 빈칸 (B)에 들어갈 말을 주어진 영영풀이를 참고하여 한 단어로 쓰시오.

> <영영풀이> to make plans or arrangements for something that will happen in the future

➡ _____

07 위 대화의 (a)~(e) 중 흐름상 어휘의 쓰임이 어색한 것은?

① (a) ② (b) ③ (c) ④ (d) ⑤ (e)

[08~09] 다음 대화를 읽고 물음에 답하시오.

> G: Why don't we make something with jean pockets?
> B: Great! _____(A)_____
> G: Which do you prefer, a pocket board or a cell phone holder?
> B: I prefer a cell phone holder. It'll be easier to make. And _____(B)_____.
> G: Okay. Let's make a cute cell phone holder together.

중요

08 위 대화의 빈칸 (A)에 들어갈 말로 알맞은 것은?

① What are you going to draw on it?
② I prefer working alone.
③ What shall we make?
④ Can I join your book-making project?
⑤ Why is that?

09 위 대화의 (B)에 들어갈 말로 알맞은 것은?

① I hate holding things in my hands.
② I love spending too much time making things.
③ I prefer working on a team.
④ I hate spending too much time making things.
⑤ I hate working with a plan.

중요

10 대화의 빈칸 (A)에 공통으로 들어갈 말로 알맞은 것은?

> (1) G: _____(A)_____, cloth dolls or digital artwork?
>   B: I like digital artwork better. Actually, I don't like dolls much.
> (2) G: _____(A)_____, paper drawings or wood block figures?
>   B: I prefer wood block figures.
>   G: Me, too. Let's go to look at some of them.
> (3) G: _____(A)_____, folding paper or making clothes?
>   B: I prefer folding paper. It's fun and a great way to relax.

① Which do you like better
② Can I join
③ What are you going to make
④ Do you wonder
⑤ Why don't we make

서답형

11 다음 대화의 빈칸에 들어갈 알맞은 말을 쓰시오.

> A: Which do you prefer, taking the bus _____ taking the subway?
> B: I prefer taking the subway. Actually, I hate taking the bus.

➡ _____

[01~02] 다음 대화를 읽고 물음에 답하시오.

Minji: Seho, the book club day is just one week away.

Seho: Right, Minji. I'm proud that we've collected so many interesting books to give away.

Minji: Now, let's prepare some gifts for visitors. Do you have any good ideas?

Seho: How about making bookmarks?

Minji: Great idea! Let's write cheerful messages on them, too.

Seho: Okay. _____(A)_____

Minji: Actually, I hate writing. I'd like to make the bookmarks.

Seho: No problem. I'll write the cheerful messages.

Minji: I'm sure they will love our bookmarks.

01 위 대화의 빈칸 (A)에 들어갈 말을 〈조건〉에 맞게 영어로 쓰시오.

┤ 조건 ├
- 'which'와 'prefer'를 이용하여 선호를 묻는 말을 쓸 것.
- 'making the bookmarks', 'writing the messages'를 사용할 것.

➡ _____

_____

02 위 대화를 읽고 다음 물음에 영어로 답하시오.

Q: What is Minji going to make for the visitors?

➡ _____

03 다음 대화의 밑줄 친 우리말을 주어진 〈조건〉에 맞게 영어로 쓰시오.

B: Which do you prefer, making masks or making food art?

G: I like both, but it is making food art that I prefer.

B: Why is that?

G: 나는 맛있는 것을 만들기를 좋아해.

┤ 조건 ├
- 'love' 'delicious'를 이용할 것.
- 동명사를 사용할 것.

➡ _____

[04~05] 다음 대화를 읽고 물음에 답하시오.

G: _____(A)_____ (don't / make / with / pockets / why / we / something / jean)

B: Great! What shall we make?

G: Which do you prefer, a pocket board or a cell phone holder?

B: I prefer a cell phone holder. It'll be easier to make. And (B)나는 뭔가를 만드는 데 시간을 너무 많이 들이는 걸 몹시 싫어해.

G: Okay. Let's make a cute cell phone holder together.

04 위 대화의 흐름상 빈칸 (A)에 주어진 단어를 알맞게 배열하여 제안하는 표현을 완성하시오.

➡ _____

05 위 대화의 밑줄 친 (B)의 우리말을 주어진 〈조건〉에 맞게 영작하시오.

┤ 조건 ├
- hate, spend, too much, things와 동명사를 이용할 것.

➡ _____

Grammar

1 the + 비교급, the +비교급

> • **The more** books we share, **the more** we learn.
> 우리가 더 많은 책을 공유할수록, 우리는 더 많이 배웁니다.

■ 형태: the+비교급(+주어+동사), the+비교급(+주어+동사)
 의미: …하면 할수록, 더 ~하다

■ 비교급 자리에는 형용사, 부사 모두 올 수 있고, 그 구분은 뒤에 이어지는 동사에 따라 달라진다.

 • **The colder** it is, **the more easily** you catch a cold.
 날씨가 더 추워질수록, 더 쉽게 감기에 걸린다.

 • **The more** money you have, **the more** money you want.
 여러분은 더 많은 돈을 가질수록, 더 많은 돈을 원하게 된다.

■ '주어+동사'를 생략하고 간단히 'the+비교급, the+ 비교급'으로 나타낼 수 있다.

 • The more, the better. 많으면 많을수록 더 좋다.

■ 접속사 'as' 또는 'if' 등을 사용하여 같은 의미의 문장을 쓸 수 있다.

 • **The more** you eat, **the fatter** you will be. = If you eat more, you will be fatter.
 당신이 더 많이 먹을수록, 더 살찌게 될 것이다.

 • **The warmer** the weather gets, **the happier** I feel. = As the weather gets warmer, I feel happier.
 날씨가 따뜻해질수록, 나는 더 행복하다.

핵심 Check

1. 다음 괄호 안의 단어를 이용하여 빈칸에 들어갈 알맞은 말을 쓰시오.

 (1) The brighter the sun is, the _____ I feel. (happy)

 (2) The harder you try, the _____ you learn. (well)

② It is[was] ··· that 강조구문

> • **It is** this filtered water **that** you can drink. 여러분이 마실 수 있는 것은 이 여과된 물입니다.

- 형태: It is[was]+강조할 부분+that+문장의 나머지 부분

  의미: ~하는 것은 바로 ···이다

- 동사를 제외한 문장의 특정 부분을 강조할 때 사용하며, 강조하고자 하는 부분을 'It is[was]'와 'that' 사이에 넣고, 문장의 나머지 부분을 'that' 뒤에 원래 순서대로 쓴다.

- 강조하는 대상을 마지막에 '바로 ···이다'에 넣어 해석한다.

- 강조하는 대상이 사람이면 that 대신 who를 사용할 수 있으며, 강조하는 대상이 사물이면 that 대신 which를, 시간이나 장소일 경우에는 when이나 where를 사용할 수 있다.

  - Jack found Ted's dog in front of the shoe store yesterday.
    ①   ②   ③   ④

① 주어 강조

= **It was** Jack **that[who]** found Ted's dog in front of the shoe store yesterday.
어제 신발가게 앞에서 Ted의 개를 찾은 것은 바로 Jack이었다.

(2) 목적어 강조

= **It was** Ted's dog **that[which]** Jack found in front of the shoe store yesterday.
어제 신발가게 앞에서 Jack이 찾은 것은 바로 Ted의 개였다.

(3) 장소를 나타내는 부사구 in front of the shoe store 강조

= **It was** in front of the shoe store **that[where]** Jack found Ted's dog yesterday.
Jack이 어제 Ted의 개를 찾은 것은 바로 신발가게 앞에서였다.

(4) 때를 나타내는 부사 yesterday 강조

= **It was** yesterday **that[when]** Jack found Ted's dog in front of the shoe store.
Jack이 Ted의 개를 신발가게 앞에서 찾은 것은 바로 어제였다.

핵심 Check

2. 다음 밑줄 친 부분을 강조하는 문장으로 바꿀 때 빈칸에 알맞은 말을 쓰시오.

(1) My mother made a chocolate cake last Saturday.

= It _____ _____ _____ _____ made a chocolate cake last Saturday.

(2) My mother made a chocolate cake last Saturday.

= It _____ _____ _____ _____ _____ my mother made last Saturday.

01 다음 우리말에 맞게 괄호 안에 주어진 단어를 이용하여 문장을 완성하시오.

(1) 우리가 더 많은 책을 공유할수록, 우리는 더 많이 배웁니다. (book, share)

➡ _____ , the more we learn.

(2) 우리가 바다 밑으로 더 깊이 갈수록, 더 어두워진다. (dark, get)

➡ The deeper we go under the sea, _____ .

(3) 더 높이 올라갈수록, 우리는 더 멀리 봐. (far, see)

➡ The higher we go up, _____ .

(4) 엄마가 크림파이를 만드신 것은 바로 지난 일요일이야. (it, that)

➡ _____ my mom made a cream pie.

02 다음 문장에서 어법상 <u>어색한</u> 부분을 바르게 고쳐 쓰시오.

(1) The longer I waited, the more angry I became.

➡ _____

(2) The hard you exercise, the stronger you will become.

➡ _____

(3) The earlier you register, the better you will get seat.

➡ _____

(4) The more books you read, the more wiser you become.

➡ _____

03 다음 〈보기〉의 문장을 참고하여 빈칸을 완성하시오.

┌─ 보기 ─
A: Junha met Seho in the shopping mall.
B: No. It was in the park that Junha met Seho. (park)
└

(1) A: Seho likes New York the most.

B: No. _____ Seho likes the most. (Paris)

(2) A: Junha walks to school every day.

B: No. _____ walks to school every day. (Minji)

01 다음 빈칸에 들어갈 말로 알맞은 것은?

> The brighter the sun is, _____ I feel.

① the happy   ② happier
③ the more happy   ④ the happily
⑤ the happier

02 다음 빈칸에 들어갈 말로 적절하지 <u>않은</u> 것은?

> The harder you try, _____ you learn.

① the more   ② the better
③ the more things   ④ the best
⑤ the sooner

03 다음 빈칸에 들어갈 말로 알맞은 것을 <u>모두</u> 고르시오.

> It was Junha _____ bought a novel in the bookstore.

① that   ② what   ③ which
④ who   ⑤ where

04 다음 중 밑줄 친 that의 쓰임이 <u>다른</u> 하나를 고르시오.

① It is Ms. Lee <u>that</u> keeps five dogs.
② It was on my birthday <u>that</u> I was given a toy car.
③ It was the museum <u>that</u> we visited yesterday.
④ It was Ted <u>that</u> won the contest.
⑤ It is clear <u>that</u> smartphones help students learn something new.

05 다음 기사의 내용과 일치하지 <u>않는</u> 것을 고르시오.

① It was Team Kim that beat the Canadian team in Gangneung in 2018.
② It was in 2018 that Team Kim beat the Canadian team in Gangneung.
③ It was by 2 points that Team Kim won the game.
④ It was Team Kim that the Canadian Team beat in Gangneung in 2018.
⑤ It was in Gangneung that Team Kim beat the Canadian team in 2018.

서답형

06 다음 문장에서 어법상 어색한 것을 바르게 고쳐 다시 쓰시오.

(1) It is Linda which doesn't like cheese cake.

   ➡ _____

(2) It is this old computer that give me a headache.

   ➡ _____

07 다음 괄호 안에 주어진 단어들을 바르게 배열하여 문장을 완성하시오.

> (you, more, the, make, mistakes), the more you will learn.

➡ _____, the more you will learn.

08 다음 문장과 같은 뜻을 가진 문장은?

> 시험이 어려울수록, 너는 더 열심히 공부해야 한다.

① The more the test is difficult, the harder you should try.
② The more the test is difficult, the hard you should try.
③ The more difficult the test is, the harder you should try.
④ The more difficult the test is, you should try harder.
⑤ The more test difficult is, the harder you should try.

09 다음 두 문장을 'the+비교급..., the+비교급 ~'을 사용하여 하나의 문장으로 완성하시오.

> • The wave rose higher.
> • We swam faster.

➡ _____

10 주어진 어휘를 이용하여 다음 우리말을 영어로 쓰시오.

> 더 일찍 떠날수록, 너는 더 빨리 도착할 것이다. (early, leave, soon, will arrive)

➡ _____

11 다음 〈보기〉와 같이 두 문장이 같은 뜻이 되도록 빈칸에 들어갈 알맞은 말을 쓰시오.

> ┤ 조건 ├
> The harder you study, the more you will learn.
> = If you study harder, you will learn more.

(1) The brighter the sun shines, the happier I feel.
➡ As the sun _____.
(2) The longer I waited, the angrier I became.
➡ As I _____.
(3) The more books you read, the more things you will know.
➡ If _____
_____.

12 ①~⑤ 중 that이 들어갈 곳으로 알맞은 것은?

> It ① was ② the chocolate cake ③ my sister ④ made ⑤ yesterday.

①　　②　　③　　④　　⑤

13 주어진 어휘를 이용하여 다음 우리말을 영어로 쓰시오. (11 글자)

> 사람들을 더 기분 좋게 만들 것은 이 아름다운 정원이다. (beautiful, better, that, make, feel)

➡ _____
_____

14 다음 괄호 안에 주어진 단어들을 바르게 배열하시오.

> The more trees I plant there, (come, birds, more, the, will).

➡ _____

15 다음 중 어색한 문장을 고르시오.

① The more you want, the more you will be disappointed.
② The younger you are, the harder you should work.
③ The more I learn English, the more I like it.
④ It was yesterday that I met Lean in the park.
⑤ It was five bottles of coke that Jack brought to the party.

16 빈칸에 공통으로 들어갈 수 있는 단어를 고르시오.

> • It was my dad _____ loved me most.
> • Jihun is the boy, _____ will have an audition this Friday.

① that   ② what   ③ which
④ who   ⑤ whom

17 빈칸에 들어갈 말을 순서대로 바르게 연결한 것은?

> In making food art, its display is important. It is an artistic display _____ _____ food look better. _____ _____ the food is, the more delicious it looks.

① which make – The pretty
② that make – The prettier
③ which makes – The pretty

④ that makes – More pretty
⑤ that makes – The prettier

18 다음 중 어법상 어색한 것을 고르시오.

> A: What happens ①when we go down ②faster?
> B: ③The more faster we go down, ④the more dangerous it ⑤gets.

①   ②   ③   ④   ⑤

19 대화의 빈칸에 쓰인 우리말 대답을 영어로 바꾸어 쓰시오.

(1) A: We went to Baker's Camp, right?
　　B: No. 우리가 갔었던 것은 바로 Makers' Camp야.

➡ _____

(2) A: Van Gogh painted *I and the Village*, right?
　　B: No. *I and the Village*를 그린 사람은 바로 Chagall이야.

➡ _____

20 다음 중 어법상 어색한 문장의 개수로 알맞은 것은?

> a. The better you know classical music, the more you will love it.
> b. It was the Internet that she bought her shirts.
> c. It is Kiyoung that love to write poems.
> d. The higher I climbed the mountain, the darker the sky is getting.
> e. The more you work out, the better you will feel.

① 1개   ② 2개   ③ 3개   ④ 4개   ⑤ 5개

01 다음 문장을 'the+비교급, the+비교급'을 이용하여 바꾸어 쓰시오.

(1) If you practice harder, you can type faster.

➡ _____

(2) As they tried more, they did better.

➡ _____

(3) If it gets colder, we need more clothes.

➡ _____

(4) As he got closer to the fire, he felt warmer.

➡ _____

(5) If you get up earlier, you can spend more time on makeup.

➡ _____

_____

02 밑줄 친 부분을 강조하는 문장으로 고쳐 쓰시오.

(1) Cats hate the smell of lemons.

➡ It is _____ .

(2) My grandmother made me banana cakes.

➡ It was _____

_____ .

(3) My grandfather told me the story.

➡ _____

_____

(4) We will attend a conference this Friday.

➡ _____

_____

(5) We saw the statue in front of the MBC building.

➡ _____

_____

03 다음 우리말에 맞게 주어진 어휘를 알맞게 배열하시오.

(1) 그가 서점에서 산 것은 똑같은 책 다섯 권이었어. (he, at the bookstore, it, bought, was, five copies of the same books, that)

➡ _____

_____

(2) 내가 잊지 못할 것은 학급 현장 학습이야. (that, forget, is, the class field trip, I, it, won't)

➡ _____

(3) 우리 모두를 깊게 연결해 준 것은 이 경험이었어. (deeply, connected, it, this experience, is, all of us, that)

➡ _____

_____

04 다음 그림을 보고 빈칸에 알맞은 말을 써 넣으시오.

(1)

In making and flying a drone, its weight is important. It is _____ that has a long battery life. The _____ the drone is, the longer it flies.

(2)

The facial design makes a mask unique.

In making a mask, the design of its face is important. It is _____ that makes a mask unique. The funnier the face is, the _____ popular it is.

06 다음 대화에서 어법상 틀린 곳을 찾아 바르게 고치시오.

A: There are many cars, so the traffic is bad.

B: You're right. The more cars there are, the more worse the traffic becomes.

_____ ⇒ _____

07 다음 문장의 밑줄 친 부분을 어법에 맞게 고쳐 쓰시오.

(1) It was her teddy bear that Cathy likes the best.

⇒ _____

(2) It was from Junsu who I first heard the news.

⇒ _____

(3) It is Minji that went to visit her aunt last Thursday.

⇒ _____
_____

(4) It is the star watching experience in Yeongwol that Minjun can't forget it.

⇒ _____
_____

(5) It was the bookstore that my dad first met my mom.

⇒ _____
_____

05 주어진 문장의 밑줄 친 부분을 괄호 안의 단어로 바꾸어 문장을 다시 쓰시오.

(1) It was yesterday that she sang the song. (tomorrow)

⇒ _____

(2) It is my friends that cheer me up all the time. (Joan)

⇒ _____

Reading

This Book Is Amazing!

Most people think of books as traditional paper books to read.
think of A as B: A를 B로 생각하다   *to부정사의 형용사적 용법*
However, there are many unique books around you. Let's learn about a
앞에 나오는 내용과 상반되는 내용을 연결하는 연결사

few of these books.
many unique books around you

Books Travel!

I found this old book on a park bench yesterday. A note on the cover
⋯ new

read, "Free Book! Take me home and read me!" Actually, this book
'~라고 쓰여 있다, ~로 해석되다'(자동사)   *= In fact. As a matter of fact: 사실*

had an ID number and was registered on a website. When I entered
등위접속사 'and'가 동사구 'had ~ number'와 'was ~ website'를 연결

the number online, I found out that the book had traveled to many
과거의 특정 시점 이전에 일어난 일은 과거완료(had+과거분사)로 표현

countries and that a number of readers in different countries had read it
두 개의 that절이 등위접속사 'and'로 연결

before me. How was that possible?
'그 책이 여러 나라를 여행하고, 나보다 앞서 많은 다른 사람들이 그 책을 읽었다'는 앞 문장의 내용

traditional 전통적인
unique 독특한
cover 커버, 표지
free 무료의
register 등록하다
a number of 많은
possible 가능한

확인문제

● 다음 문장이 본문의 내용과 일치하면 T, 일치하지 않으면 F를 쓰시오.

1 Most people consider books as traditional paper books to read. ☐

2 There are only a few unique books around you. ☐

3 The writer found an old book on a park bench yesterday. ☐

4 There was a note on the back cover of the book. ☐

5 The book which the writer found had an ID number and was registered on a website. ☐

6 The writer was the first reader of the book. ☐

There is a book-sharing project. First, register your book online
register ~ and get ~: 명령문
and get an ID number. Next, leave it in a public place. When the next
= your book
reader finds your book and reports back to the website, you can check
_V1_   _V2_
where your book is. This way, the whole world can become a big
간접의문문('의문사+주어+동사'의 어순)
library. The more books we share, the more we learn.
The+비교급+주어+동사 …, the+비교급+주어+동사 ~: …하면 할수록, 더 ~하다

The Drinkable Book

This tiny book is really important to people in my town. It provides
_아주 작은_
both the information and the tools necessary to make clean drinking
both A and B: A와 B 둘 다   _to부정사의 부사적 용법_
water.

It is called the Drinkable Book. You cannot actually drink the book,
수동태
but you can use it as a filter. Simply tear out a page and pour dirty
~으로(전치사)
water on it. As the water goes through the page, it changes into clean
the page that you tear out
drinking water. It is this filtered water that you can drink. This is
'You can drink this filtered water.'에서 'this filtered water'를 강조하기 위해 쓰인 강조구문
possible because the book is made of special filter paper. This amazing
amazed(✕)
book saves the lives of many children from diseases that come from
주격 관계대명사절: 앞의 선행사 'diseases'를 수식
dirty water.

project 기획, 프로젝트

leave 남겨 두다

report 알리다, 보고하다

this way 이렇듯, 이런 식으로

tiny 아주 작은

provide 제공하다

both … and ~ …와 ~ 둘 다

necessary 필요한

simply 그냥, 그저, 간단히

tear ~을 찢다, 뜯어내다(tear-tore-torn)

pour 붓다, 따르다

disease 병, 질병

확인문제

● 다음 문장이 본문의 내용과 일치하면 T, 일치하지 않으면 F를 쓰시오.

1 When we join a book-sharing project, we should register our book online and get an ID number. ☐

2 We should leave the book in a private place. ☐

3 As we share more books, we learn more. ☐

4 You can actually drink the Drinkable Book. ☐

5 You can use the book as a filter by simply tearing out a page and pouring dirty water on it. ☐

6 This amazing book saves the lives of many children from diseases that come from water shortage. ☐

The Tree-Book-Tree Project

This is the most amazing book that I have ever seen. After you
<small>that+주어+have ever+과거분사: 최상급 표현 뒤에서 '주어가 …해 본 중에서 가장 ~한'</small>

finish reading this book, plant it and water it. You will see new leaves
<small>finish는 목적어로 동명사를 취함.</small> <small>지각동사 see+목적어+현재분사: …가 ~하는 것을 보다</small>

growing on the book. In some bookstores in my town, you can see a
<small>지각동사 see+목적어+현재분사: …가 ~하는 것을 보다</small>

copy of this book producing new leaves.

The secret is that the book has seeds in each page. It is these tiny
<small>each+단수명사</small> <small>'These tiny seeds change</small>

seeds that change the book into a tree. This book was made by a small
<small>the book into a tree.'에서 주어 'These tiny seeds'를 강조하기 위한 'It ~ that …' 강조구문 be made by: '~에 의해 만들어지다'</small>

children's book publisher in Argentina. Though the company does

not print this book anymore, this special project makes us think about
<small>not+anymore = no more</small> <small>사역동사 makes+목적어+동사원형</small>

where books come from.
<small>간접의문문('의문사+주어+동사'의 어순)</small>

These are just a few of the unique books you can find. What other
<small>books와 you 사이에 목적격 관계대명사 that[which] 생략</small>

unique books do you want to make? What special project would you
<small>want는 목적어로 to부정사를 취함</small>

like to do with the books? The bigger your imagination is, the more
<small>would like는 목적어로 to부정사를 취함</small> <small>The+비교급+주어+동사 …, the+비교급+주어+동사 ~: …하면 할수록, 더 ~하다</small>

wonderful your books will become.

---

bookstore 서점
produce 생산하다, 산출하다
publisher 출판업자, 출판사
not ~ anymore 더 이상 ~ 않다
print 인쇄하다, 발행하다

📎 **확인문제**

● 다음 문장이 본문의 내용과 일치하면 T, 일치하지 <u>않으면</u> F를 쓰시오.

1 If you plant the book and water it after you finish reading it, you will see new leaves growing on the book. ☐

2 In many bookstores all around the world, you can see a copy of this book producing new leaves. ☐

3 This book has seeds in each page. ☐

4 A big children's book publisher in Argentina made this book. ☐

5 The Tree-Book-Tree Project makes us think about where books come from. ☐

6 As your imagination is bigger, your library will become more wonderful. ☐

● 우리말을 참고하여 빈칸에 알맞은 말을 쓰시오.

1   This Book Is _____!

2   Most people think of books as _____ _____ _____ to read.

3   However, there are many _____ books around you.

4   Let's learn about _____ _____ of these books.

5   Books _____!

6   I _____ this old book on a park bench yesterday.

7   A note on the cover _____, " _____ Book!

8   _____ _____ _____ and read me!"

9   Actually, this book had an _____ _____ and _____ _____ on a website.

10   When I entered the number online, I found out that the book _____ _____ to many countries and that a number of readers in different countries _____ _____ it before me.

11   _____ was that possible?

12   There is a _____ _____.

13   First, _____ your book online and _____ an ID number.

14   Next, _____ _____ in a public place.

15 When the next reader finds your book and _____ _____ to the website, you can check _____ _____ _____ _____.

16 This way, the whole world can become _____ _____ _____.

17 _____ _____ _____ we share, _____ _____ we learn.

18 The _____ Book

19 _____ _____ _____ is really important to people in my town.

20 It provides _____ _____ _____ _____ _____ _____ necessary to make clean drinking water.

21 It _____ _____ the Drinkable Book.

22 You cannot actually drink the book, but you can use it _____ _____ _____.

23 Simply _____ _____ a page and _____ dirty water _____ it.

24 _____ the water goes through the page, it _____ _____ clean drinking water.

25 _____ _____ this filtered water _____ you can drink.

26 This is possible because the book is made of _____ _____ _____.

27 This _____ book _____ the lives of many children _____ _____ that come from dirty water.

15 다음 독자가 여러분의 책을 발견해서 그 웹사이트에 다시 알릴 때, 여러분은 책이 어디 있는지 확인할 수 있습니다.

16 이런 식으로, 전 세계가 하나의 큰 도서관이 될 수 있습니다.

17 우리가 더 많은 책을 공유할수록, 우리는 더 많이 배웁니다.

18 마실 수 있는 책

19 이 작은 책은 우리 마을 사람들에게는 정말로 중요합니다.

20 그것은 깨끗한 마실 물을 만드는 데 필요한 정보와 도구 둘 다를 제공합니다.

21 그것은 '마실 수 있는 책'이라고 불립니다.

22 여러분은 실제로 그 책을 마실 수는 없지만, 그것을 필터로 사용할 수 있습니다.

23 그냥 한 페이지를 떼어 내서 그 위에 더러운 물을 부으세요.

24 물이 그 페이지를 통과하면서, 깨끗한 마실 물로 바뀝니다.

25 여러분이 마실 수 있는 것은 이 여과된 물입니다.

26 책이 특별한 여과지로 만들어졌기 때문에 이것이 가능합니다.

27 이 놀라운 책은 더러운 물로 생기는 질병으로부터 많은 어린이의 생명을 구합니다.

28 The _____ _____

29 This is _____ _____ _____ _____ that I have ever
    seen.

30 After you finish _____ this book, _____ it and _____ it.

31 You will see new leaves _____ on the book.

32 In some bookstores in my town, you can see _____ _____
    _____ this book _____ new leaves.

33 The secret is that the book _____ _____ in each page.

34 It is _____ _____ _____ that change the book into a
    tree.

35 This book _____ _____ _____ a small children's book
    publisher in Argentina.

36 Though the company does _____ print this book _____, this
    special project makes us _____ about where books come from.

37 These are _____ _____ _____ of the unique books you
    can find.

38 _____ _____ _____ _____ do you want to make?

39 What special project _____ you _____ _____ _____
    with the books?

40 _____ _____ your imagination is, _____ _____
    _____ your books will become.

28 나무-책-나무 프로젝트

29 이것은 제가 지금까지 본 것 중
    에서 가장 놀라운 책입니다.

30 여러분이 이 책을 다 읽은 후에,
    그것을 심고 물을 주세요.

31 여러분은 책에서 새잎이 자라는
    것을 보게 될 거예요.

32 우리 마을의 몇몇 서점에서, 여
    러분은 이 책 한 권이 새잎을 내
    는 것을 볼 수 있습니다.

33 비밀은 책이 각 페이지 안에 씨
    앗을 갖고 있다는 것입니다.

34 책을 나무로 변화시키는 것은
    이 아주 작은 씨앗들이에요.

35 이 책은 아르헨티나에 있는 한
    작은 아동 도서 출판사에 의해
    만들어졌습니다.

36 그 회사가 더는 이 책을 발행하
    지는 않지만, 이 특별한 프로젝
    트는 우리에게 책이 어디에서
    오는지에 대해 생각하게 해 줍
    니다.

37 이것들은 여러분이 찾을 수 있
    는 독특한 책 중의 단지 몇 가지
    입니다.

38 여러분은 어떤 다른 독특한 책
    을 만들기 원하나요?

39 여러분은 책으로 어떤 특별한
    프로젝트를 하고 싶나요?

40 여러분의 상상이 크면 클수록,
    여러분의 책은 더 훌륭해질 것
    입니다.

● 우리말을 참고하여 본문을 영작하시오.

1 이 책은 놀라워요!

➡ _____

2 대부분의 사람은 책을 읽기 위한 전통적인 종이책으로 생각합니다.

➡ _____

3 하지만, 여러분 주변에는 독특한 책이 많이 있습니다.

➡ _____

4 이러한 책 중 몇 가지에 대해 배워 봅시다.

➡ _____

5 책이 여행합니다!

➡ _____

6 저는 어제 공원 벤치에서 이 낡은 책을 발견했습니다.

➡ _____

7 표지 위의 쪽지에 "공짜 책이에요!

➡ _____

8 저를 집으로 데려가서 읽어 주세요!"라고 쓰여 있었습니다.

➡ _____

9 사실, 이 책은 ID 번호가 있고 웹사이트에 등록되어 있었어요.

➡ _____

10 제가 온라인으로 그 번호를 입력했을 때, 저는 그 책이 많은 나라를 여행하고 다른 나라의 많은 독자가 저보다 앞서 이 책을 읽었다는 것을 알아냈습니다.

➡ _____

_____

11 그게 어떻게 가능했을까요?

➡ _____

12 책을 공유하는 프로젝트가 있습니다.

➡ _____

13 우선, 온라인에 여러분의 책을 등록하고 ID 번호를 얻으세요.

➡ _____

14 그다음, 그것을 공공장소에 놓아두세요.

➡ _____

15 다음 독자가 여러분의 책을 발견해서 그 웹사이트에 다시 알릴 때, 여러분은 책이 어디 있는지 확인할 수 있습니다.

➡ _____

_____

16 이런 식으로, 전 세계가 하나의 큰 도서관이 될 수 있습니다.

➡ _____

17 우리가 더 많은 책을 공유할수록, 우리는 더 많이 배웁니다.

➡ _____

18 마실 수 있는 책

➡ _____

19 이 작은 책은 우리 마을 사람들에게는 정말로 중요합니다.

➡ _____

20 그것은 깨끗한 마실 물을 만드는 데 필요한 정보와 도구 둘 다를 제공합니다.

➡ _____

21 그것은 '마실 수 있는 책'이라고 **불립**니다.

➡ _____

22 여러분은 실제로 그 책을 마실 수는 없지만, 그것을 필터로 사용할 수 있습니다.

➡ _____

23 그냥 한 페이지를 떼어 내서 그 위에 더러운 물을 부으세요.

➡ _____

24 물이 그 페이지를 통과하면서, 깨끗한 마실 물로 바뀝니다.

➡ _____

25 여러분이 마실 수 있는 것은 이 여과된 물입니다.

➡ _____

26 책이 특별한 여과지로 만들어졌기 때문에 이것이 가능합니다.

➡ _____

27 이 놀라운 책은 더러운 물로 생기는 질병으로부터 많은 어린이의 생명을 구합니다.

➡ _____

28 나무-책-나무 프로젝트

➡ _____

29 이것은 제가 지금까지 본 것 중에서 가장 놀라운 책입니다.

➡ _____

30 여러분이 이 책을 다 읽은 후에, 그것을 심고 물을 주세요.

➡ _____

31 여러분은 책에서 새잎이 자라는 것을 보게 될 거예요.

➡ _____

32 우리 마을의 몇몇 서점에서, 여러분은 이 책 한 권이 새잎을 내는 것을 볼 수 있습니다.

➡ _____

33 비밀은 책이 각 페이지 안에 씨앗을 갖고 있다는 것입니다.

➡ _____

34 책을 나무로 변화시키는 것은 이 아주 작은 씨앗들이에요.

➡ _____

35 이 책은 아르헨티나에 있는 한 작은 아동 도서 출판사에 의해 만들어졌습니다.

➡ _____

36 그 회사가 더는 이 책을 발행하지는 않지만, 이 특별한 프로젝트는 우리에게 책이 어디에서 오는지에 대해 생각하게 해 줍니다.

➡ _____

_____

37 이것들은 여러분이 찾을 수 있는 독특한 책 중의 단지 몇 가지입니다.

➡ _____

38 여러분은 어떤 다른 독특한 책을 만들기 원하나요?

➡ _____

39 여러분은 책으로 어떤 특별한 프로젝트를 하고 싶나요?

➡ _____

40 여러분의 상상이 크면 클수록, 여러분의 책은 더 훌륭해질 것입니다.

➡ _____

[01~03] 다음 글을 읽고 물음에 답하시오.

Most people think of books as traditional paper books (A)to read. ⓐ , there are many unique books around you. Let's learn about a few of these books.

01 위 글의 빈칸 ⓐ에 들어갈 알맞은 말을 고르시오.

① That is
② Therefore
③ As a result
④ However
⑤ For example

02 위 글의 밑줄 친 (A)to read와 to부정사의 용법이 같은 것을 모두 고르시오.

① It's time for you to finish the work.
② This book was easy to read.
③ It was hard for me to solve the problem.
④ He was tall enough to play basketball.
⑤ She is the last person to do it.

03 위 글의 뒤에 올 내용으로 가장 알맞은 것을 고르시오.

① the decrease of traditional paper books
② the explanation of some unique books
③ various electronic books
④ the popularity of traditional paper books
⑤ the decrease of unique books

[04~06] 다음 글을 읽고 물음에 답하시오.

Books Travel!

I found this old book ⓐ a park bench yesterday. A note ⓑ the cover read, "Free Book! Take me home and read me!" Actually, this book had an ID number and was registered ⓒ a website. When I entered the number online, I found out that the book had traveled to many countries and that ⓓa number of readers in different countries had read it before me. How was that possible?

04 위 글의 빈칸 ⓐ~ⓒ에 공통으로 들어갈 알맞은 전치사를 고르시오.

① in
② on
③ to
④ at
⑤ from

서답형

05 위 글의 밑줄 친 ⓓa number of와 바꿔 쓸 수 있는 한 단어를 쓰시오.

➡ _____

06 According to the passage, which is NOT true?

① The writer found a free old book yesterday.
② The writer could take the book home and read it.
③ The book had an ID number.
④ The writer found out that the book had traveled to many countries.
⑤ The writer was the first reader of the book.

[07~09] 다음 글을 읽고 물음에 답하시오.

There is a book-sharing project. First, register your book online and get an ID number. ⓐNext, leave it in a private place. When the next reader finds your book and reports back to the website, you can check where your book is. This way, the whole world can become a big library. The more books we share, the more we learn.

서답형

07 What is the first step in the book-sharing project? Fill in the blanks (A) and (B) with suitable words.

The first step in the book-sharing project is to (A)_____ your book online and (B)_____ an ID number.

서답형

08 위 글의 밑줄 친 ⓐ에서 흐름상 어색한 부분을 찾아 고치시오.

_____ ➡ _____

중요

09 위 글의 주제로 알맞은 것을 고르시오.

① the way to register your book online
② the difficulty in getting an ID number
③ how to report back to the website on the book
④ the project to share books
⑤ the way to check where the book is

[10~11] 다음 글을 읽고 물음에 답하시오.

The Drinkable Book

This tiny book is really important to people in my town. It provides both the information and the tools necessary to make clean ⓐdrinking water.

It is called the Drinkable Book. You cannot actually drink the book, but you can use it as a filter. Simply tear out a page and pour dirty water on it. ⓑ물이 그 페이지를 통과하면서, 깨끗한 마실 물로 바뀝니다. It is this filtered water that you can drink. This is possible because the book is made of special filter paper. This amazing book saves the lives of many children from diseases that come from dirty water.

10 위 글의 밑줄 친 ⓐdrinking과 문법적 쓰임이 다른 것을 고르시오.

① She bought a swimming suit.
② He is in the waiting room now.
③ You can smoke only in a smoking room.
④ He is a walking dictionary.
⑤ He is wearing a hearing aid.

서답형

11 위 글의 밑줄 친 ⓑ의 우리말에 맞게 주어진 어휘를 이용하여 13 단어로 영작하시오.

As, goes through, into

➡ _____

_____

[12~14] 다음 글을 읽고 물음에 답하시오.

The Tree-Book-Tree Project

This is the most amazing book ___ⓐ___ I ⓑ have ever seen. ⓒAfter you finish to read this book, plant it and water it. You will see new leaves growing on the book. In some bookstores in my town, you can see a copy of this book producing new leaves.

12 위 글의 빈칸 ⓐ에 들어갈 알맞은 말을 고르시오.

① where ② how ③ what

④ that ⑤ when

13 위 글의 밑줄 친 ⓑ의 현재완료와 용법이 같은 것을 **모두** 고르시오.

① I <u>have been</u> to Busan twice.

② <u>Have</u> you <u>been</u> to the bank yet?

③ I <u>have</u> never <u>read</u> this novel.

④ She <u>has been</u> sick since yesterday.

⑤ The train <u>has</u> just <u>arrived</u>.

서답형

14 위 글의 밑줄 친 ⓒ에서 어법상 **틀린** 부분을 찾아 고치시오.

_____ ➡ _____

[15~18] 다음 글을 읽고 물음에 답하시오.

There is a book-sharing project. First, register your book online and get an ID number. Next, (A)<u>leave</u> it in a public place. When the next reader finds your book and reports back _____ⓐ_____ the website, you can check where your book is. This way, the whole world can become a big _____ⓑ_____. The more books we share, the more we learn.

15 위 글의 빈칸 ⓐ에 들어갈 알맞은 전치사를 고르시오.

① from ② to

③ for ④ of

⑤ on

16 위 글의 빈칸 ⓑ에 들어갈 알맞은 말을 고르시오.

① museum ② publishing company

③ bookstore ④ shopping center

⑤ library

17 위 글의 밑줄 친 (A)leave와 같은 의미로 쓰인 것을 고르시오.

① You can <u>leave</u> the cooking to me.

② When will the plane <u>leave</u> for Dallas?

③ <u>Leave</u> the key on the table.

④ She took a month's paid <u>leave</u>.

⑤ <u>Leave</u> the door open, please.

18 Which question CANNOT be answered after reading the passage?

① What is the first step to join the book-sharing project?

② Where should you leave your book after the first step?

③ What should the next reader do after finding your book?

④ How long does it usually take for the next reader to find your book?

⑤ When can you check where your book is?

[19~21] 다음 글을 읽고 물음에 답하시오.

Most people (A)<u>think of</u> books as traditional paper books to read. However, there are many unique books around you. Let's learn about a few of these books.

_____ⓐ_____

I found this old book on a park bench yesterday. (①) A note on the cover read, "Free Book! (②) Take me home and read me!" (③) Actually, this book had an ID number and was registered on a website. (④) When I entered the number online, I found out that the book had traveled to many countries and that a number of readers in different countries had read it before me. (⑤)

19 위 글의 빈칸 ⓐ에 들어갈 제목으로 알맞은 것을 고르시오.

① Register Your Book on a Website

② The Drinkable Book

③ Books Travel!

④ How to Get an ID Number for a Book

⑤ The Tree-Book-Tree Project

20 위 글의 밑줄 친 (A)think of와 바꿔 쓸 수 없는 말을 고르시오.

① regard   ② look upon

③ consider   ④ show

⑤ view

21 위 글의 흐름으로 보아, 주어진 문장이 들어가기에 가장 적절한 곳은?

> How was that possible?

①   ②   ③   ④   ⑤

[22~24] 다음 글을 읽고 물음에 답하시오.

The Drinkable Book

This tiny book is really important to people in my town. It provides both the information and the tools necessary to make clean drinking water.

It is called the Drinkable Book. You cannot actually drink the book, but you can use it ⓐ as a filter. Simply tear out a page and pour dirty water on it. As the water goes through the page, ⓑit changes into clean drinking water. It is this filtered water that you can drink. This is possible because the book is made of special filter paper. This amazing book saves the lives of many children from diseases that come from dirty water.

22 위 글의 밑줄 친 ⓐas와 같은 의미로 쓰인 것을 고르시오.

① As I entered the room, they applauded.

② This plastic bag served as a hat.

③ Her anger grew as she talked.

④ She is as tall as you are.

⑤ Leave it as it is.

23 위 글의 밑줄 친 ⓑit이 가리키는 것을 본문에서 찾아 쓰시오.

➡ _____

24 위 글의 주제로 알맞은 것을 고르시오.

① the importance of a book which gives precious information

② the way to use tools necessary to make clean drinking water

③ how to make special filter paper

④ various ways to save the lives of many children from diseases

⑤ the book which provides the tools necessary to make clean drinking water

[25~26] 다음 글을 읽고 물음에 답하시오.

The secret is that the book has seeds in each page. (A)[It is / They are] these tiny seeds that change the book into a tree. This book was made by a small children's book publisher in Argentina. Though the company does not print this book anymore, this special project makes us (B)[think / to think] about where books come from.

These are just a few of the unique books you can find. What other unique books do you want to make? What special project would you like (C)[doing / to do] with the books? The bigger your imagination is, the more wonderful your books will become.

서답형

25 위 글의 괄호 (A)~(C)에서 문맥이나 어법상 알맞은 낱말을 골라 쓰시오.

➡ (A) _____ (B) _____ (C) _____

26 Which question CANNOT be answered after reading the passage?

① What does the book have in each page?

② Who made this book?

③ When was this book first published?

④ Is this book still printed?

⑤ Through this special project, what can we think about?

[27~28] 다음 글을 읽고 물음에 답하시오.

The Tree-Book-Tree Project

This is the most amazing book that I have ever seen. After you finish reading this book, plant it and water it. You will see new leaves growing on the book. In some bookstores in my town, you can see a copy of this book producing new leaves.

The secret is that the book has seeds in each page. It is these tiny seeds that change the book into a tree. (A)This book was made by a small children's book publisher in Argentina. Though the company does not print this book anymore, this special project makes us think about _____ⓐ_____.

서답형

27 위 글의 빈칸 ⓐ에 다음 문장을 알맞은 형태로 쓰시오.

Where does books come from?

➡ _____

28 위 글을 밑줄 친 (A)This book에 대한 설명으로 옳지 <u>않은</u> 것을 고르시오.

① It is the most amazing book that the writer has ever seen.

② If you plant it and water it, you will see new leaves growing on the book.

③ It has seeds in each page.

④ A small children's book publisher in Argentina made it.

⑤ Even now the publishing company prints this book.

[29~30] 다음 글을 읽고 물음에 답하시오.

These are just a few of the unique books you can find. What other unique books do you want to make? What special project would you like to do with the books? ⓐ The bigger your imagination is, the more wonderful your books will become.

29 위 글의 앞에 올 내용으로 가장 알맞은 것을 고르시오.

① the history of books

② the explanation about a few unique books we can find

③ various kinds of books that people like most

④ a recent survey showing people's taste in books

⑤ the imagination about books

서답형

30 위 글의 밑줄 친 ⓐ를 다음과 같이 바꿔 쓸 때, 어법상 틀린 부분을 찾아 고치시오. (2 군데)

As your imagination is the bigger, your books will become the more wonderful.

_____ ➡ _____

_____ ➡ _____

[01~03] 다음 글을 읽고 물음에 답하시오.

(A)[Almost / Most] people think of books as traditional paper books to read. However, there are many (B)[ordinary / unique] books around you. Let's learn about a few of these books.

Books Travel!

I found this old book on a park bench yesterday. A note on the cover read, "Free Book! Take me home and read me!" Actually, this book had an ID number and was registered on a website. When I entered the number online, I found out that the book had traveled to many countries and that (C)[a / the] number of readers in different countries had read it before me. How was ⓐthat possible?

01 위 글의 괄호 (A)~(C)에서 알맞은 낱말을 골라 쓰시오.

➡ (A) _____ (B) _____ (C) _____

02 위 글의 밑줄 친 ⓐthat이 가리키는 것을 영어로 쓰시오.

➡ _____
_____
_____

03 본문의 내용과 일치하도록 다음 빈칸 (A)~(C)에 알맞은 단어를 쓰시오.

The old book that the writer found on a park bench yesterday had (A)_____ _____ _____ and was registered (B)_____ _____ _____. Anyone who found it could take it home and read it because it was a (C)_____ book.

[04~06] 다음 글을 읽고 물음에 답하시오.

There is a book-sharing project. First, ___ⓐ___ your book online and get an ID number. Next, leave it in a public place. When the next reader finds your book and reports back to the website, you can check where your book is. This way, the whole world can become a big library. ⓑThe more books we share, the more we learn.

04 주어진 영영풀이를 참고하여 빈칸 ⓐ에 철자 r로 시작하는 단어를 쓰시오.

to put your name on an official list, in order to be able to do something or to receive a service

➡ _____

05 위 글의 밑줄 친 ⓑ를 다음과 같이 바꿔 쓸 때 빈칸에 들어갈 알맞은 말을 쓰시오.

As we share _____ _____, we learn _____.

06 본문의 내용과 일치하도록 다음 빈칸 (A)~(D)에 알맞은 단어를 쓰시오.

1. Register your book and get (A)_____ _____ _____.
2. Leave your book anywhere in (B)_____ _____ _____.
3. Someone picks up your book and reports back to (C)_____ _____.
4. Check (D)_____ your book goes and who reads it.

[07~09] 다음 글을 읽고 물음에 답하시오.

The Drinkable Book

This tiny book is really important to people in my town. It provides both the information and the tools necessary to make clean drinking water.

It is called the Drinkable Book. You cannot actually drink the book, but you can use it as a filter. Simply tear out a page and pour dirty water on it. As the water goes through the page, it changes into clean drinking water. ⓐ여러분이 마실 수 있는 것은 이 여과된 물입니다. This is possible because the book is made of special filter paper. This amazing book saves the lives of many children from diseases that come from dirty water.

07 다음 문장에서 위 글의 내용과 <u>다른</u> 부분을 찾아서 고치시오.

> As the Drinkable Book is made of special filter paper, you can not only drink the book but you can use it as a filter.

➡ _____ ➡ _____

08 위 글의 밑줄 친 ⓐ의 우리말에 맞게 주어진 어휘를 알맞게 배열하시오.

> filtered water / can / is / you / this / that / drink / it

➡ _____

09 본문의 내용과 일치하도록 다음 빈칸에 알맞은 단어를 쓰시오.

> Thanks to the Drinkable Book, many children can protect themselves from diseases that come from _____.

[10~12] 다음 글을 읽고 물음에 답하시오.

The Tree-Book-Tree Project

This is the most amazing book that I have ever seen. After you finish reading this book, plant it and water it. You will see new leaves growing on the book. In some bookstores in my town, you can see a copy of this book ___ⓐ___ new leaves.

The secret is that the book has seeds in each page. It is these tiny seeds that change the book into a tree. This book was made by a small children's book publisher in Argentina. ⓑThough the company does not print this book anymore, this special project makes us think about where books come from.

10 위 글의 빈칸 ⓐ에 produce를 알맞은 형태로 쓰시오.

➡ _____

11 위 글의 밑줄 친 ⓑ를 다음과 같이 바꿔 쓸 때 빈칸에 들어갈 알맞은 말을 두 단어로 쓰시오.

> Though the company prints this book
> _____ _____

12 What is the secret of the book on which new leaves grow? Answer in English beginning with "It's that ～". (9 words)

➡ _____

교과서

구석구석

해석

Express Yourself C

In making and flying a drone, its weight is important. It is a light drone that
= When you make and fly a drone. 'A light drone has a long battery life.'에서 주어 'A light drone'을 강조하기

has a long battery life. The lighter the drone is, the longer it flies.
위한 'It is … that ~' 강조구문   The+비교급+주어+동사 …, the+비교급+주어+동사 ~: …하면 할수록, 더 ~하다

구문해설 • drone: 드론, (무선 조종되는) 무인 비행 물체   • weight: 무게   • light: 가벼운   • battery
life: 건전지 수명

드론을 만들어 날릴 때, 그것
의 무게가 중요하다. 긴 건전
지 수명을 가지는 것은 가벼
운 드론이다. 드론이 가벼울
수록, 더 오래 난다.

Link to the World

This is called Dalhang-ari, a moon jar, because it looks like a full moon. In the
　　　　　　수동태　　　　　　　　　　　　　　　　　　　　　　~처럼 생기다

past, it was impossible to make this large round jar by hand. The larger a jar
　　　　　　가주어　　　　　진주어　　　　　　　　　　　the 비교급

was, the more difficult it was to make. It was a potter that solved this problem.
　　the 비교급　　　　　　　　　　　　　It ~ that 강조구문

A smart potter put two large bowls together to make this moon jar.
　　　　　　　　　　　　　　　　　　　　　부사적 용법(목적)

구문해설 • by hand: 손으로   • potter: 도공   • put ~ together: 합치다   • bowl: 사발

이것은 보름달처럼 생겨서 달
항아리라고 불린다. 과거에는
손으로 이렇게 크고 둥근 항
아리를 만드는 게 불가능했
다. 항아리가 클수록, 만들기
가 더 어려웠다. 이 문제를 해
결한 것은 한 도공이었다. 현
명한 도공은 두 개의 큰 사발
을 합쳐서 이 달항아리를 만
들었다.

Learning Diary – Listen & Speak 2

A: Which do you prefer, going camping or going swimming?
선호를 묻는 표현으로 prefer 대신 like better를 사용할 수 있다.

B: I prefer going camping. Actually, I hate going swimming. How about you?
　　　　　　　　　　　　　　　　　　　　　　목적어로 사용된 동명사

A: Well, I prefer going swimming.

구문해설 • prefer: 선호하다   • actually: 사실   • hate: 싫어하다

A: 너는 캠핑 가기와 수영하
러 가기 중에서 어떤 것을
더 좋아하니?

B: 나는 캠핑 가기를 더 좋아
해. 사실, 나는 수영하러
가기를 몹시 싫어해. 너는
어때?

A: 음, 나는 수영하러 가기를
더 좋아해.

영역별 핵심문제

Words & Expressions

01 다음 주어진 두 단어의 관계가 같도록 빈칸에 알맞은 단어를 쓰시오.

> disease – illness : furnish – _____

02 다음 문장의 빈칸 (a)와 (b)에 들어갈 단어가 바르게 짝지어진 것은?

> • I'll ask my friend to ___(a)___ the score of the game.
> • The ___(b)___ ants worked together to lift the leaf.

① break down – useful
② find out – tiny
③ stand up for – necessary
④ give away – giant
⑤ get over – tiny

[03~04] 다음 영영풀이에 해당하는 것을 고르시오.

03

> to produce words, numbers, pictures, etc. on paper by using a machine

① bridge   ② hunt
③ publish   ④ production
⑤ print

04

> to pull apart or to pull pieces off

① tear   ② seat
③ reply   ④ pour
⑤ vote

05 다음 대화의 빈칸에 들어갈 말을 〈영영풀이〉를 참고하여 쓰시오.

> A: Can I join your book-making project?
> B: Sure. Which do you prefer, paper books or digital books?
> A: I prefer digital books. Actually, I hate making paper books.
> B: Okay. Let me _____ you to the digital book team.

> 〈영영풀이〉 to tell someone another person's name the first time that they meet

➡ _____

06 다음 밑줄 친 부분의 뜻이 잘못된 것은?

① I looked happy, but I was <u>actually</u> sad. (사실)
② The people are looking at the <u>artwork</u> in the museum. (예술품)
③ Most curtains are made of <u>cloth</u>. (천)
④ I was asked to <u>prepare</u> a report for our next meeting. (준비하다)
⑤ You must <u>register</u> on the Internet to join the club. (설치하다)

Conversation

07 다음 대화의 흐름상 밑줄 친 단어의 쓰임이 <u>어색한</u> 것을 찾아 바르게 고치시오.

> G: (a)<u>Which</u> do you prefer, flying kites (b)<u>and</u> flying drones?
> B: I prefer (c)<u>flying</u> kites.
> G: (d)<u>Why</u> is that?
> B: I (e)<u>hate</u> working with machines.

_____ ➡ _____

08 주어진 문장을 알맞은 대화 순서로 배열한 것은?

> (A) I love making something delicious.
> (B) I like both, but it is making food art that I prefer.
> (C) Which do you prefer, making masks or making food art?
> (D) Why is that?

① (B)-(A)-(C)-(D) ② (B)-(D)-(C)-(A)
③ (C)-(B)-(D)-(A) ④ (D)-(A)-(C)-(B)
⑤ (D)-(B)-(A)-(C)

09 다음 짝지어진 대화 중 어색한 것은?

① A: Which do you prefer, raising dogs or raising cats?
　 B: I prefer raising dogs. Actually, I hate raising cats.
② A: Which do you prefer, watching sports or playing sports?
　 B: I prefer watching sports. Actually, I hate playing sports.
③ A: Which do you prefer, climbing a mountain or going to the beach?
　 B: I prefer climbing a mountain. Actually, I love going to the beach most.
④ A: Which do you prefer, riding a bike or riding a skateboard?
　 B: I prefer riding a bike. Actually, I hate riding a skateboard.
⑤ A: We went to Bakers' Camp, right?
　 B: No. It was Makers' Camp that we went to.

10 다음 대화의 흐름상 빈칸 (A)에 들어갈 말로 알맞은 것은?

> B: Why don't we make a bag with old jeans?
> G: Great! What kind of bag are we going to make?
> B: Which do you prefer, a shoulder bag or a hand bag?
> G: I prefer a shoulder bag. Actually, I hate holding things in my hands.
> B: Okay. _____(A)

① Who is going to make a shoulder bag?
② How about making a hand bag?
③ Actually I hate making a shoulder bag.
④ Let's make a shoulder bag together.
⑤ I prefer a hand bag.

11 대화의 제목으로 가장 적절한 것은?

> Minji: Seho, the book club day is just one week away.
> Seho: Right, Minji. I'm proud that we've collected so many interesting books to give away.
> Minji: Now, let's prepare some gifts for visitors. Do you have any good ideas?
> Seho: How about making bookmarks?
> Minji: Great idea! Let's write cheerful messages on them, too.
> Seho: Okay. Which do you prefer, making the bookmarks or writing the messages?
> Minji: Actually, I hate writing. I'd like to make the bookmarks.
> Seho: No problem. I'll write the cheerful messages.
> Minji: I'm sure they will love our bookmarks.

① The Pleasure of Giving Away Gifts
② Preparing for Book Club Day
③ How to Make Bookmarks
④ The Reason Why Minji Hates Writing
⑤ Things That Book Club Does

12 다음 중 어법상 <u>어색한</u> 문장을 고르시오.

① The more you have, the more you want.

② The higher I climbed, the colder I felt.

③ It is we that helped the stray dog.

④ It was in their car that Dave ate the hamburger by himself.

⑤ It is Ashley that go jogging every morning.

13 다음 글의 밑줄 친 단어를 알맞은 형태로 바꾸어 빈칸에 쓰시오.

> In making and flying a kite, its tail is important. It is the <u>length</u> of a tail that makes a kite fly <u>well</u>. The (a)_____ the tail is, the (b)_____ it flies.

14 다음 주어진 문장과 같은 뜻의 문장을 고르시오.

> As students are happier, they are more likely to enjoy their studies.

① The happier students are, the more they are likely to enjoy their studies.

② The happier students are, the more likely they are to enjoy their studies.

③ The more students are happy, the more likely they are to enjoy their studies.

④ The more happy students are, the more likely they are to enjoy their studies.

⑤ The happier students are, the likely they are more to enjoy their studies.

15 다음 중 어법상 <u>어색한</u> 문장의 개수로 알맞은 것은?

> a. It was Jack that he broke the vase.
> b. It was to the gym that the teacher went.
> c. It was Jessica that likes Korean dramas.
> d. The more information you provide, the well we can help you.
> e. The more money you make, the more you will buy things.
> f. The harder he practiced, the more beautiful he got to dance.

① 1개　② 2개　③ 3개　④ 4개　⑤ 5개

16 다음 우리말을 주어진 어휘를 이용하여 영어로 옮기시오.

(1) 그 불에 더 가까이 갈수록, 우리는 더 따뜻함을 느꼈다. (close, get, warm, feel)

➡ _____

_____

(2) 침대 아래에서 내가 찾은 것은 바로 그 잃어버린 열쇠야. (it, lost, found)

➡ _____

_____

(3) 그 아기가 토끼를 그린 곳은 바로 벽이야. (it, wall, draw, rabbit)

➡ _____

_____

Reading

[17~19] 다음 글을 읽고 물음에 답하시오.

Most people think of books as traditional paper books to read. However, there are many ___ⓐ___ books around you. Let's learn about a few of these books.

Books Travel!

I found this old book on a park bench yesterday. A note on the cover read, "Free Book! Take me home and read me!" Actually, this book had an ID number and was registered on a website. When I ⓑentered the number online, I found out that the book had traveled to many countries and that a number of readers in different countries had read it before me. How was that possible?

17 위 글의 빈칸 ⓐ에 들어갈 알맞은 말을 고르시오.

① usual
② normal
③ routine
④ unique
⑤ typical

18 위 글의 밑줄 친 ⓑentered와 같은 의미로 쓰인 것을 고르시오.

① She knocked the door before she entered.
② The idea never entered his head.
③ He entered his name and address in the blanks.
④ Several new companies have now entered the market.
⑤ 1,000 children entered the competition.

19 위 글을 읽고 대답할 수 없는 것을 고르시오.

① Where did the writer find the old book?
② When did the writer find the old book?
③ What was written on a note on the book cover?
④ What was the ID number of the book?
⑤ When the writer entered the ID number online, what did the writer find out?

[20~22] 다음 글을 읽고 물음에 답하시오.

___ⓐ___

This tiny book is really important to people in my town. It provides both the information and the tools necessary ⓑto make clean drinking water.

It is called the Drinkable Book. You cannot actually drink the book, but you can use it as a filter. Simply tear out a page and pour dirty water on it. As the water goes through the page, it changes into clean drinking water. It is this filtered water that you can drink. ⓒThis is possible because the book is made of special filter paper. This amazing book saves the lives of many children from diseases that come from dirty water.

20 위 글의 빈칸 ⓐ에 들어갈 제목으로 알맞은 것을 고르시오.

① The Tree-Book-Tree Project
② All Drinking Water Must Be Filtered
③ The Drinkable Book
④ The Tools Necessary to Save Children's Lives
⑤ Books Travel!

21 다음 〈보기〉에서 위 글의 밑줄 친 ⓑto make와 to부정사의 용법이 다른 것의 개수를 고르시오.

┌─ 보기 ─┐
① His fault is to talk too much.
② I hurried to the station only to miss the train.
③ He was the first man to land on the moon.
④ I make it a rule to take a walk early in the morning.
⑤ He must be a gentleman to behave like that.
└────────┘

① 1개 ② 2개 ③ 3개 ④ 4개 ⑤ 5개

22 위 글의 밑줄 친 ⓒThis가 가리키는 내용을 우리말로 쓰시오.

➡ _____

_____

_____

[23~24] 다음 글을 읽고 물음에 답하시오.

The secret is that the book has seeds in each page. It is these tiny seeds that change the book into a tree. This book was made ⓐ a small children's book publisher in Argentina. Though the company does not print this book anymore, this special project makes us think about where books come from.

These are just a few of the unique books you can find. What other unique books do you want to make? What special project would you like to do with the books? ⓑThe bigger your imagination is, the more your books will become wonderful.

23 위 글의 빈칸 ⓐ에 들어갈 알맞은 말을 고르시오.

① from ② for ③ into
④ by ⑤ of

24 위 글의 밑줄 친 ⓑ에서 어법상 틀린 부분을 찾아 고치시오.

➡ _____

_____

[25~26] 다음 글을 읽고 물음에 답하시오.

There is a book-sharing project. First, register your book online and get an ID number. Next, leave it in a public place. When the next reader finds your book and reports back to the website, ⓐ여러분은 책이 어디 있는지 확인할 수 있습니다. This way, the whole world can become a big library. The more books we share, the more we learn.

25 위 글의 밑줄 친 ⓐ의 우리말에 맞게 주어진 어휘를 알맞게 배열하시오.

you, your, where, is, can, check, book

➡ _____

26 According to the passage, which is NOT true?

① When you join a book-sharing project, you should register your book online and get an ID number first.
② You should leave your book in a public place.
③ The next reader should report back to the website when he or she finds your book.
④ After the next reader reports back to the website, you can locate your book.
⑤ As we have more big libraries, we share more books.

단원별 예상문제

01 출제율 90%

다음 짝지어진 단어의 관계가 같도록 빈칸에 알맞은 단어를 쓰시오.

> collect – collection : connect – _____

02 출제율 95%

다음 영영풀이에 해당하는 단어는?

> feeling pleased about something that you have done or something that you own

① cheerful   ② proud   ③ actual
④ public   ⑤ necessary

03 출제율 90%

밑줄 친 부분의 표현을 이용하여 〈조건〉에 맞게 빈칸 (A)를 알맞게 채우시오.

> ┌─── 조건 ───┐
> hate를 써서 싫어하는 것을 표현하는 문장을 쓰시오.

> A: Which do you prefer, working with a plan or working without a plan?
> B: I prefer working without a plan. Actually,
> _____
>   (A)
> A: You and I prefer the same thing!

➡ _____

[04~05] 다음 대화를 읽고 물음에 답하시오.

> B: Why don't we make a bag with old jeans?
>
> (A) Which do you prefer, a shoulder bag or a hand bag?
>
> (B) I prefer a shoulder bag. Actually, I hate holding things in my hands.
>
> (C) Great! What kind of bag are we going to make?
>
> (D) Okay. Let's make a shoulder bag together.

04 출제율 100%

위 대화의 (A)~(D)를 알맞게 배열하시오.

➡ _____

05 출제율 90%

위 대화를 읽고 다음 질문에 영어로 답하시오.

> Q: What are the speakers going to make?

➡ _____

06 출제율 95%

다음 짝지어진 대화 중 어법상 어색한 것은?

① A: Which do you prefer, baseball or soccer?
  B: I prefer soccer.

② A: Which do you prefer, taking the bus or take the subway?
  B: I prefer taking the subway.

③ A: I prefer digital books. Actually, I hate making paper books.
  B: Okay. Let me introduce you to the digital book team.

④ A: I like both, but it is making food art that I prefer.
  B: Why is that?

⑤ A: Which do you like better, cloth dolls or digital artwork?
  B: I like digital artwork better. Actually, I don't like dolls much.

07 다음 대화의 빈칸에 알맞은 것은?

> B: _____, working with a plan or working without a plan?
> G: I like working with a plan better.
> B: Me, too! You and I prefer the same thing!

① What do you say to
② Do you think of
③ Which do you prefer
④ Would you like
⑤ Are you going to

08 다음 대화에서 주어진 문장이 들어갈 위치로 알맞은 것은?

> G: Why don't we make something with jean pockets? (A)
> B: Great! What shall we make? (B)
> G: Which do you prefer, a pocket board or a cell phone holder? (C)
> B: I prefer a cell phone holder. (D) And I hate spending too much time making things.
> G: Okay. (E) Let's make a cute cell phone holder together.

> It'll be easier to make.

① (A) ② (B) ③ (C) ④ (D) ⑤ (E)

09 다음 대화의 빈칸에 들어갈 말로 알맞은 것은?

> A: Can I join your book-making project?
> B: Sure. Which do you prefer, paper books _____ digital books?
> A: I prefer digital books. Actually, I hate making paper books.
> B: Okay. Let me introduce you to the digital book team.

① or ② of ③ and ④ for ⑤ so

10 다음 대화의 빈칸 (A)에 들어갈 말로 알맞은 것은?

> G: Junha, what are you doing with jeans?
> B: I'm making a pencil case for you.
> G: That's great! What are you going to draw on it?
> B: _____(A)_____
> G: I prefer cats. They're lovely.
> B: Okay. Let me draw a lovely cat on this pencil case.
> G: Thanks! I can't wait for it!.

① What animal are you drawing?
② Why don't we draw cats?
③ Do you like animals?
④ I think cats are smarter than pandas.
⑤ Which do you prefer, pandas or cats?

11 다음 밑줄 친 ①~⑤에서 어법상 어색한 부분을 모두 찾아 바르게 고치시오.

> This is ①called Dalhang-ari, a moon jar, because it ②looks a full moon. In the past, it was impossible to make this large round jar by hand. ③The large a jar was, the more difficult it was to make. It was a potter ④who solved this problem. A smart potter put two large bowls together ⑤to make this moon jar.

➡ _____

12 다음 중 밑줄 친 it의 쓰임이 나머지 넷과 다른 하나는?

① It is Ken that often fights with his brother.
② It is natural that kids like to run around and play.
③ It was Tom and Jack that we met on our way back home.
④ It was Woojin that broke my favorite mug.
⑤ It is iced Americano that my mom likes most.

13 다음 글에서 밑줄 친 우리말을 괄호 안에 주어진 단어를 활용하여 영어로 옮기시오.

> In 3D printing, the size of an object is important. (1)당신의 인쇄 시간에 영향을 주는 것은 크기이다.(size, influence, the time of your print) The larger the object is, (2)당신은 더 오래 기다려야 할 것이다.(long, will, wait)

(1) _____

(2) _____

15 다음 빈칸 (A)와 (B)에 알맞은 단어를 넣어 밑줄 친 ⓑThis book에 대한 소개를 완성하시오.

> This book has (A)_____ in each page, so if you plant the book and water it, these tiny seeds change the book into (B)_____ _____.

[16~18] 다음 글을 읽고 물음에 답하시오.

> **Books Travel!**
> I found ①this old book on a park bench yesterday. A note on the cover ⓐread, "Free Book! Take ②me home and read me!" ⓑActually, this book had an ID number and was registered on a website. When I entered the number online, I found out that ③the book had traveled to many countries and that a number of readers in different countries had read ④it before ⑤me. How was that possible?

[14~15] 다음 글을 읽고 물음에 답하시오.

> ⓐ_____
> This is the most amazing book that I have ever seen. After you finish reading this book, plant it and water it. You will see new leaves growing on the book. In some bookstores in my town, you can see a copy of this book producing new leaves.
> The secret is that the book has seeds in each page. It is these tiny seeds that change the book into a tree. ⓑThis book was made by a small children's book publisher in Argentina. Though the company does not print this book anymore, this special project makes us think about where books come from.

16 밑줄 친 ①~⑤ 중에서 가리키는 대상이 나머지 넷과 다른 것은?

① ② ③ ④ ⑤

14 위 글의 빈칸 ⓐ에 들어갈 제목으로 알맞은 것을 고르시오.

① How to Recycle the Used Book
② The Tree-Book-Tree Project
③ Where Do Books Come from?
④ Books Travel!
⑤ The Drinkable Book

17 위 글의 밑줄 친 ⓐread와 같은 의미로 쓰인 것을 고르시오.

① She's still learning to read.
② The sign read 'No admittance.'
③ A man came to read the gas meter.
④ I can't read your writing.
⑤ She read us a story.

18 위 글의 밑줄 친 ⓑActually와 바꿔 쓸 수 없는 말을 모두 고르시오.

① In reality
② In fact
③ Especially
④ In particular
⑤ As a matter of fact

[19~21] 다음 글을 읽고 물음에 답하시오.

The Drinkable Book

This tiny book is really important to people in my town. It provides both the information and the tools necessary to make clean drinking water.

It is called the Drinkable Book. (①) Simply tear out a page and pour dirty water on it. (②) As the water goes through the page, it changes ___ⓐ___ clean drinking water. (③) It is this filtered water that you can drink. (④) This is possible because the book is made of special filter paper. (⑤) This amazing book saves the lives of many children ___ⓑ___ diseases that come from dirty water.

19 위 글의 빈칸 ⓐ와 ⓑ에 들어갈 전치사가 바르게 짝지어진 것은?

	ⓐ	ⓑ		ⓐ	ⓑ
①	for	from	②	into	for
③	into	from	④	for	to
⑤	on	for			

20 위 글의 흐름으로 보아, 주어진 문장이 들어가기에 가장 적절한 곳은?

You cannot actually drink the book, but you can use it as a filter.

① ② ③ ④ ⑤

21 How is it possible to make clean drinking water? Fill in the blanks with the suitable words.

As the Drinkable Book is made of _____ _____ _____, it is possible to make clean drinking water simply by pouring dirty water on a page torn out from the Drinkable Book.

[22~23] 다음 글을 읽고 물음에 답하시오.

The Tree-Book-Tree Project

This is the most amazing book that I have ever seen. After you finish reading this book, plant it and water it. You will see new leaves growing on the book. In some bookstores in my town, you can see a copy of this book producing new leaves.

The secret is that the book has seeds in each page. It is these tiny seeds that change the book into a tree. ⓐThis book was made by a small children's book publisher in Argentina. Though the company does not print this book anymore, this special project makes us think about where books come from.

22 위 글의 밑줄 친 ⓐ를 능동태로 고치시오.

➡ _____

_____

23 What does the Tree-Book-Tree Project make us think about? Answer in English in a full sentence. (9 words)

➡ _____

01 다음 대화를 읽고 질문에 영어로 답하시오.

> G: Why don't we make something with jean pockets?
> B: Great! What shall we make?
> G: Which do you prefer, a pocket board or a cell phone holder?
> B: I prefer a cell phone holder. It'll be easier to make. And I hate spending too much time making things.
> G: Okay. Let's make a cute cell phone holder together.

Q: Why does the boy prefer a cell phone holder? Write two things.

➡ _____
_____
_____

02 다음 대화의 밑줄 친 우리말을 〈조건〉에 맞게 쓰시오.

> B: Which do you prefer, making masks or making food art?
> G: I like both, but 내가 더 좋아하는 것은 푸드 아트 만들기야.

┤ 조건 ├
• 강조구문과 동명사를 이용하시오.
• make / food art / prefer를 이용할 것.

➡ _____

03 다음 대화를 읽고 질문에 영어로 답하시오.

> Minji: Seho, the book club day is just one week away.
> Seho: Right, Minji. I'm proud that we've collected so many interesting books to give away.

> Minji: Now, let's prepare some gifts for visitors. Do you have any good ideas?
> Seho: How about making bookmarks?
> Minji: Great idea! Let's write cheerful messages on them, too.
> Seho: Okay. Which do you prefer, making the bookmarks or writing the messages?
> Minji: Actually, I hate writing. I'd like to make the bookmarks.
> Seho: No problem. I'll write the cheerful messages.
> Minji: I'm sure they will love our bookmarks.

Q: What is Seho going to do about making bookmarks?

➡ _____
_____

04 다음 문장에서 어법상 틀린 곳이 있으면 바르게 고치시오.

> (1) This called Dalhang-ari, a moon jar.
> (2) The larger a jar was, the more it was difficult to make.
> (3) It was a potter which solved this problem.

➡ (1) _____
(2) _____
(3) _____

05 다음 주어진 〈조건〉에 맞게 문장을 바꾸어 쓰시오.

> (1) I waited for him for a long time.
> (2) As my son grew bigger, I got more worried.

┤ 조건 ├
(1) 'It ... that' 강조구문으로 밑줄 친 부분을 강조
(2) 'the+비교급, the+비교급'을 사용

(1) _____
(2) _____

06 괄호 안에 주어진 표현을 사용하여 우리말을 영어로 옮기시오.

(1) (*the Mona Lisa*)

A: Leonardo da Vinci painted *The Starry Night*, right?

B: No, Leonardo da Vinci가 그린 것은 바로 모나리자야.

(2) (speak, can, well)

A: English is still difficult for me. What should I do?

B: The only way is to practice more. The more you practice, 너는 더 잘 말할 수 있어.

(1) _____

_____

(2) _____

[07~09] 다음 글을 읽고 물음에 답하시오.

ⓐ대부분의 사람은 책을 읽기 위한 전통적인 종이 책으로만 생각합니다. However, there are many unique books around you. Let's learn about a few of ⓑthese books.

Books Travel!

I found this old book on a park bench yesterday. A note on the cover read, "Free Book! Take me home and read me!" Actually, this book had an ID number and was registered on a website. ⓒWhen I entered the number online, I found out that the book had traveled to many countries and that a number of readers in different countries read it before me. How was that possible?

07 위 글의 밑줄 친 ⓐ의 우리말에 맞게 주어진 어휘를 이용하여 11 단어로 영작하시오.

> think of

➡ _____

_____

08 위 글의 밑줄 친 ⓑthese books가 가리키는 것을 본문에서 찾아 쓰시오.

➡ _____

09 위 글의 밑줄 친 ⓒ에서 어법상 틀린 부분을 찾아 고치시오.

_____ ➡ _____

[10~12] 다음 글을 읽고 물음에 답하시오.

The Drinkable Book

This tiny book is really important to people in my town. It provides both the information and the tools necessary to make clean drinking water. ⓐIt is called the Drinkable Book. You cannot actually drink the book, but you can use it as a filter. Simply tear out a page and pour dirty water on it. As the water goes through the page, it changes into clean drinking water. It is this (A)[filtering / filtered] water that you can drink. This is possible because the book is made (B)[from / of] special filter paper. This (C)[amazing / amazed] book saves the lives of many children from diseases that come from dirty water.

10 위 글의 밑줄 친 ⓐ를 능동태로 고치시오.

➡ _____

11 위 글의 괄호 (A)~(C)에서 문맥이나 어법상 알맞은 낱말을 골라 쓰시오.

➡ (A) _____ (B) _____ (C) _____

12 본문의 내용과 일치하도록 다음 빈칸 (A)~(D)에 알맞은 단어를 쓰시오.

The Drinkable Book provides (A)_____ _____ necessary to make clean drinking water. When you (B)_____ _____ a page of the book and (C)_____ dirty water on it, the water changes into (D)_____ drinking water.

01 주어진 〈보기〉의 문장과 같이 선호를 묻는 말과 좋아하는 것과 싫어하는 것을 표현하는 대화를 완성하시오.

┌─ 보기 ┐

A: Which do you prefer, working alone or working on a team?

B: I prefer working alone. Actually, I hate working on a team.

☐ working alone   ☐ working with a plan   ☐ working with numbers and texts

☐ working on a team   ☐ working without a plan   ☐ working with pictures and music

02 〈보기〉를 참고하여, 친구에게 옳은 답을 알려주는 문장을 완성하시오.

┌─ 보기 ┐

A: Edison invented the telephone, right?

B: No, it was Bell that invented the telephone. (Bell)

(1) A: You can visit the Leaning Tower in Naples, right?

B: No, _____. (in Pisa)

(2) A: The Curies discovered the lasers, right?

B: No, _____. (radium)

(3) A: French is spoken all over the world, right?

B: No, _____. (English)

03 다음 내용을 바탕으로 작품 제작 과정에서 어떤 점이 중요한지 설명하는 글을 쓰시오.

MAKING AND FLYING A KITE

The length of a tail makes a kite fly well

In making and flying (A)_____, its tail is important. It is (B)_____ of a tail that makes a kite fly well. The longer the tail is, (C)_____ it flies.

단원별 모의고사

01 다음 단어에 대한 영어 설명이 <u>어색한</u> 것은?

① drinkable: clean and safe to drink

② filter: to remove unwanted substances from liquids or gases

③ actually: used to refer to what is true or real

④ huge: extremely small

⑤ register: to put someone's or something's name on an official list

02 다음 짝지어진 단어의 관계가 같도록 주어진 철자로 시작하는 알맞은 말을 쓰시오.

necessary – unnecessary : like – d_____

03 다음 영영풀이에 해당하는 단어를 고르시오.

a person or company that prints books

① manager   ② bookstore

③ publisher   ④ disease

⑤ filter

04 다음 빈칸에 들어갈 말로 알맞은 것은?

A: Which do you prefer, taking the bus or taking the subway?

B: I prefer taking the subway. Actually,

_____.

① taking the bus is not expensive

② I hate taking the bus

③ I prefer taking the bus

④ I don't like taking the subway

⑤ you had better take the bus

05 다음 대화의 밑줄 친 (A)를 'It ~ that ...' 강조구문을 이용하여 쓰시오.

G: Which do you prefer, flying kites or flying drones?

B: I prefer flying kites.

G: Why is that?

B: (A)I hate working with machines.

➡ _____

06 다음 대화의 빈칸에 들어갈 말로 알맞은 것은?

G: Why don't we make something with jean pockets?

B: Great! What shall we make?

G: Which do you prefer, a pocket board or a cell phone holder?

B: I prefer a cell phone holder. _____ And I hate spending too much time making things.

G: Okay. Let's make a cute cell phone holder together.

① The better the cell phone is, the more expensive it will be.

② I hate making a cell phone holder.

③ It'll be easier to make.

④ I hate making food art.

⑤ It'll be a bit expensive to buy.

07 대화의 밑줄 친 우리말에 맞게 주어진 단어를 이용하여 영어로 쓰시오.

> G: Junha, what are you doing with jeans?
>
> B: I'm making a pencil case for you.
>
> G: That's great! What are you going to draw on it?
>
> B: Which do you prefer, pandas or cats?
>
> G: I prefer cats. They're lovely.
>
> B: Okay. Let me draw a lovely cat on this pencil case.
>
> G: Thanks! 몹시 기다려진다!(can / wait / it)

➡ _____

[08~09] 다음 대화를 읽고 물음에 답하시오.

> Minji: Seho, the book club day is just one week away.
>
> Seho: Right, Minji. I'm proud that we've collected so many interesting books to give away.
>
> Minji: Now, let's prepare some gifts for visitors. (A)_____
>
> Seho: How about making bookmarks?
>
> Minji: Great idea! Let's write cheerful messages on them, too.
>
> Seho: Okay. (B)_____
>
> Minji: Actually, (C)_____ I'd like to make the bookmarks.
>
> Seho: No problem. I'll write the cheerful messages.
>
> Minji: I'm sure they will love our bookmarks.

08 위 대화의 빈칸 (A)~(C)에 들어갈 말을 〈보기〉에서 찾아 쓰시오.

> ┤ 보기 ├
> • I hate writing.
> • Do you have any good ideas?
> • Which do you prefer, making the bookmarks or writing the messages?

➡ (A) _____

  (B) _____

  _____

  (C) _____

09 What have Minji and Seho done?

➡ _____

  _____

10 다음 중 어법상 어색한 문장을 고르시오.

① The more he gets, the more he wants.

② The faster you go up, the faster you go down.

③ The hotter it gets, the more people you will see near the sea.

④ The more foolish you are, the easier you believe what others say.

⑤ The longer he stayed there, the less he liked the people.

11 다음 주어진 문장과 같은 의미의 문장을 바르게 쓴 것을 고르시오.

> As you go farther, it is harder to come back.

① The more you go far, the harder it is to come back.

② The more you go far, the more hard it is to come back.

③ The farther you go, the harder it is to come back.

④ The farther you go, it is the harder to come back.

⑤ The farther you go, the more it is hard to come back.

12 다음 대화의 빈칸에 알맞은 것은?

> A: Did Mr. Kim buy shoes for his wife?
> B: No. It _____ for his wife. (a ring)

① is a ring that he buys

② is a ring what he bought

③ was a ring that he bought

④ was a ring that he buys

⑤ was a ring who he bought

13 다음 문장의 밑줄 친 부분을 강조하는 문장으로 다시 쓰시오.

(1) He became President in 2017.

➡ It _____.

(2) Dash chose what to eat at dinner.

➡ It _____.

14 다음 글에서 밑줄 친 우리말을 괄호 안의 단어를 활용하여 영어로 옮기시오.

> I'd like to make special cookies. (1)내가 설탕을 덜 사용할수록, 쿠키는 더 선상에 좋아진다.(little sugar, healthy) (2)모든 사람을 건강하게 만들 것은 이 건강에 좋은 쿠키이다.(these, will make, healthy, everyone)

(1) _____

(2) _____

_____

[15~17] 다음 글을 읽고 물음에 답하시오.

> **Books Travel!**
> I found this old book on a park bench yesterday. A note on the cover read, "(A) Free Book! Take me home and read me!" Actually, this book had an ID number and was registered on a website. When I entered the number online, I found out that the book ____ⓐ____ to many countries and that a number of readers in different countries had read it before me. How was that possible?

15 위 글의 빈칸 ⓐ에 travel을 알맞은 형태로 쓰시오.

➡ _____

16 위 글의 밑줄 친 (A)Free와 같은 의미로 쓰인 것을 고르시오.

① He held out his free hand and I took it.

② He lives free from care.

③ Admission is free.

④ Is this seat free?

⑤ You are free to come and go as you please.

17 위 글의 주제로 알맞은 것을 고르시오.

① the typical thoughts that many people have about books
② a unique book around you
③ a traditional place to borrow books
④ the cheapest way to buy a book
⑤ a traditional paper book to read

[18~19] 다음 글을 읽고 물음에 답하시오.

There is a book-sharing project. First, register your book online and get an ID number. Next, leave it in a public place. When the next reader finds your book and reports back to the website, you can check where your book is. This way, the whole world can become a big library. ⓐ우리가 더 많은 책을 공유할수록, 우리는 더 많이 배웁니다.

18 위 글의 밑줄 친 ⓐ의 우리말에 맞게 주어진 어휘를 이용하여 9 단어로 영작하시오.

the more

➡ _____

19 다음 중 전 세계가 하나의 큰 도서관이 될 수 있는 절차에 해당하지 않는 것을 고르시오.

① 책을 공유하는 프로젝트에 참가한다.
② 우선, 온라인에 여러분의 책을 등록한다.
③ 여러분의 책의 ID 번호를 얻는다.
④ 등록한 책을 공공장소에 놓아둔다.
⑤ 독자가 여러분의 책을 발견해서 가져가면, 여러분은 그 사실을 웹사이트에 다시 알려준다.

[20~22] 다음 글을 읽고 물음에 답하시오.

The Drinkable Book
①This tiny book is really important to people in my town. ②It provides both the information and the tools necessary to make clean drinking water.
③It is called the Drinkable Book. You cannot actually drink the book, but you can use ④ it as a filter. Simply tear out a page and pour dirty water on ⑤it. As the water goes through the page, it changes into clean drinking water. It is this filtered water that you can drink. This is possible because the book is made of special filter paper. This ⓐamaze book saves the lives of many children from diseases that come from dirty water.

20 밑줄 친 ①~⑤ 중에서 가리키는 대상이 나머지 넷과 다른 것은?

①   ②   ③   ④   ⑤

21 위 글의 밑줄 친 ⓐamaze를 알맞은 형으로 고치시오.

➡ _____

22 According to the passage, which is NOT true?

① The Drinkable Book provides both the information and the tools necessary to make clean drinking water.
② You can use the Drinkable Book as a filter.
③ You can make clean drinking water simply by pouring dirty water on a page torn out from the Drinkable Book.
④ You can drink the water filtered through the page torn out from the Drinkable Book.
⑤ The Drinkable Book saves the lives of many children from diseases that come from malnutrition.

Lesson 7

Fact, Opinion or Fake

 의사소통 기능

- 의견 묻기
  How do you feel about this drama?

- 이의 제기하기
  I don't agree (with you).

 언어 형식

- 간접화법
  Garcia-Fuller **said** she was teaching her students how to tell fake news from real news.

- 명사절을 이끄는 접속사 if
  You also have to check **if** they are based on facts.

Words & Expressions

Key Words

- **actually**[ǽktʃuəli] (부) 실제로, 사실
- **appear**[əpíər] (동) ~인 것 같다
- **artwork**[ɑ́:rtwərk] (명) 예술 작품
- **attack**[ətǽk] (동) 공격하다
- **boring**[bɔ́:riŋ] (형) 지루한
- **check**[tʃek] (동) 확인하다
- **cheer**[tʃiər] (동) 환호하다
- **cleaner**[klí:nər] (명) 세제, 청소기
- **clown**[klaun] (명) 광대
- **comfortable**[kʌ́mfərtəbl] (형) 편안한
- **complete**[kəmplí:t] (형) 완전한
- **cool**[ku:l] (형) 멋있는, 시원한
- **critically**[krítikəli] (부) 비판적으로
- **cute**[kju:t] (형) 귀여운
- **evidence**[évədəns] (명) 증거
- **false**[fɔ:ls] (형) 거짓의, 잘못된
- **friendly**[fréndli] (형) 친절한
- **funny**[fʌ́ni] (형) 우스운
- **healthy**[hélθi] (형) 건강한
- **information**[ìnfərméiʃən] (명) 정보
- **light**[lait] (형) 가벼운
- **major**[méidʒər] (형) 주요한, 주된
- **octopus**[ɑ́ktəpəs] (명) 문어
- **offer**[ɔ́:fər] (동) 제공하다
- **perfect**[pə́:rfikt] (형) 완벽한

- **performance**[pərfɔ́:rməns] (명) 공연, 수행
- **prefer**[prifə́:r] (동) 선호하다
- **provide**[prəváid] (동) 제공하다
- **recently**[rí:sntli] (부) 최근에
- **save**[seiv] (동) 구하다
- **scared**[skɛərd] (형) 겁먹은
- **scary**[skɛ́əri] (형) 무서운
- **search**[sə:rtʃ] (동) 찾다, 검색하다
- **seem**[si:m] (동) ~인 것 같다
- **sink**[siŋk] (동) 가라앉다
- **site**[sait] (명) 장소
- **skill**[skil] (명) 기술, 실력
- **smart**[smɑ:rt] (형) 똑똑한
- **snake**[sneik] (명) 뱀
- **source**[sɔ:rs] (명) 근원, 출처
- **spread**[spred] (형) 퍼진 (동) 퍼지다
- **support**[səpɔ́:rt] (동) 지지하다, 후원하다
- **tooth**[tui:θ] (명) 이, 치아
- **totally**[tóutəli] (부) 전적으로
- **touching**[tʌ́tʃiŋ] (형) 감동적인
- **unclear**[ənklíər] (형) 불확실한
- **unique**[ju:ní:k] (형) 독특한
- **untrue**[əntrú:] (형) 사실이 아닌
- **wear**[wɛər] (동) 착용하다

Key Expressions

- **along with** ~와 함께
- **be based on** ~에 바탕을 두다
- **be made out of** ~로부터 만들어지다
- **by the way** 그런데
- **get along well with** ~와 잘 지내다
- **get scared** 겁먹다
- **give up** 포기하다
- **laugh out loud** 큰 소리로 웃다
- **look like** ~처럼 보이다

- **made up** 꾸며낸, 지어낸
- **make sense** 의미가 통하다
- **pass away** 돌아가시다
- **pay attention to** ~에 주의를 기울이다
- **slow down** 속도를 줄이다
- **take a break** 휴식을 취하다
- **tell A from B** A와 B를 구별하다
- **too good to be true** 너무 좋아서 믿어지지 않는
- **turn out** 판명되다

Word Power

※ 서로 비슷한 뜻을 가진 어휘

- □ **appear** ~인 것 같다 - **seem** ~인 것 같다
- □ **attack** 공격하다 - **strike** 치다, 공격하다
- □ **evidence** 증거 - **proof** 증거
- □ **major** 주요한, 주된 - **principal** 주된
- □ **recently** 최근에 - **lately** 최근에
- □ **totally** 전적으로 - **wholly** 전적으로

- □ **artwork** 예술 작품 - **craft** 공예품
- □ **check** 확인하다 - **examine** 조사하다
- □ **false** 거짓의, 잘못된 - **fake** 거짓의
- □ **offer** 제공하다 - **provide** 제공하다, **supply** 공급하다
- □ **search** 찾다 - **investigate** 조사하다
- □ **unclear** 불확실한 - **uncertain** 불확실한

※ 서로 반대의 뜻을 가진 어휘

- □ **attack** 공격하다 ↔ **defend** 방어하다
- □ **comfortable** 편안한 ↔ **uncomfortable** 불편한
- □ **false** 거짓의 ↔ **true** 진실인
- □ **light** 가벼운 ↔ **heavy** 무거운
- □ **perfect** 완벽한 ↔ **imperfect** 불완전한
- □ **untrue** 사실이 아닌 ↔ **true** 사실인

- □ **boring** 지루한 ↔ **exciting** 흥미로운
- □ **complete** 완전한 ↔ **incomplete** 불완전한
- □ **friendly** 친절한 ↔ **unfriendly** 불친절한
- □ **major** 주요한, 주된 ↔ **minor** 사소한
- □ **sink** 가라앉다 ↔ **float** 떠오르다

※ 명사 - 형용사

- □ **comfort** 편안함 - **comfortable** 편안한
- □ **health** 건강 - **healthy** 건강한

- □ **evidence** 증거 - **evident** 명백한
- □ **skill** 기술, 실력 - **skillful** 능숙한

※ 동사 - 명사

- □ **inform** 알려주다 - **information** 정보

- □ **perform** 공연하다 - **performance** 공연, 수행

English Dictionary

- □ **attack** 공격하다
  → to try to hurt or damage someone or something using physical violence
  물리적인 폭력을 사용하여 다치게 하거나 손상을 주려고 하다

- □ **clown** 광대
  → a performer in a circus who wears funny clothes and bright make-up, and does silly things in order to make people laugh
  서커스에서 우스운 옷을 입고 밝은 화장을 하고 사람들을 웃게 하려고 어리석은 행동을 하는 공연자

- □ **critically** 비판적으로
  → in a way that expresses disapproval
  불찬성을 표현하는 방식으로

- □ **evidence** 증거
  → anything that causes you to believe that something is true
  당신이 어떤 것이 사실이라고 믿도록 만드는 어떤 것

- □ **false** 거짓의, 잘못된
  → incorrect, untrue, or mistaken
  정확하지 않거나 사실이 아닌, 또는 잘못된

- □ **lie** 거짓말
  → an untrue statement
  사실이 아닌 진술

- □ **major** 주된, 주요한
  → very important and serious
  매우 중요하고 진지한

- □ **octopus** 문어
  → a soft sea creature with eight long arms
  여덟 개의 긴 다리를 가진 연한 바다 생물

- □ **opinion** 의견
  → what you think or believe about something
  무엇에 관하여 생각하거나 믿고 있는 것

- □ **sink** 가라앉다
  → to disappear below the surface of the water
  수면 아래로 사라지다

- □ **spread** 퍼지다
  → to open it out or arrange it over a place or surface
  한 장소나 표면 위에 펼치거나 배열하다

- □ **support** 지지하다
  → to give assistance, approval, comfort, or encouragement to someone
  어떤 사람에게 도움, 동의, 위로, 격려 등을 주다

- □ **totally** 전적으로
  → completely, absolutely
  완전하게, 절대적으로

서답형

01 다음 문장의 빈칸에 〈영어 설명〉에 맞게 한 단어로 쓰시오.

In my _____, English is the most difficult subject.
〈영어 설명〉 a thought or belief about something or someone

02 다음 빈칸에 공통으로 들어갈 말로 가장 적절한 것은?

• This new trend _____s to be continuing for a while.
• A new vending machine will _____ at a subway station in Tokyo.

① check   ② spread
③ report   ④ appear
⑤ provide

03 다음 빈칸에 들어갈 말이 알맞게 짝지어진 것은?

(A) My teacher got upset because my homework wasn't _____.
(B) We must find the _____ of the information first.

① false – source
② complete – resource
③ critical – impressed
④ complex – resource
⑤ complete – source

[04~05] 다음 설명에 해당하는 단어를 고르시오.

04
to try to hurt or damage someone or something using physical violence

① save   ② attack
③ support   ④ search
⑤ offer

05
a performer in a circus who wears funny clothes and bright make-up, and does silly things in order to make people

① snake   ② octopus
③ clown   ④ source
⑤ crown

06 짝지어진 단어의 관계가 나머지 넷과 다른 것은?

① inform – information
② evidence – evident
③ comfort – comfortable
④ skill – skillful
⑤ health – healthy

서답형

07 다음 우리말에 맞게 주어진 단어를 이용하여 두 단어로 쓰시오.

그의 이야기는 거짓으로 밝혀졌다. (turn)

➡ His story _____ to be a lie.

서답형

08 다음 짝지어진 단어의 관계가 같도록 알맞은 말을 쓰시오.

evidence – proof : fake – _____

중요

01 〈보기〉에서 알맞은 단어를 선택하여 문장의 빈칸을 완성하시오. (필요하면 변형하여 쓰시오.)

보기

critical   scare   spread   sink

(1) The story quickly _____ to everyone.
(2) The workers must think _____ to solve problems.
(3) The little boy is _____ of monsters.
(4) If a boat has a hole in it, the boat will _____.

02 대화의 빈칸에 〈영영풀이〉에 해당하는 단어를 주어진 철자로 쓰시오.

G: How do you feel about this drama?
B: I think it's very t_____. The boy gave up his life to save his sister.

<영영풀이> making you feel pity, sympathy, sadness, etc.

➡ _____

중요

03 다음 우리말과 같은 표현이 되도록 문장의 빈칸을 채우시오.

(1) 모든 승객들은 지하철에서 편안한 시간을 가질 권리가 있습니다.
➡ All passengers have a right to have a c_____ time in the subway.
(2) 매일 같은 것을 연습하는 것은 지루한 일입니다.
➡ Practicing the same thing every day is b_____.

(3) 온실가스 배출은 지구 온난화의 주요한 원인들 중 하나입니다.
➡ Greenhouse gas emission is one of the m_____ causes of global warming.
(4) 신호등이 노란색으로 바뀌는 것을 볼 때는 속도를 낮춰라.
➡ S_____ down when you see the traffic light turn yellow.

04 영영풀이에 해당하는 단어를 〈보기〉에서 찾아 첫 번째 빈칸에 쓰고, 두 번째 빈칸에는 우리말 뜻을 쓰시오.

보기

sink   support   octopus   spread

(1) _____: to give assistance, approval, comfort, or encouragement to someone: _____
(2) _____: to open it out or arrange it over a place or surface: _____
(3) _____: to disappear below the surface of the water: _____
(4) _____: a soft sea creature with eight long arms: _____

난이도

05 다음 문장의 빈칸에 들어갈 말을 〈보기〉의 단어를 이용하여 완성하시오.

보기

attention   tell   make up

(1) Students should _____ their teacher.
(2) His parents taught him how to _____ right _____ wrong.
(3) The story about the pink horse was _____.

교과서

Conversation

① 의견 묻기

- **How do you feel about this drama?** 이 드라마에 대해서 어떻게 생각하니?

■ 'How do you feel about ~?'은 '~을[~에 대해] 어떻게 생각해?'라는 의미로 상대방에게 어떤 대상에 대한 의견을 물을 때 사용하는 표현이다. 'What do you think about ~?(~에 대하여 어떻게 생각하니?)', 'What's your opinion about ~?(~에 대한 의견이 무엇이니?)', 'What do you say about ~?(~에 대하여 어떻게 생각하십니까?)'와 같은 표현을 사용하여 의견을 물어볼 수 있다. 'How do you like ~?'는 '~가 마음에 드니?'의 의미로 상대방이 만족하는지 등의 의견을 물어보는 표현이다.

■ 경험한 일을 바탕으로 하여 상대방의 의견이나 감정을 물을 때는 'Do you find it ~?(너는 ~하다고 생각하니?)'를 사용할 수 있다. 주로 가목적어 it을 사용하여 'find it+형용사+to부정사'의 형태가 되고 목적격보어로 쓰이는 다양한 형용사 다음에 진목적어인 to부정사가 따라온다.

■ 상대방의 의견을 물어보는 표현으로 'Would you find it easy/hard to ~ if you had the chance to ~?(만약 네가 ~할 기회가 있다면 너는 ~하는 것이 쉽다고/어렵다고 생각하니?)'를 사용할 수 있고, think를 사용하여 'Do you think it is easy/hard to ~?(너는 ~하는 것이 쉽다고/어렵다고 생각하니?)'와 같이 물어볼 수 있다.

상대방의 의견 묻기

- How do you feel about ~? ~에 대하여 어떻게 생각하니?
- What do you think about ~? ~에 대하여 어떻게 생각하니?
- What's your opinion about ~? ~에 대한 의견이 무엇이니?
- What do you say about ~? ~에 대하여 어떻게 생각하십니까?
- Do you find it ~? 너는 ~하다고 생각하니?
- Do you think it is easy/hard to ~? 너는 ~을 쉽다고/어렵다고 생각하니?

핵심 Check

1. 다음 우리말을 주어진 단어를 포함하여 영작하시오.

   G: Look at those shoes the girl is wearing. I think they're great. <u>그것에 대하여 어떻게 생각하니?</u> (feel, how)

   B: I think they look light and comfortable.

   G: Right. I want to buy them for the school field trip.

   ➡ _____

2 이의 제기하기

> • I don't agree (with you). 저는 동의하지 않아요.

■ 'I don't agree with you.(나는 동의하지 않아요.)'는 상대와 의견이 달라서 동의하지 않고 상대의 의견에 이의를 제기하는 말이다. 'I have a different idea.(나는 생각이 달라.)', 'I don't think so.(나는 그렇게 생각하지 않아.)', 'I don't believe so.(그렇게 생각하지 않습니다.)', 'I disagree with you.(저는 반대합니다.)'도 이의를 제기하는 표현이다.

■ 상대방의 말이나 의견에 동의할 때는 'You can say that again.'이라고 한다. 'I agree with you.'라고 할 수도 있다. 상대방에게 자신의 말에 대하여 동의를 구할 때 간단하게는 부가의문문을 덧붙여서 나타낼 수 있고, 구체적으로 'Don't you agree (with me)?'라고 하거나 '제 생각에 동의하지 않으세요?'의 의미로 'Don't you think so?'라고 할 수도 있다.

■ 상대방의 표현에 동의할 때는 '나도 그래.'의 의미로 'Me, too.' 또는 'So+동사+주어.'의 형태를 쓴다. 이때 사용하는 동사는 be동사, do, does, did를 포함하는 조동사들이다. 부정문에 이어지는 경우에는 so 대신 neither를 사용하여 'Neither+동사+주어.'라고 하거나 'Me neither.'라고 할 수 있다.

이의 제기하기

- • I don't agree with you. 나는 동의하지 않아.
- • I don't think so. 나는 그렇게 생각하지 않아.
- • I disagree with you. 저는 반대합니다.
- • I have a different idea. 나는 생각이 달라.
- • I don't believe so. 저는 그렇게 생각하지 않습니다.

동의하기

- • You can say that again. 네 말이 맞아.
- • So am/do I. 나도 마찬가지야.
- • Me, neither. 나도 그래. (부정의 대답)
- • I agree with you. 네 말에 동의해
- • Me, too. 나도 그래. (긍정의 대답)

핵심 Check

2. 다음 대화의 내용으로 보아, 밑줄 친 말 대신 쓰기에 <u>어색한</u> 것은?

> G: I like the coat the boy is wearing. I think it's warm and light.
> B: Well, <u>I don't agree with you.</u> Actually, I bought one last week. It's not so warm, and it's much heavier than it looks.
> G: Really? I don't believe it.

① I don't think so.
② I have a different idea.
③ You can say that again.
④ I don't believe so.
⑤ I disagree with you.

Step UP - Real-life Scene

Alex: Big Mouth's show is really cool. ❶How do you feel about it?

Somi: Well, ❷I don't think it's that great.

Alex: Come on. I love Mr. Big Mouth. He always ❸makes me laugh out loud.

Somi: He's funny, but ❹don't believe everything he says.

Alex: All right. Oh, look at his photo of an octopus. ❺He said it lives in a tree.

Somi: It doesn't make sense.

Alex: He took the photo when it was climbing the tree. I don't think he's lying. It's a great photo.

Somi: ❻I don't agree with you. It's a fake photo. An octopus can't live out of the sea.

Alex: Big Mouth 쇼는 정말 굉장해. 너는 어떻게 생각하니?

소미: 글쎄, 나는 그렇게 대단한 것 같지 않아.

Alex: 왜 그래. 나는 Big Mouth 씨를 진짜 좋아해. 그는 언제나 나를 큰 소리로 웃게 해 줘.

소미: 웃기긴 하지만, 그가 하는 모든 말을 믿지는 마.

Alex: 알았어. 오, 그가 찍은 문어 사진을 봐. 그가 말하기를 그건 나무에 산대.

소미: 말도 안 돼.

Alex: 그는 문어가 나무에 기어 올라갈 때 사진을 찍었대. 그가 거짓말하고 있는 것 같지는 않아. 대단한 사진이야.

소미: 나는 네 말에 동의하지 않아. 그건 가짜 사진이야. 문어는 바다 밖에서는 살 수 없다고.

❶ 'How do you feel about ~?(~에 대해 어떻게 생각하니?)'의 뜻으로 상대방의 의견이나 느낌을 묻는 표현이다.

❷ 'I don't think (that)+주어+동사 ~.'는 '~하지 않다고 생각해.'라는 의미로 목적어를 이끄는 접속사 'that'이 생략되어 있다.

❸ 'make'는 사역동사로 'make+목적어(me)+목적격보어(동사원형: laugh)' 형태를 가진다. '~가 …하도록 하게 하다[시키다]'로 해석한다. 'out loud'는 '큰 소리로'의 뜻으로 'aloud'로 바꾸어 사용할 수 있다.

❹ '~하지 마'라는 의미로 명령문을 부정할 때 'Don't'나 'Never'를 사용한다. 'everything'과 'he says' 사이에는 목적격 관계대명사 'that'이 생략되어 있다.

❺ 동사 'said' 뒤에는 목적어를 이끄는 접속사 'that'이 생략되어 있다.

❻ 상대방의 말에 동의하지 않을 때 사용하는 표현으로 'I don't think so.'로 바꾸어 표현할 수 있다.

Check(√) True or False

(1) Alex thinks that Mr. Big Mouth's photo is real. T ☐ F ☐

(2) Alex said the octopus in the photo lives in a tree. T ☐ F ☐

Start Off - Listen & Talk A 1

G: ❶Look at those shoes the girl is wearing. I think they're great. How do you feel about them?

B: I think they ❷look light and comfortable.

G: Right. I ❸want to buy them for the school field trip.

G: 저 여자애가 신고 있는 신발 좀 봐. 멋있는 것 같아. 너는 저 신발을 어떻게 생각해?

B: 가볍고 편안해 보여.

G: 맞아. 난 학교 체험 학습 때 신으려고 저걸 사고 싶어.

❶ 'the girl is wearing'은 선행사 'those shoes'를 수식하는 목적격 관계대명사절로 관계대명사 'that' 또는 'which'가 생략되어 있다.

❷ 'look+형용사' 형태로 '~하게 보인다'라는 의미이다.

❸ 'want'는 목적어로 to부정사를 취하는 동사이다.

Check(√) True or False

(3) The girl thinks those shoes the girl is wearing are great. T ☐ F ☐

(4) The boy agrees with the girl. T ☐ F ☐

Get Ready 2

(1) G: ❶There's no monkey like this in the world. Its nose is too big. I think it's fake.

B: I don't agree. I saw that kind of monkey on TV. It's real.

(2) G: This animal has a long nose and two long, sharp teeth. ❷What do you think of it? Is it real?

B: Well, let's search the Internet and check it together.

G: That's a good idea.

(3) B: What do you think of this animal?

G: It doesn't have legs, but it doesn't ❸look like a snake. It's very strange.

B: I think so, too.

(4) B: This monkey is very small. Is it real?

G: I don't know. Let's visit some animal fact sites and check it together.

B: That's a good idea.

❶ 'There is+단수명사'로 '~가 있다'는 의미이고, 'no'는 'not ~ any'의 의미로 명사를 부정할 때 사용한다.

❷ What do you think of[about] ~?: '~에 대해 어떻게 생각하니?'의 의미로 상대방이 생각을 물어볼 때 사용한다.

❸ 'look like+명사'는 '~처럼 보인다'라는 의미이다.

Start Off - Listen & Talk A 2

G: I like the coat the boy is wearing. I think it's warm and light.

B: Well, I don't agree with you. ❷Actually, I bought one last week. It's not so warm, and it's ❸much heavier than it looks.

G: Really? I don't believe it.

❶ 'the coat'와 'the boy' 사이에 목적격 관계대명사 'that/which'가 생략되어 있다.

❷ 'Actually'는 앞 문장의 말에 대해 강조하여 말할 때 사용하는 부사로 '사실'의 뜻이다.

❸ 'much'는 비교급을 강조하는 말로 '훨씬, 한층'의 의미로 해석한다. 'much' 대신에 'still, even, far, a lot'을 사용할 수 있다.

Start Off - Listen & Talk B

G: ❶How do you feel about this drama?

B: I think it's very touching. The boy gave up his life to save his sister. It's the best drama of this year.

G: I don't agree. It's not a good drama.

B: Come on. ❷Why do you think so?

G: It doesn't ❸seem real. And it's ❹a little boring.

❶ How do you feel about ~?: '~에 대해 어떻게 생각하니?'의 뜻으로 상대방의 의견이나 느낌을 묻는 표현이다.

❷ '왜 그렇게 생각하니?'의 의미로 'What makes you think so?'와 같은 표현이다.

❸ 'seem+형용사' 형태로 '~하게 보이다'로 해석한다.

❹ 'a little'은 부사구로 형용사 'boring'을 수식하고 '약간, 조금'의 뜻이다.

Start Off - Speak Up

A: How do you feel about this ad?

B: I think it's great. ❶It shows the phone is strong.

A: I don't agree. We should not believe every ad.

❶ 동사 'shows' 뒤에는 목적절을 이끄는 접속사 'that'이 생략되어 있다.

Start Off - Express Yourself A

1. G: How do you feel about these animals?

B: They are very cute, but ❶I think cats don't get along well with dogs.

G: I don't agree. And these two are good friends. They are enjoying the trip together.

2. G: How do you feel about this kid here?

B: I think she is very pretty. ❷By the way, why did she cut her hair?

G: Can you guess?

B: Well, girls these days prefer short hair.

G: I don't agree with that. Most girls like long hair better than short hair. And this kid here is not a girl. In fact, he is a boy.

B: Really?

G: Yes. He grew his hair ❸to help sick children.

3. G: How do you feel about the teddy bears?

B: They are cute. Is there ❹anything special about them?

G: They were made out of a police officer's uniform.

B: Oh, I see.

G: This police officer made them for the kids. Their dad was a police officer, and he ❺ passed away recently.

B: That's very touching.

❶ 동사 'think' 뒤에는 목적절을 이끄는 접속사 'that'이 생략되어 있다. 'get along with ~'는 '~와 사이좋게 지내다, 잘 지내다'라는 뜻이다.

❷ 'By the way'는 대화나 글의 화제를 전환할 때 사용하는 표현으로 '그런데'의 의미이다.

❸ 'to help'는 부정사의 부사적 용법의 '목적'으로 '~하기 위해'의 의미이다. 'so as to'나 'in order to'로 바꾸어 쓸 수 있다.

❹ 부정대명사 'anything'은 형용사가 뒤에서 수식을 한다. '-thing, -one, -body'로 끝나는 부정대명사는 형용사가 반드시 뒤에서 수식을 해야 한다.

❺ 'pass away'는 '돌아가시다'라는 의미이다.

다음 우리말과 일치하도록 빈칸에 알맞은 말을 쓰시오.

Get Ready 2

(1) **G:** There's no monkey _____ this in the world. Its nose is too big. _____ _____ it's _____.

   B: I don't _____. I saw that _____ of monkey on TV. It's _____.

(2) **G:** This animal has a long nose and two long, _____ _____. _____ _____ _____ _____ _____ _____ it? Is it _____?

   B: Well, let's _____ the Internet and _____ it together.

   G: That's a good idea.

(3) **B:** _____ do you think of this animal?

   G: It doesn't have legs, but it doesn't _____ _____ a snake. It's very _____.

   B: I think so, _____.

(4) **B:** _____ monkey is very small. Is it _____?

   G: I don't know. _____ visit some animal _____ sites and check it together.

   B: That's a good idea.

Start Off - Listen & Talk A

1. **G:** Look at those shoes the girl is wearing. I think they're great. _____ _____ _____ _____ _____ them?

   B: I think they look _____ and _____.

   G: Right. I want _____ _____ them for the _____ _____ _____.

2. **G:** I like the coat the boy _____ _____. I think it's warm and light.

   B: Well, I don't _____ _____ you. _____, I bought one last week. It's not so warm, and it's _____ _____ than it looks.

   G: Really? I don't _____ it.

Start Off - Listen & Talk B

G: _____ do you _____ about this drama?

B: I think it's very _____. The boy _____ _____ his life _____ his sister. It's the best drama of this year.

G: I don't agree. It's not a good drama.

B: Come on. _____ do you think so?

G: It doesn't _____ _____. And it's _____ _____ _____.

해석

(1) G: 세상에 이런 원숭이는 없어. 코가 너무 크잖아. 나는 그것이 가짜라고 생각해.
   B: 나는 동의하지 않아. 저런 종류의 원숭이를 TV에서 본 적이 있어. 그건 진짜야.
(2) G: 이 동물은 긴 코와 두 개의 길고 날카로운 이빨을 가지고 있어. 그것을 어떻게 생각해? 진짜일까?
   B: 음, 인터넷을 찾아보고 함께 확인해 보자.
   G: 좋은 생각이야.
(3) B: 이 동물을 어떻게 생각해?
   G: 그것은 다리가 없지만 뱀처럼 보이지는 않아. 정말 이상하네.
   B: 나도 그렇게 생각해.
(4) B: 이 원숭이는 정말 작다. 진짜일까?
   G: 모르겠어. 동물 사실 확인 사이트를 방문해서 함께 확인해 보자.
   B: 좋은 생각이야.

1. G: 저 여자애가 신고 있는 신발 좀 봐. 멋있는 것 같아. 너는 저 신발을 어떻게 생각해?
   B: 가볍고 편안해 보여.
   G: 맞아. 난 학교 체험 학습 때 신으려고 저걸 사고 싶어.
2. G: 저 남자애가 입고 있는 코트가 마음에 들어. 따뜻하고 가벼울 것 같아.
   B: 글쎄, 나는 동의하지 않아. 사실 나는 지난주에 저것을 샀어. 그렇게 따뜻하지도 않고 보기보다 훨씬 더 무거워.
   G: 정말로? 믿을 수가 없어.

G: 이 드라마를 어떻게 생각하니?
B: 난 아주 감동적이라고 생각해. 소년이 그의 여동생을 구하기 위해 자신의 생명을 포기했잖아. 올해 최고의 드라마야.
G: 난 동의하지 않아. 그건 좋은 드라마가 아니야.
B: 이런, 왜 그렇게 생각해?
G: 현실적으로 보이지 않아. 그리고 약간 지루해.

Start Off - Speak Up

A: _____ do you feel _____ this _____?
B: I think it's great. It _____ the phone is strong.
A: I don't agree. We _____ _____ believe every ad.

Step Up - Real-life Scene

Alex: Big Mouth's show is really _____. _____ _____ _____ _____ _____ it?

Somi: Well, I don't think it's _____ great.

Alex: Come on. I love Mr. Big Mouth. He always _____ me _____ out _____.

Somi: He's funny, but don't believe everything he says.

Alex: All right. Oh, look at his photo of an _____. He said it lives in a tree.

Somi: It doesn't _____ _____.

Alex: He took the photo _____ it was _____ the tree. I don't think he's _____. It's a great photo.

Somi: I don't _____ _____ you. It's a _____ photo. An octopus can't live _____ _____ the sea.

Express Yourself A

1. G: _____ do you feel _____ these animals?
   B: They are very cute, but I think cats don't _____ _____ well _____ dogs.
   G: I don't agree. And _____ _____ are good friends. They are _____ the trip _____.

2. G: How do you feel about this kid here?
   B: I think she is very pretty. _____ _____ _____, why did she cut her hair?
   G: Can you _____?
   B: Well, girls these days _____ short hair.
   G: I don't agree _____ that. Most girls like long hair _____ _____ short hair. And this kid here is not a girl. _____ _____, he is a boy.
   B: Really?
   G: Yes. He grew his hair _____ _____ sick children.

3. G: How do you _____ _____ the teddy bears?
   B: They are cute. Is there _____ _____ about them?
   G: They _____ _____ out of a police officer's _____.
   B: Oh, I see.
   G: This police officer made them for the kids. Their dad was a police officer, and he _____ _____ recently.
   B: That's very _____.

A: 이 광고를 어떻게 생각하니?
B: 굉장하다고 생각해. 그건 그 전화기가 튼튼하다는 것을 보여주고 있어.
A: 나는 동의하지 않아. 우리는 모든 광고를 믿어서는 안 돼.

Alex: Big Mouth 쇼는 정말 굉장해. 너는 어떻게 생각하니?
소미: 글쎄, 나는 그렇게 대단한 것 같지 않아.
Alex: 왜 그래. 나는 Big Mouth 씨를 진짜 좋아해. 그는 언제나 나를 큰 소리로 웃게 해 줘.
소미: 웃기긴 하지만, 그가 하는 모든 말을 믿지는 마.
Alex: 알았어. 오, 그가 찍은 문어 사진을 봐. 그가 말하기를 그건 나무에 산대.
소미: 말도 안 돼.
Alex: 그는 문어가 나무에 기어 올라갈 때 사진을 찍었대. 그가 거짓말하고 있는 것 같지는 않아. 대단한 사진이야.
소미: 나는 네 말에 동의하지 않아. 그건 가짜 사진이야. 문어는 바다 밖에서는 살 수 없다고.

1. G: 이 동물들을 어떻게 생각해?
   B: 아주 귀엽지만, 고양이는 개와 잘 어울리지 못한다고 생각해.
   G: 나는 동의하지 않아. 그리고 이 둘은 좋은 친구야. 그들은 함께 즐겁게 여행하고 있어.
2. G: 여기 이 아이를 어떻게 생각해?
   B: 매우 예쁘다고 생각해. 그런데 그녀는 왜 머리카락을 잘랐니?
   G: 짐작할 수 있어?
   B: 음, 요새 여자아이들은 짧은 머리를 더 좋아하더라.
   G: 난 그것에 동의하지 않아. 대부분의 여자아이는 짧은 머리보다 긴 머리를 좋아해. 그리고 여기 이 아이는 여자아이가 아니야. 사실, 이 아이는 남자아이야.
   B: 정말이니?
   G: 응. 그는 아픈 아이들을 돕기 위해 머리를 길렀어.
3. G: 곰 인형들을 어떻게 생각해?
   B: 귀여워. 뭔가 특별한 점이 있니?
   G: 그것들은 한 경찰관의 제복으로 만들어졌어.
   B: 아, 그렇구나.
   G: 이 경찰이 아이들을 위해 그것들을 만들어 줬어. 그들의 아빠는 경찰관이었고, 최근에 세상을 떠나셨어.
   B: 아주 감동적이야.

01 우리말에 맞도록 주어진 단어를 활용하여 빈칸을 채우시오.

> 이 동물을 어떻게 생각해? (think)

➡ _____ do you _____ _____ this animal?

02 다음 대화의 빈칸에 들어갈 말로 어색한 것은?

> A: _____ classical music?
> B: I love it. It makes me calm down and feel happy.

① How do you feel about
② What do you think about
③ What do you say about
④ What do you know about
⑤ What's your opinion about

03 다음 대화의 빈칸에 들어갈 말로 알맞지 <u>않은</u> 것은?

> A: What do you think of listening to music while studying math?
> B: I think it's very helpful.
> A: _____

① I agree with you.
② I don't think so.
③ I've never done that.
④ I couldn't agree more.
⑤ I can't agree with you more.

04 다음 대화의 밑줄 친 말의 의도로 알맞은 것은?

> G: I like the coat the boy is wearing. I think it's warm and light.
> B: Well, <u>I don't agree with you.</u> Actually, I bought one last week. It's not so warm, and it's much heavier than it looks.

① 관심 표현하기   ② 이의 제기하기
③ 동의하기   ④ 의견 표현하기
⑤ 의도 표현하기

[01~02] 다음 대화를 읽고 물음에 답하시오.

G: How do you feel about this drama?
B: I think it's very (a)(touch). The boy gave up his life to save his sister. It's the best drama of this year.
G: _____(A)_____ It's not a good drama.
B: Come on. Why do you think so?
G: It doesn't seem real. And it's a little (b)(bore).

01 위 대화의 빈칸 (A)에 들어갈 말로 알맞은 것은?

① I couldn't agree more.
② I think so, too.
③ I can't agree with you more.
④ I don't agree.
⑤ You can say that again.

서답형

02 위 대화의 (a)와 (b)의 단어를 알맞은 형태로 고쳐 쓰시오.

(a) _____ (b) _____

[03~04] 다음 대화를 읽고 물음에 답하시오.

Alex: Big Mouth's show is really cool. How do you feel about it?
Somi: Well, I don't think it's that great.
Alex: Come on. I love Mr. Big Mouth. He always makes me laugh out loud.
Somi: He's funny, but don't believe everything he says.
Alex: All right. Oh, look at his photo of (a)an octopus. He said (b)it lives in a tree.
Somi: (c)It doesn't make sense.
Alex: He took the photo when (d)it was climbing the tree. I don't think he's lying. It's a great photo.
Somi: I don't agree with you. It's a fake photo. (e)It can't live out of the sea.

03 위 대화를 읽고 답할 수 없는 질문은?

① What are they talking about?
② What are they watching now?
③ Why does Alex like Mr. Big Mouth?
④ Does Somi agree with Alex about the photo?
⑤ Does Alex know a lot about an octopus?

04 위 대화의 (a)~(e) 중 가리키는 대상이 다른 하나는?

① (a)　② (b)　③ (c)　④ (d)　⑤ (e)

[05~06] 다음 대화를 읽고 물음에 답하시오.

G: I like the coat the boy is wearing. I think it's warm and light.
B: Well, I don't agree with you. _____(A)_____, I bought one last week. It's not so warm, and it's _____(B)_____ heavier than it looks.
G: Really? I don't believe it.

05 위 대화의 빈칸 (A)에 들어갈 말로 알맞은 것은?

① Therefore　② For example
③ Actually　④ However
⑤ On the other hand

06 위 대화의 흐름상 (B)에 들어갈 말로 알맞지 않은 것은?

① much　② very
③ even　④ still
⑤ a lot

서답형

07 다음 대화의 빈칸에 들어갈 단어를 주어진 영영풀이를 보고 3단어로 쓰시오.

> G: How do you feel about these animals?
> B: They are very cute, but I think cats don't _____ _____ well _____ dogs.
> G: I don't agree. And these two are good friends. They are enjoying the trip together.

> <영영풀이> If two or more people get along, they have a friendly relationship.

➡ _____

[08~09] 다음 대화를 읽고 물음에 답하시오.

> G: (A)How do you feel about this kid here?
> B: I think she is very pretty. By the way, why did she cut her hair?
> G: Can you guess?
> B: Well, girls these days prefer short hair.
> G: I don't agree with that. Most girls like long hair better than short hair. And this kid here is not a girl. In fact, he is a boy.
> B: Really?
> G: Yes. He grew his hair to help sick children.

08 위 대화의 밑줄 친 (A)와 바꾸어 쓸 수 있는 말은?

① What do you know about this kid here?
② Have you ever met this kid here?
③ Why do you think so about this kid here?
④ What did you say to this kid here?
⑤ What's your opinion about this kid here?

09 위 대화를 읽고 Fact에 해당하는 문장을 고르시오.

① Girls these days prefer short hair.
② This kid is very pretty.
③ Every girl likes long hair better than short hair.
④ This kid grew his hair to help sick children.
⑤ This kid here is a girl.

[10~11] 다음 대화를 읽고 물음에 답하시오.

> (1) G: This animal has a long nose and two long, sharp teeth. _____(A)_____ it? Is it _____(a)_____ ?
> B: Well, let's search the Internet and check it together.
> G: That's a good idea.
> (2) B: _____(A)_____ this animal?
> G: It doesn't have legs, but it doesn't look like a snake. It's very _____(b)_____ .
> B: I think so, too.

10 위 대화의 빈칸 (A)에 공통으로 들어갈 말은?

① What do you think of
② Have you ever heard of
③ How did you like
④ How about seeing
⑤ Why did you feel so about

11 위 대화의 흐름상 빈칸 (a)와 (b)에 들어갈 말로 알맞은 것은?

① fake – real   ② interesting – real
③ real – strange   ④ real – boring
⑤ fake – disappointing

[01~02] 다음 대화를 읽고 물음에 답하시오.

Alex: (A)Big Mouth's show is really cool.
_____(A)_____
Somi: Well, I don't think it's that great.
Alex: Come on. I love Mr. Big Mouth. He always makes me laugh out loud.
Somi: He's funny, but don't believe everything he says.
Alex: All right. Oh, look at his photo of an octopus. He said it lives in a tree.
Somi: It doesn't make sense.
Alex: He took the photo when it was climbing the tree. I don't think he's lying. It's a great photo.
Somi: _____(B)_____ It's a fake photo. An octopus can't live out of the sea.

01 위 대화의 빈칸 (A)와 (B)에 들어갈 말을 〈조건〉에 맞게 영어로 쓰시오.

┤ 조건 ├
(A) • Big Mouth's show에 대한 의견을 묻는 표현을 사용할 것.
   • 'feel'과 'it'을 사용할 것.
(B) • 'agree'를 이용하여 상대방의 의견에 동의하지 않는 표현을 사용할 것. (5 words)

(A) _____
(B) _____

02 위 대화를 읽고 다음 물음에 영어로 답하시오. (Because를 사용할 것.)

Q: Why does Alex like Mr. Big Mouth?

➡ _____

03 다음 대화의 빈칸 (A)와 (B)에 아래의 〈조건〉에 맞게 알맞은 표현을 쓰시오.

B: _____(A)_____ these animals?
G: They are very cute, but _____(B)_____ .
B: I don't agree. And these two are good friends. They are enjoying the trip together.

┤ 조건 ├
(A) 'about', 'think'를 이용하여 상대방의 의견을 묻는 표현을 쓸 것.
(B) '고양이는 개와 잘 어울리지 못한다고 생각해.'라는 이견을 말하는 표현을 쓸 것.

(A) _____
(B) _____

04 대화의 흐름상 빈칸 (A)에 들어갈 말을 〈조건〉에 맞게 쓰시오.

G: I like the coat the boy is wearing. I think it's warm and light.
B: Well, _____(A)_____ . Actually, I bought one last week. It's not so warm, and it's much heavier than it looks.
G: Really? I don't believe it.

┤ 조건 ├
'agree'를 이용할 것 (5 words)

➡ _____

Grammar

① 간접화법

> • Garcia-Fuller **said** she was teaching her students how to tell fake news from real news.
>
> Garcia-Fuller는 그녀가 자신의 학생들에게 가짜 뉴스와 진짜 뉴스를 구분하는 방법을 가르치고 있다고 말했다.

■ 직접화법: 다른 사람의 말을 따옴표(" ")로 묶어 그대로 되풀이하여 전달한다.

   간접화법: 따옴표 없이 전하는 이의 입장에서 시제나 인칭을 바꿔 내용을 전달한다.

■ 직접화법의 간접화법으로의 전환

 (1) 평서문
   • 전달동사를 바꾼다. say → say, say to 사람 → tell 사람
   • 전달하는 내용의 콤마(,)와 따옴표(" ")를 없애고 접속사 'that'을 넣는다. (단, 생략 가능)
   • 전달동사가 현재이면 시제를 그대로 사용하고 전달동사가 과거라면, 시제의 일치 법칙에 맞게 시제를 바꾼다. (현재 → 과거, 현재완료 또는 과거 → 과거완료)
 ※ 시제의 일치의 예외: 전할 말이 전하는 시점에서도 여전히 사실일 경우에는 현재 시제를 과거로 바꾸는 것이 필수적인 것은 아니며, 현재 시제를 그대로 사용할 수도 있다. 또한 전할 말이 역사적인 사실일 경우 과거시제를 유지한다.
   • 인칭대명사를 전달자의 입장에 맞게 바꾼다.
     ex) 따옴표 속 'I'는 문장의 주어, 따옴표 속 'you'는 듣는 이로 바꾼다.
   • 지시대명사와 부사를 전달자의 입장에 맞게 바꾼다.
     here → there   this → that   now → then   today → that day
     tonight → that night   yesterday → the day before, the previous day
     tomorrow → the next day, the following day
 (2) 의문문
   • 전달동사를 바꾼다. say 또는 say to → ask
   • 전달하는 내용의 콤마(,)와 따옴표(" ")를 없애고 간접의문문으로 전환한다. 물음표(?)는 마침표로 바꾼다.
   • 시제, 인칭대명사, 지시대명사, 부사 등을 적절하게 바꾼다.
 (3) 명령문
   • 전달동사를 어조에 따라 tell, ask, order, advise 등으로 바꾼다.
   • 명령문의 동사원형을 긍정은 to부정사로, 부정은 not to 또는 never to부정사로 바꾼다.

핵심 Check

1. 다음 괄호 안에서 알맞은 것을 고르시오.
   (1) Tom (said to / told) her that he wanted to play soccer then.
   (2) My mom said that dinner (is / was) ready.

❷ 명사절을 이끄는 접속사 if

• You also have to check **if** they are based on facts.
여러분은 그것들이 사실에 기반을 둔 것인지를 확인해 보아야 합니다.

■ 형태: if 주어+동사
의미: ~인지 아닌지

■ 명사절을 이끌며 주로 동사의 목적어로 쓰인다.

• I don't know **if** she works for the company. 나는 그녀가 그 회사에서 일하는지 아닌지 모르겠다.

■ 명사절을 이끄는 접속사 'if'는 좀 더 격식을 갖춘 표현인 'whether'로 대체할 수 있다. 단, 'whether'는 주어, 보어, 동사의 목적어, 전치사의 목적어 자리에 모두 쓰일 수 있고, 'if'는 동사의 목적어 자리에 주로 쓰인다.

• He asked **if** I could speak English. = He asked **whether** I could speak English.
그는 내가 영어를 말할 수 있는지 물었다.

• **If** it will snow or not doesn't matter. (×) → **Whether** it will snow or not doesn't matter. (○)
눈이 올지 안 올지는 중요하지 않다.

■ 'if'는 'or not'을 함께 사용할 때 문장 끝에만 사용 가능하며, 'whether'는 바로 다음이나 문장 끝에 'or not'을 붙여 쓸 수도 있다.

• Tell me **if** or not she is married. (×)

• Tell me **if** she is married or not. (○)

• Tell me **whether** or not she is married. (○)

• Tell me **whether** she is married or not. (○)

■ '만일 ~라면'의 뜻으로 쓰인 'if'는 조건을 나타내는 부사절의 접속사이고 미래시제를 현재시제로 나타내는 반면, 명사절의 'if'는 정해진 시제를 그대로 쓴다.

• **If** you do well on the next exam, I will buy you the latest smart phone.
만일 다음 시험을 잘 본다면, 나는 너에게 최신식 스마트폰을 사줄 거야.

• I'm not sure **if** you will do well on the next exam. 나는 네가 다음 시험을 잘 볼지 확신하지 못한다.

핵심 Check

2. 다음 괄호 안에서 알맞은 것을 고르시오.

(1) (If / Whether) you succeed or fail depends on your effort.

(2) I'm not sure (if / whether) or not he will come.

01 〈보기〉를 참고하여 A의 질문에 대한 B의 응답을 따옴표 안에 주어진 문장을 사용하여 빈칸에 알맞은 형태로 써 넣으시오.

┤ 보기 ├

"You have blue eyes like me."

A: What did the man say to his sister?

B: He told her that <u>she had blue eyes like him.</u>

(1) "You are very tall."

A: What did the woman say to her brother?

B: She told him that _____ .

(2) "I'm very happy to meet you."

A: What did the woman say to her brother?

B: She told him that _____ .

(3) "I'm not crying."

A: What did the woman say to her brother?

B: She told him that _____ .

(4) "You look great."

A: What did the man say to his sister?

B: He told her that _____ .

02 다음 문장에서 어법상 어색한 부분을 바르게 고쳐 쓰시오.

(1) I wonder that she will like my present.

➡ _____

(2) I don't know if or not he will give me flowers.

➡ _____

(3) I want to know if will he throw the ball.

➡ _____

(4) The question is if they believe what I said or not.

➡ _____

Grammar 시험대비 실력평가 Step3

---

01 다음 중 간접화법으로의 전환이 올바르지 않은 것을 고르시오.

① Sarah said, "I am so happy."
= Sarah said that she was so happy.

② Suji said, "I will be back in ten minutes."
= Suji said that she would be back in ten minutes.

③ Minsu said to her, "You look tired today."
= Minsu told her that she looked tired that day.

④ Jason said to me, "I ate lunch."
= Jason told me that he has eaten lunch.

⑤ She said to him, "You are very tall."
= She told him that he was very tall.

서답형

02 다음 괄호 안에 주어진 어구를 바르게 배열하여 문장을 완성하시오.

(if, will, I, he, my ball, wonder, catch).

➡ _____

03 다음 중 밑줄 친 if의 뜻이 나머지 넷과 다른 것은?

① I'm not sure if he is single.

② I don't know if he will come back from his long journey.

③ Mom doesn't remember if she turned off the gas or not.

④ What he has to do is to see if anyone is in the building.

⑤ You can see the animal if it is in a good mood.

04 다음 중 내용상 어색한 문장을 고르시오.

① He told me that he wanted to help me.

② She told me that she had gone on a picnic the day before.

③ He told me that my mom would come.

④ Jaeho said that he would be busy tomorrow.

⑤ Jenny said that she had already read that book.

05 다음 빈칸에 들어갈 말로 적절한 것을 고르시오.

He asked me _____ or not I could help him.

① if   ② what   ③ that
④ whether   ⑤ how

서답형

06 다음 직접화법을 간접화법으로 바꾼 문장에서 어법상 어색한 것을 바르게 고쳐 다시 쓰시오.

(1) I said to Amy, "I want to play with you now."
➡ I told Amy that I wanted to play with her now.
➡ _____

(2) Mom said to me, "Are you finished with your homework?"
➡ Mom told me if I was finished with my homework.
➡ _____

07 다음 중 빈칸에 들어갈 단어가 다른 하나를 고르시오.

① _____ you aren't busy, we will watch the TV show.

② Do you know _____ the news is true?

③ I knew _____ it rained yesterday as the road was wet this morning.

④ I can help you _____ you want.

⑤ He wondered _____ he could get the diamond ring.

08 다음 주어진 화법 전환에서 어색한 부분을 바르게 고친 것은?

> She said to me, "What do you want to buy?"
> → She ①said to me ②what ③I ④wanted ⑤to buy.

① said to → asked

② what → that

③ I → she

④ wanted → did I want

⑤ to buy → buy

09 빈칸에 들어갈 말을 순서대로 바르게 연결한 것은?

> • I wonder _____ you made this reusable tote bag.
> • What I want to know is _____ she remembers my name.

① that – if   ② that – whether

③ if – whether   ④ whether – if

⑤ if – that

10 다음 괄호 안에 주어진 어구를 바르게 배열하여 문장을 완성하시오.

> I am (if, do, on, not, I, well, the test, sure)

➡ _____

11 다음 문장과 같은 뜻을 가진 것은?

> She said to him, "I want to stay with you forever."

① She said to him that she wanted to stay with me forever.

② She asked him that she wanted to stay with him forever.

③ She told him that she wanted to stay with him forever.

④ She said to him that she wanted to stay with you forever.

⑤ She told him that I wanted to stay with you forever.

12 다음 두 문장을 접속사를 사용하여 한 문장으로 연결하시오.

> • Will they give me a big hand?
> • I'm not sure.

➡ _____

_____

13 주어진 어휘를 이용하여 다음 우리말을 영어로 쓰시오.

> 나의 언니는 내가 그 시험에서 부정행위를 했는지 안 했는지 의심한다. (if, doubt, cheat, the test)

➡ _____

14 다음 중 어법상 <u>어색한</u> 문장을 고르시오.

① Tom says that he likes Amy.
② My sister told me that she meets Tom by chance the day before.
③ She told me that she had received the gift that day.
④ She advised me to take the medicine regularly.
⑤ My brother asked me where I had put his glasses.

15 빈칸에 들어갈 말을 순서대로 바르게 연결한 것은?

> • _____ he will come or not is another matter.
> • The detective must find out _____ the document is fake or not.

① That – if
② Whether – that
③ If – whether
④ That – whether
⑤ Whether – if

16 다음 빈칸에 들어갈 수 <u>없는</u> 것은?

> The old lady _____ me to keep an eye on her dog.

① asked
② told
③ ordered
④ begged
⑤ made

17 다음 우리말을 영어로 바르게 옮긴 것은?

> 그녀가 지금 회의 중인지 내가 확인할게.

① Let me check that she's in the meeting now.
② Let me check if she's in the meeting now.
③ Let me to check if she's in the meeting now.
④ Let me check if or not she's in the meeting now.
⑤ Let me check that she's in the meeting or not now.

18 다음 중 어법상 <u>어색한</u> 문장의 개수로 알맞은 것은?

> a. Mom ordered me to brush my teeth before breakfast.
> b. She told that she was not ready for the race.
> c. The doctor said me that I should take a rest for a few days.
> d. I told my father to not smoke indoors.
> e. They wanted to know if I was satisfied with the result.

① 1개
② 2개
③ 3개
④ 4개
⑤ 5개

서답형

19 다음 괄호 안에서 알맞은 말을 고르시오.

(1) She (said to / asked) me where I was going.
(2) John (says / says to) that he has a dream of being a musical actor.
(3) My teacher asked me (if / that) I could lend him a pen.
(4) Tom said that he (feels / felt) sick that day.
(5) Our science teacher said that the Earth (is / was) round.

01 명사절의 접속사(if, whether, that)를 사용하여 두 문장을 한 문장으로 쓰시오.

(1) • I wonder.
   • Did the plane arrive on time?
   ➡ _____

(2) • I asked.
   • Was she married?
   ➡ _____

(3) • Is the meeting ready?
   • The question is this.
   ➡ _____

(4) • I think.
   • He is very honest.
   ➡ _____

(5) • Will she attend the audition?
   • It depends on her physical condition.
   ➡ _____
   _____

02 다음 문장을 간접화법으로 바꾸어 쓰시오.

(1) He said to me, "I really appreciate your help."
   ➡ _____

(2) My roommate said to me, "I will be late tonight."
   ➡ _____
   _____

03 다음 빈칸에 알맞은 말을 쓰시오.

(1) He said, "I know the answer."
   ➡ He said that _____ _____ the answer.

(2) Jane said, "_____ _____ to be a teacher."
   ➡ Jane said that she wanted to be a teacher.

(3) He said to me, "I will help you."
   ➡ He told me that _____ _____ _____ _____.

04 잘못된 부분을 바르게 고쳐 문장을 다시 쓰시오.

(1) John said Mary, "I love you."
   ➡ _____

(2) She told him that she is sorry.
   ➡ _____

(3) I told my dad that I would call you later.
   ➡ _____

(4) Mr. Brown said me that he wanted me to study more.
   ➡ _____
   _____

(5) My mom said this dish tasted good.
   ➡ _____

05 다음 두 문장을 간접화법을 이용하여 하나의 문장으로 바꾸어 쓰시오.

> • He said to her.
> • What is the weather like in New York today?

➡ _____
_____

06 다음 문장을 어법에 맞게 고쳐 쓰시오.

(1) I understand if you don't want to talk about it.

➡ _____

(2) Whether you are a boy or a girl make no difference to me.

➡ _____
_____

(3) If you will succeed or not depends on your efforts.

➡ _____
_____

(4) I am not sure that there is life on other planets.

➡ _____
_____

(5) Tell me that you have any plans for your future.

➡ _____
_____

07 〈보기〉에 주어진 문장과 접속사 'if, that, whether'를 각각 한번만 써서 문장의 빈칸을 완성하시오.

> ┤ 보기 ├
> • He had lied to his family.
> • She will have a garage sale in her backyard.
> • We have enough money to buy the new car.

(1) Our question is _____
_____.

(2) He admitted _____.

(3) I asked my grandmother _____
_____.

08 다음 그림 속 내용을 다른 사람에게 전달하는 문장으로 완성하시오.

(1)

Are you hungry?
Why does she look angry?

> The man asked if the cat _____ and he wondered _____.

(2)

You are very cute.
Does she like this food?

> The man said the cat _____ and he wondered _____.

Reading

How to Be a Smart News Reader

In October 2016, stories about scary clowns shook schools across the
Washington area, but Danina Garcia-Fuller's students didn't believe
them a bit.

"Some people were getting scared because they saw things on social
media," said Patricia Visoso, one of Garcia-Fuller's students. "But
they never checked up on who was saying this." The stories were
actually made by teenagers, not by major newspapers or TV stations.
They offered no hard evidence that clowns really were trying to attack
students. The story turned out to be a complete lie.
"I think a lot of people just look at one thing and believe it's true,"
Patricia's classmate Ivy-Brooks said. "It's really important to look at
the right sources and to pay attention to what is real and what is fake."
Like Garcia-Fuller's students, many teenagers in America are
learning to think critically about information they're seeing in the news
and on the Internet. This skill is getting more important these days as
stories can spread very fast, and anyone can make a website full of
false information.

scary 무서운	
clown 광대	
area 지역, 구역	
a bit 조금, 약간	
scared 무서워하는	
social media 소셜 미디어	
check up on ~을 확인하다	
major 주요한, 중대한	
hard 명백한	
evidence 증거	
attack 공격하다	
turn out ~인 것으로 드러나다, 밝혀지다	
complete 완벽한, 완전한	
lie 거짓말	
source 자료, 출처	
pay attention to ~에 주목하다, 유의하다	
critically 비판적으로	
spread 퍼지다	
false 틀린, 거짓의	

 확인문제

● 다음 문장이 본문의 내용과 일치하면 T, 일치하지 않으면 F를 쓰시오.

1 Danina Garcia-Fuller's students didn't believe stories about scary clowns a bit. ☐

2 The stories about scary clowns were actually made by major newspapers or TV
   stations. ☐

3 Ivy-Brooks said a lot of people just looked at one thing and believed it was true. ☐

4 These days, anyone can make a website full of true information. ☐

Garcia-Fuller said she was teaching her students how to tell fake news from real news.
직접화법: Garcia-Fuller said, "I am teaching my students how to tell fake news from real news."

"One of the first steps is to slow down. If a story or a photo seems too good to be true, stop and think: Is there any evidence that supports what the writer says? And where is this coming from?"
one of+복수명사: '~ 중 하나'라는 뜻   to slow down: to부정사의 명사적 용법
If: '만약 ~한다면'이라는 조건의 의미를 지니는 부사절을 이끎.
너무 좋아서 믿어지지 않는. too+형용사/부사+to부정사: 너무 …해서 ~할 수 없다   주격 관계대명사
what: 선행사를 포함한 관계대명사, '~한 것'

Garcia-Fuller's students also learn how to tell fact from opinion in the news. "Opinions are good to read," said 15-year-old McKenzie Campbell, "but you also have to check if they are based on facts."
how+to부정사: ~하는 방법   tell A from B: A와 B를 구분하다
형용사 'good'을 수식하는 to부정사의 부사적 용법
= whether. if: ~인지 아닌지 (명사절을 이끎)

Garcia-Fuller also said sometimes it can be very hard to be a smart news reader. She tests her students with a website that appears to provide information on an animal called a tree octopus. The site is full of information on this animal, along with a few unclear photos of octopuses in trees. But like the story of scary clowns, it's totally made up.
said 다음에 접속사 'that' 생략   가주어   진주어
주격 관계대명사(= which)
appear to+동사원형: ~인 것 같다   'an animal' 뒤에 'which is' 생략
~와 함께

The lesson, Garcia-Fuller tells her students, is to "check the information you're seeing once more carefully" and to "question everything, even things that I say."
to부정사의 명사적 용법
information' 다음에 목적격 관계대명사 'that(which)' 생략   to부정사의 명사적 용법
목적격 관계대명사, 생략가능.

tell … from ~ …를 ~와 구분하다
slow down (속도, 활동)을 늦추다
support 지지하다, 지원하다
be based on ~에 기초하다, 근거하다
appear 나타나다, ~인 것 같다
octopus 문어
site 사이트, 현장, 위치
unclear 불확실한, 불분명한
totally 완전히
be made up ~로 꾸며지다
question 의심하다, 의문을 갖다

📎 확인문제

● 다음 문장이 본문의 내용과 일치하면 T, 일치하지 않으면 F를 쓰시오.

1 Garcia-Fuller said she was teaching her students how to distinguish fake news from real news. ☐

2 Garcia-Fuller's students also learn how to tell fake news from opinion in the news. ☐

3 Garcia-Fuller said sometimes it can be very hard to be a smart news reader. ☐

4 Unlike the story of scary clowns, the information on a tree octopus is true. ☐

● 우리말을 참고하여 빈칸에 알맞은 말을 쓰시오.

1 How to Be a _____ _____ _____

2 In October 2016, stories about scary clowns _____ _____ across the Washington area, but Danina Garcia-Fuller's students _____ _____ them _____ _____.

3 "Some people were _____ _____ because they saw things on social media," said Patricia Visoso, one of Garcia-Fuller's students.

4 "But they never _____ _____ _____ who was saying this."

5 The stories _____ _____ _____ by teenagers, not by major newspapers or TV stations.

6 They offered _____ _____ _____ that clowns really were trying to attack students.

7 The story _____ _____ _____ _____ a complete lie.

8 "I think a lot of people _____ _____ _____ _____ _____ and believe it's true," Patricia's classmate Ivy-Brooks said.

9 "It's really important _____ _____ _____ _____ _____ and to pay attention to _____ _____ _____ and _____ _____ _____."

10 _____ Garcia-Fuller's students, many teenagers in America are learning _____ _____ _____ about information they're seeing in the news and _____ _____ _____.

11 This skill is _____ _____ _____ these days as stories can spread very fast, and anyone can make a website full of false information.

1 현명한 뉴스 독자가 되는 방법

2 2016년 10월, 무서운 광대들에 관한 이야기가 워싱턴 지역 전역의 학교에 충격을 안겼지만, Danina Garcia-Fuller의 학생들은 조금도 그 이야기들을 믿지 않았다.

3 "몇몇 사람들은 그들이 소셜 미디어에 올라온 것들을 봤기 때문에 무서워했어요."라고 Garcia-Fuller의 학생 중 한 명인 Patricia Visoso가 말했다.

4 "하지만 그들은 이것을 누가 말하고 있는지를 전혀 확인하지 않았어요."

5 그 이야기들은 실제로 주요 신문사나 TV 방송국이 아닌 10대들이 지어냈다.

6 그들은 광대들이 정말로 학생들을 공격하려고 한다는 명백한 증거를 하나도 제공하지 않았다.

7 그 이야기는 결국 완벽한 거짓말인 것으로 드러났다.

8 "많은 사람이 단지 한 가지만을 보고 그것이 사실이라고 믿는 것 같아요.라고 Patricia의 반 친구인 Ivy-Brooks가 말했다.

9 올바른 출처를 살펴보고, 무엇이 진짜이고 무엇이 가짜인지에 주의를 기울이는 것은 정말 중요해요."

10 Garcia-Fuller의 학생들처럼, 많은 미국의 10대들은 뉴스 속 그리고 인터넷상에서 보고 있는 정보에 관해 비판적으로 생각하는 것을 배워 나가고 있다.

11 이 기능은 최근 더 중요해지고 있는데, 이야기들은 아주 빠른 속도로 퍼져 나갈 수 있고 누구나 허위 정보로 가득 찬 웹사이트를 만들어 낼 수 있기 때문이다.

12 Garcia-Fuller said she was teaching her students _____ _____ _____ fake news _____ real news.

13 "_____ _____ _____ _____ _____ is to slow down.

14 If a story or a photo seems _____ _____ _____ _____, stop and think.

15 Is there any evidence that supports _____ _____ _____ _____?

16 And where is this _____ _____?"

17 Garcia-Fuller's students also learn _____ _____ _____ fact _____ opinion in the news.

18 "Opinions are good to read," said 15-year-old McKenzie Campbell, "but you also have to check they _____ _____ facts."

19 Garcia-Fuller also said sometimes it can be very hard to be _____ _____ _____ _____.

20 She tests her students with a website that _____ _____ _____information on an animal called a tree octopus.

21 The site is full of information on this animal, _____ _____ a few unclear photos of octopuses in trees.

22 But _____ the story of scary clowns, it's totally _____ _____.

23 The lesson, Garcia-Fuller tells her students, is to "check the information you're seeing _____ _____ _____" and to "_____ _____, even things that I say."

12 Garcia-Fuller는 그녀가 자신의 학생들에게 가짜 뉴스를 진짜 뉴스로부터 구분하는 방법을 가르치고 있다고 말했다.

13 "첫 단계 중 하나는 속도를 늦추는 것(천천히 생각하는 것)입니다.

14 만약 어떤 이야기나 어떤 사진이 진짜라고 하기엔 너무 좋아 보인다면, 멈춰서 생각해 보세요.

15 글쓴이가 말하고 있는 것을 뒷받침하는 어떠한 증거라도 있나요?

16 그리고 이 정보가 어디서 온 것인가요?"

17 Garcia-Fuller의 학생들은 또한 뉴스에서 사실을 의견과 구분하는 방법에 대해서도 배운다.

18 "의견들은 읽을 만한 가치가 있습니다,"라고 15살인 McKenzie Campbell이 말했다. "하지만 여러분은 그것들이 사실에 기반을 둔 것인지를 확인해 보아야 합니다."

19 Garcia-Fuller는 또한 때때로 현명한 뉴스 독자가 되는 것이 아주 어려울 수도 있다고 말했다.

20 그녀는 자신의 학생들을 '나무 문어'라는 이름의 동물에 대한 정보를 제공하는 것처럼 보이는 웹사이트로 시험한다.

21 그 사이트는 나무 위에 있는 문어들의 몇몇 불확실한 사진과 함께, 이 동물에 대한 정보로 가득 차 있다.

22 하지만 무서운 광대들의 이야기와 마찬가지로, 그것은 완전히 꾸며진 것이다.

23 Garcia-Fuller가 그녀의 학생들에게 말하는 교훈은 '당신이 보고 있는 정보를 한 번만 더 신중하게 확인해 보라'는 것과 '모든 것, 심지어 내가 말하는 것에도 의문을 가져 보라'는 것이다.

● 우리말을 참고하여 본문을 영작하시오.

1 현명한 뉴스 독자가 되는 방법

➡ _____

2 2016년 10월, 무서운 광대들에 관한 이야기가 워싱턴 지역 전역의 학교에 충격을 안겼지만,
Danina Garcia-Fuller의 학생들은 조금도 그 이야기들을 믿지 않았다.

➡ _____

_____

3 "몇몇 사람들은 그들이 소셜 미디어에 올라온 것들을 봤기 때문에 무서워했어요."라고 Garcia-Fuller의
학생 중 한 명인 Patricia Visoso가 말했다.

➡ _____

_____

4 "하지만 그들은 이것을 누가 말하고 있는지를 전혀 확인하지 않았어요."

➡ _____

5 그 이야기들은 실제로 주요 신문사나 TV 방송국이 아닌 10대들이 지어냈다.

➡ _____

6 그들은 광대들이 정말로 학생들을 공격하려고 한다는 명백한 증거를 하나도 제공하지 않았다.

➡ _____

7 그 이야기는 결국 완벽한 거짓말인 것으로 드러났다.

➡ _____

8 "많은 사람이 단지 한 가지만을 보고 그것이 사실이라고 믿는 것 같아요."라고 Patricia의
반 친구인 Ivy-Brooks가 말했다.

➡ _____

_____

9 "올바른 출처를 살펴보고, 무엇이 진짜이고 무엇이 가짜인지에 주의를 기울이는 것은 정말 중요해요."

➡ _____

_____

10 Garcia-Fuller의 학생들처럼, 많은 미국의 10대들은 뉴스 속 그리고 인터넷상에서 보고 있는 정보에 관해
비판적으로 생각하는 것을 배워 나가고 있다.

➡ _____

_____

11 이 기능은 최근 더 중요해지고 있는데, 이야기들은 아주 빠른 속도로 퍼져 나갈 수 있고 누구나 허위 정보로
가득 찬 웹사이트를 만들어 낼 수 있기 때문이다.

➡ _____

_____

12 Garcia-Fuller는 그녀가 자신의 학생들에게 가짜 뉴스를 진짜 뉴스로부터 구분하는 방법을 가르치고 있다고 말했다.

➡ _____

13 "첫 단계 중 하나는 속도를 늦추는 것(천천히 생각하는 것)입니다.

➡ _____

14 만약 어떤 이야기나 어떤 사진이 진짜라고 하기엔 너무 좋아 보인다면, 멈춰서 생각해 보세요.

➡ _____

15 글쓴이가 말하고 있는 것을 뒷받침하는 어떠한 증거라도 있나요?

➡ _____

16 그리고 이 정보가 어디서 온 것인가요?"

➡ _____

17 Garcia-Fuller의 학생들은 또한 뉴스에서 사실을 의견과 구분하는 방법에 대해서도 배운다.

➡ _____

18 "의견들은 읽을 만한 가치가 있습니다,"라고 15살인 McKenzie Campbell이 말했다. "하지만 여러분은 그것들이 사실에 기반을 둔 것인지를 확인해 보아야 합니다."

➡ _____

_____

19 Garcia-Fuller는 또한 때때로 현명한 뉴스 독자가 되는 것이 아주 어려울 수도 있다고 말했다.

➡ _____

20 그녀는 자신의 학생들을 '나무 문어'라는 이름의 동물에 대한 정보를 제공하는 것처럼 보이는 웹사이트로 시험한다.

➡ _____

_____

21 그 사이트는 나무 위에 있는 문어들의 몇몇 불확실한 사진과 함께, 이 동물에 대한 정보로 가득 차 있다.

➡ _____

_____

22 하지만 무서운 광대들의 이야기와 마찬가지로, 그것은 완전히 꾸며진 것이다.

➡ _____

23 Garcia-Fuller가 그녀의 학생들에게 말하는 교훈은 '당신이 보고 있는 정보를 한 번만 더 신중하게 확인해 보라'는 것과 '모든 것, 심지어 내가 말하는 것에도 의문을 가져 보라'는 것이다.

➡ _____

_____

[01~03] 다음 글을 읽고 물음에 답하시오.

In October 2016, stories about scary clowns shook schools across the Washington area, but Danina Garcia-Fuller's students didn't believe them a bit.

"Some people were getting scared because they saw things ⓐ social media," said Patricia Visoso, one of Garcia-Fuller's students. "But they never checked up ⓑ who was saying this." The stories were actually made by teenagers, not by major newspapers or TV stations. ©They offered no hard evidence that clowns really were trying to attack students. The story turned out to be a complete lie.

01 위 글의 빈칸 ⓐ와 ⓑ에 들어갈 전치사가 바르게 짝지어진 것은?

ⓐ ⓑ	ⓐ ⓑ
① to – on	② on – in
③ to – in	④ in – to
⑤ on – on	

02 위 글의 밑줄 친 ©They가 가리키는 것을 본문에서 찾아 쓰시오.

➡ _____

03 According to the passage, which is NOT true?

① In October 2016, schools across the Washington area were shocked at stories about scary clowns.

② Danina Garcia-Fuller's students didn't believe the stories about scary clowns a bit.

③ Some people who were getting scared because they saw things on social media never found out who was saying this.

④ The stories about scary clowns were not made by teenagers but by major newspapers or TV stations.

⑤ The story about scary clowns proved to be a complete lie.

[04~06] 다음 글을 읽고 물음에 답하시오.

"I think a lot of people just look at one thing and believe it's true," Patricia's classmate Ivy-Brooks said. "It's really important to look at the right (A)[sources / resources] and to pay attention to what is real and what is fake."

(B)[Alike / Like] Garcia-Fuller's students, many teenagers in America are learning to think ⓐ about information they're seeing in the news and on the Internet. This skill is getting more important these days as stories can spread very fast, and anyone can make a website full of (C)[false / true] information.

04 위 글의 빈칸 ⓐ에 들어갈 알맞은 말을 고르시오.

① unquestioningly

② conformingly

③ adaptationally

④ critically

⑤ unconditionally

05 위 글의 괄호 (A)~(C)에서 문맥이나 어법상 알맞은 낱말을 골라 쓰시오.

➡ (A) _____ (B) _____ (C) _____

서답형

06 다음 문장에서 위 글의 내용과 <u>다른</u> 부분을 찾아서 고치시오.

> Patricia's classmate Ivy-Brooks thinks many people look at everything and believe it's true.

_____ ➡ _____

[07~09] 다음 글을 읽고 물음에 답하시오.

Garcia-Fuller also said sometimes it can be very hard to be a smart news reader. ⓐ <u>She tests her students with a website that is appeared to provide information on an animal called a tree octopus.</u> The site is full of information on this animal, ⓑ<u>along with</u> a few unclear photos of octopuses in trees. But like the story of scary clowns, it's totally made up.

The lesson, Garcia-Fuller tells her students, is to "check the information you're seeing once more carefully" and to "question everything, even things that I say."

서답형

07 위 글의 밑줄 친 ⓐ에서 어법상 틀린 부분을 찾아 고치시오.

_____ ➡ _____

서답형

08 위 글의 밑줄 친 ⓑalong with와 바꿔 쓸 수 있는 단어를 쓰시오. (two words)

➡ _____

09 위 글을 읽고 알 수 <u>없는</u> 것을 고르시오.

① According to Garcia-Fuller, sometimes what can be very hard?

② Is it always easy to be a smart news reader?

③ What does the website with which Garcia-Fuller tests her students seem to provide?

④ What is the website with which Garcia-Fuller tests her students full of?

⑤ Who made up the information on the tree octopus?

[10~12] 다음 글을 읽고 물음에 답하시오.

Garcia-Fuller said she was teaching her students how to ⓐ<u>tell</u> fake news from real news.

"One of the first steps is to slow down. If a story or a photo seems too good to be true, stop and think: Is there any evidence ⓑ<u>that</u> supports what the writer says? And where is this coming from?"

Garcia-Fuller's students also learn how to tell fact from opinion in the news. "Opinions are good to read," said 15-year-old McKenzie Campbell, "but you also have to check if they are based on facts."

10 위 글의 밑줄 친 ⓐtell과 바꿔 쓸 수 있는 말을 <u>모두</u> 고르시오.

① know   ② protect

③ talk   ④ distinguish

⑤ keep

중요

11 위 글의 밑줄 친 ⓑthat과 문법적 쓰임이 같은 것을 <u>모두</u> 고르시오.

① She was so tired that she couldn't think properly.

② This is all that matters.

③ The rumor that he married Kate is not true.

④ She said that the story was true.

⑤ Where's the letter that came yesterday?

12 위 글의 주제로 알맞은 것을 고르시오.

① the best way to teach students the importance of real news

② the reason to stop and think when a story seems too good to be true

③ how to tell fake news from real news and fact from opinion in the news

④ how to find out the evidence that supports what the writer says

⑤ the opinions which are based on facts

[13~14] 다음 글을 읽고 물음에 답하시오.

> "I think a lot of people just look at one thing and believe it's true," Patricia's classmate Ivy-Brooks said. "It's really important to look at the right sources and to pay attention to what is real and what is fake."
>
> Like Garcia-Fuller's students, many teenagers in America are learning to think critically about information they're seeing in the news and on the Internet. This skill is getting more important these days as stories can spread very fast, and anyone can make a website ⓐunderline full of false information.

서답형

13 위 글의 밑줄 친 ⓐfull of false information 앞에 생략된 말을 쓰시오.

➡ _____

14 Which question CANNOT be answered after reading the passage?

① According to Ivy-Brooks, what do many people look at when they believe it's true?

② What are many teenagers in America learning?

③ Where are many teenagers in America

seeing information?

④ Are many teenagers in America learning to think critically about information?

⑤ Why do people make a website full of false information?

[15~16] 다음 글을 읽고 물음에 답하시오.

> Garcia-Fuller said she was teaching her students how to tell fake news from real news.
>
> "One of the first steps is to slow down. If a story or a photo seems too good to be true, stop and think: ⓐ글쓴이가 말하고 있는 것을 뒷받침하는 어떠한 증거라도 있나요? And where is this coming from?"
>
> Garcia-Fuller's students also learn how to tell fact from opinion in the news. "Opinions are good to read," said 15-year-old McKenzie Campbell, "but you also have to check if ⓑunderline they are based on facts."

서답형

15 위 글의 밑줄 친 ⓐ의 우리말에 맞게 주어진 어휘를 알맞게 배열하시오.

| the writer / that / there / supports / any evidence / is / says / what / ? |

➡ _____

_____

서답형

16 위 글의 밑줄 친 ⓑthey가 가리키는 것을 본문에서 찾아 쓰시오.

➡ _____

[17~19] 다음 글을 읽고 물음에 답하시오.

In October 2016, stories about scary clowns shook schools across the Washington area, but Danina Garcia-Fuller's students didn't believe them a bit. (①)

"Some people were getting scared because they saw things on social media," said Patricia Visoso, one of Garcia-Fuller's students. (②) The stories were actually made by teenagers, not by major newspapers or TV stations. (③) They offered no hard evidence @that clowns really were trying to attack students. (④) The story turned out to be a complete lie. (⑤)

17 위 글의 흐름으로 보아, 주어진 문장이 들어가기에 가장 적절한 곳은?

> "But they never checked up on who was saying this."

①   ②   ③   ④   ⑤

18 위 글의 밑줄 친 @that과 문법적 쓰임이 같은 것을 모두 고르시오.

① There was no hope that she would recover her health.
② She said that the story was true.
③ No one can deny the fact that you are guilty.
④ It's true that we were a little late.
⑤ The trouble is that we are short of money.

19 위 글의 제목으로 알맞은 것을 고르시오.

① Scary Clowns Shook Schools across the Washington Area
② Danina Garcia-Fuller's Smart Students
③ Hey, Be Careful in Believing Things on Social Media!

④ Stories on Social Media Made by Teenagers
⑤ Why Don't You Believe Things on Social Media?

[20~21] 다음 글을 읽고 물음에 답하시오.

Garcia-Fuller also said sometimes it can be very hard to be a smart news reader. She tests her students with a website that appears to provide information on an animal @ a tree octopus. The site is full of information on this animal, along with a few unclear photos of octopuses in trees. But like the story of scary clowns, it's totally made up.

The ⓑlesson, Garcia-Fuller tells her students, is to "check the information you're seeing once more carefully" and to "question everything, even things that I say."

서답형

20 위 글의 빈칸 @에 call을 알맞은 형태로 쓰시오.

➡ _____

21 위 글의 밑줄 친 ⓑlesson과 같은 의미로 쓰인 것을 고르시오.

① What did we do last lesson?
② Let her fate be a valuable lesson to you.
③ We studied lesson Five today.
④ She was preparing a lesson plan for a class she was teaching.
⑤ No talking was allowed during the lesson.

[01~04] 다음 글을 읽고 물음에 답하시오.

In October 2016, stories about scary clowns shook schools across the Washington area, but Danina Garcia-Fuller's students didn't believe them a bit.
ⓐ"Some people were getting scared because they saw things on social media," said Patricia Visoso, one of Garcia-Fuller's student. "But they never checked up on who was saying this." ⓑThe stories were actually made by teenagers, not by major newspapers or TV stations. They offered no hard evidence that clowns really were trying to attack students. ⓒThe story turned out to be a complete lie.

01 위 글의 밑줄 친 ⓐ에서 어법상 틀린 부분을 찾아 고치시오.

_____ ➡ _____

02 위 글의 밑줄 친 ⓑ를 다음과 같이 바꿔 쓸 때 빈칸에 들어갈 알맞은 단어를 쓰시오.

The stories were actually made _____ by major newspapers or TV stations _____ by teenagers.

03 위 글의 밑줄 친 ⓒ를 복문으로 바꾸시오.

➡ _____

04 본문의 내용과 일치하도록 다음 빈칸 (A)와 (B)에 알맞은 단어를 쓰시오.

Some people were getting scared of the stories about scary clowns because they saw things (A)_____ _____ _____, but they never checked up on who was saying the story, which turned out to be (B)_____ _____ _____.

[05~07] 다음 글을 읽고 물음에 답하시오.

"I think a lot of people just look at one thing and believe it's true," Patricia's classmate Ivy-Brooks said. "It's really important to look at the right sources and to pay attention to what is real and what is fake."
Like Garcia-Fuller's students, many teenagers in America are learning to think critically about information they're seeing in the news and on the Internet. ⓐThis skill is getting more important these days as stories can spread very fast, and anyone can make a website ⓑfull of false information.

05 위 글의 밑줄 친 ⓐThis skill이 가리키는 것을 본문에서 찾아 쓰시오.

➡ _____
_____

06 위 글의 밑줄 친 ⓑfull of와 바꿔 쓸 수 있는 말을 쓰시오.

➡ _____

07 According to Patricia's classmate Ivy-Brooks, what is really important? Answer in English in a full sentence beginning with "It".

➡ _____
_____
_____

[08~11] 다음 글을 읽고 물음에 답하시오.

ⓐGarcia-Fuller said she was teaching her students how to tell fake news from real news.

"One of the first steps (A)[are / is] to slow down. If a story or a photo seems (B)[good enough / too good] to be true, stop and think: Is there any evidence that (C)[denies / supports] what the writer says? And where is this coming from?"

ⓑGarcia-Fuller's students also learn how to tell fact from opinion in the news. "Opinions are good to read," said 15-year-old McKenzie Campbell, "but you also have to check if they are based on facts."

08 위 글의 밑줄 친 ⓐ를 직접화법으로 고칠 때, 빈칸 (A)와 (B)에 들어갈 알맞은 말을 쓰시오.

> Garcia-Fuller said, "(A)_____ _____
> teaching (B)_____ students how to tell
> fake news from real news."

09 위 글의 괄호 (A)~(C)에서 문맥이나 어법상 알맞은 낱말을 골라 쓰시오.

➡ (A) _____ (B) _____ (C) _____

10 위 글의 밑줄 친 ⓑ를 다음과 같이 바꿔 쓸 때 빈칸에 들어갈 알맞은 말을 두 단어로 쓰시오.

> Garcia-Fuller's students also learn how
> _____ _____ tell fact from opinion
> in the news.

11 What's one of the first steps to tell fake news from real news? Fill in the blanks (A)~(C) with suitable words.

> It's to (A)_____ _____. When it
> seems that a story or a photo is so good
> that it can't be true, you must (B)_____
> and think if there is (C)_____ _____
> that supports the writer's word and the
> source of this.

[12~14] 다음 글을 읽고 물음에 답하시오.

Garcia-Fuller also said sometimes it can be very hard to be a smart news reader. She tests her students with a website that appears to provide information on an animal called a tree octopus. The site is full of information on ⓐthis animal, along with a few unclear photos of octopuses in trees. But like the story of scary clowns, it's totally made up.

The lesson, Garcia-Fuller tells her students, is to "check the information you're seeing once more carefully" and to "question everything, even ⓑthings that I say."

12 위 글의 밑줄 친 ⓐthis animal이 가리키는 것을 본문에서 찾아 쓰시오.

➡ _____

13 위 글의 밑줄 친 ⓑthings that과 바꿔 쓸 수 있는 한 단어를 쓰시오.

➡ _____

14 What is the lesson that Garcia-Fuller gives to her students? Fill in the blanks (A) and (B) with suitable words.

> It's to "check the information you're
> seeing (A)_____ _____ _____ "
> and to "(B)_____ _____, even things
> that she says."

교과서

구석구석

After You Read A

• In October 2016, stories about scary clowns shook schools across the
in: 시간과 함께 쓰여 '(특정 기간)에'   about: 주제와 연관성의 의미로 '…에 관한'   across: 장소와 함께 쓰여 '~에 걸쳐, 온 …에'
Washington area.

↓ how+to부정사: '…하는 방법'
• Garcia-Fuller's students also learn how to tell fact from opinion in the news.
tell A from B: A와 B를 구분하다

• The site is full of information on this animal, along with a few unclear
be full of: ~로 가득 차 있다   = together with
photos of octopuses in trees.

구문해설 • scary: 무서운 • clown: 광대 • area: 지역, 구역 • tell … from ~: …를 ~와 구분하다
• site: 사이트, 현장, 위치 • unclear: 불확실한, 불분명한 • octopus: 문어

해석

• 2016년 10월, 무서운 광대들에 관한 이야기가 워싱턴 지역 전역의 학교에 충격을 안겼다.

• Garcia-Fuller의 학생들은 또한 뉴스에서 사실을 의견과 구분하는 방법에 대해서도 배운다.

• 그 사이트는 나무 위에 있는 문어들의 몇몇 불확실한 사진과 함께, 이 동물에 대한 정보로 가득 차 있다.

Do It Yourself

Team NW danced on the stage during the school festival. They wondered if
전치사 '~ 동안' 'wonder'의 목적어를 이끄는 접속사로 '~인지 아닌지' = whether
the students and teachers would like their dancing. But they performed much
비교급 강조(훨씬)
better than any other team. A lot of students stood up and cheered loudly when
비교급 than any other+단수명사   = Many   부사로 동사 'cheered'를 수식
the team danced. Ms. Yu, the P.E. teacher, said it was the performance of the year.
Ms. Yu를 설명하는 동격어구

구문해설 • stage: 무대 • festival: 축제 • wonder: 궁금해 하다 • perform: 공연하다
• cheer: 환호하다 • performance: 공연

NW 팀은 학교 축제 기간에 무대에서 춤을 선보였다. 그들은 학생들과 선생님들이 그들의 춤을 좋아할지 확신이 서지 않았다. 하지만 그들은 다른 어떠한 팀보다 훨씬 더 멋지게 공연을 해냈다. 그 팀이 춤출 때 많은 학생이 일어서서 크게 환호했다. 체육 선생님인 유 선생님은 그해 최고의 공연이라고 말씀하셨다.

Link to the World

Fact

• This drawing, *Don Quixote*, is one of Picasso's works.
one of 복수명사

• Picasso drew it in 1955 with black lines against a white background.

Opinion

• I don't know if the man on the horse is brave, but he looks very tired and
~인지 아닌지
hungry. I think he needs some food and water.

• I think this artwork shows the most interesting part of Cervantes' novel *Don*
뒤에 접속사 that 생략
Quixote.

구문해설 • drawing: 그림 • work: 작품 • artwork: 미술작품 • novel: 소설

사실
• 이 그림 '돈키호테'는 피카소의 작품 중 하나이다.
• 피카소는 이 그림을 1955년에 흰 배경과 대비를 이루는 검은 선들로 그렸다.
의견
• 말 위에 올라탄 남자가 용감한지는 잘 모르겠지만, 그는 매우 피곤하고 굶주려 보인다. 내 생각에는 그에게 약간의 음식과 물이 필요한 것 같다.
• 나는 이 미술품이 세르반테스의 소설인 '돈키호테'의 가장 흥미로운 부분을 보여 주고 있다고 생각한다.

Words & Expressions

01 다음 주어진 두 단어의 관계가 같도록 빈칸에 알맞은 단어를 쓰시오.

> boring – exciting : defend – _____

02 다음 문장의 빈칸 (a)와 (b)에 들어갈 단어로 바르게 짝지어진 것은?

> • This book _____(a)_____ a true story.
> • The story about the pink horse _____
>   _____(b)_____.

① gets along with – was slowed down
② gives up – was got over
③ is based on – was made up
④ stands up for – got scared
⑤ looks like – passed away

03 다음 밑줄 친 부분의 뜻이 **잘못된** 것은?

① You look pretty <u>cool</u> with that new haircut. (멋진)
② This sentence doesn't <u>make sense</u>. (타당하다, 말이 되다)
③ The roller coaster looked so <u>scary</u> that we didn't ride it. (무서운)
④ My teacher got upset because my homework wasn't <u>complete</u>. (완료하다)
⑤ The <u>major</u> roads in this city are always busy. (주요한)

[04~05] 다음 영영풀이에 해당하는 것을 고르시오.

04
> anything that causes you to believe that something is true

① performance   ② source
③ skill   ④ evidence
⑤ site

05
> in a way that expresses disapproval

① critically   ② friendly
③ totally   ④ recently
⑤ unclearly

06 다음 대화의 빈칸에 들어갈 말을 〈영영풀이〉를 참고하여 네 글자(four letters)로 된 한 단어를 쓰시오.

> G: There's no monkey like this in the world. Its nose is too big. I think it's _____.
> B: I don't agree. I saw that kind of monkey on TV. It's real.

> 〈영영풀이〉 not real, but made to look or seem real

➡ _____

Conversation

07 다음 대화의 밑줄 친 단어를 알맞은 형으로 고치시오.

> G: Look at those shoes the girl is wearing. I think they're great. How do you feel about them?
>
> B: I think they look light and comfort.

➡ _____

08 다음 대화의 빈칸에 'B'의 입장에서 할 말로 알맞은 것은?

> G: There's no monkey like this in the world. Its nose is too big. I think it's fake.
>
> B: I don't agree. I saw that kind of monkey on TV. It's _____.

① fake　　　　　　② exciting
③ real　　　　　　④ an opinion
⑤ a lie

09 다음 짝지어진 대화 중 어색한 것은?

① A: Let's take a lunch break. I want to eat some healthy food.
　B: Sounds great! I'm ready to eat anything.

② A: How do you feel about this bird?
　B: I think it looks clean. It's a perfect pet for us.

③ A: What do you think of this dog?
　B: I think it looks friendly.

④ A: This monkey is a perfect pet for us. Don't you agree?
　B: Yes, I agree.

⑤ A: How do you feel about this ad?
　B: I think it's great. We should not believe every ad.

[10~12] 다음 대화를 읽고 물음에 답하시오.

> Alex: Big Mouth's show is really cool. How do you feel about it?
>
> Somi: Well, (a)I don't think it's that great.
>
> Alex: Come on. I love Mr. Big Mouth. He always (b)makes me laugh out loud.
>
> Somi: He's funny, but (c)don't believe everything he says.
>
> Alex: All right. Oh, look at his photo of an octopus. He said it lives in a tree.
>
> Somi: (d)It makes sense.
>
> Alex: He took the photo when it was climbing the tree. I don't think he's lying. It's a great photo.
>
> Somi: (e)I don't agree with you. It's a fake photo. An octopus can't live out of the sea.

10 위 대화의 흐름상 밑줄 친 (a)~(e) 중 어휘의 쓰임이 어색한 것은?

① (a)　② (b)　③ (c)　④ (d)　⑤ (e)

11 위 대화의 제목으로 가장 적절한 것은?

① How to Make a Popular Show
② Big Mouth's Show: Real or Fake?
③ Truth Becoming Falsehood
④ Where an Octopus Lives
⑤ Big Mouth's Show Alex Really Likes

12 위 대화의 내용과 일치하지 않는 것을 고르시오.

① Alex and Somi are looking at a photo of an octopus.
② Alex likes Mr. Big Mouth because he makes him laugh out loud.
③ Somi warns Alex not to trust Mr. Big Mouth.
④ Alex doesn't think a picture of an octopus climbing a tree is real.
⑤ Somi doesn't agree with Alex because an octopus can't live out of the sea.

Grammar

13 주어진 문장의 밑줄 친 if와 용법이 같은 것은?

> This test tells if a student understands what she learned.

① You don't have to come if you don't want to.
② I am worrying if I can receive the support fund.
③ We will leave if everyone is ready.
④ You can see this movie if you are over 18 years old.
⑤ I won't go there if you don't come.

14 다음 글에서 어법상 어색한 부분을 찾아 바르게 고치시오.

> Opinion
> • I don't know ①that the man on the horse ②is brave, but he looks very ③tired and hungry. I think he ④needs some food and water.
> • I think this artwork shows ⑤the most interesting part of Cervantes' novel *Don Quixote*.

_____ ➡ _____

15 다음 두 문장이 같은 뜻이 되도록 빈칸에 들어갈 알맞은 것은?

> He said to me, "Who brought this gecko home?"
> = He asked me _____.

① who brought that gecko home
② who had brought this gecko home
③ who that gecko had brought home
④ who had brought that gecko home
⑤ who that gecko brought home

16 다음 중 어법상 어색한 문장의 개수로 알맞은 것은?

> a. Do you know if will it be rainy tomorrow?
> b. I am not sure that he can finish his project.
> c. Jenny told me that she was sleepy then.
> d. Tell me do you have the time.
> e. He asked me if I want something to eat.
> f. Mom asked me not to lose my umbrella again.

① 1개   ② 2개   ③ 3개   ④ 4개   ⑤ 5개

17 다음 두 문장이 같은 뜻이 되도록 빈칸에 들어갈 알맞은 것은?

> Mr. Hong said to me, "You can come to my house for dinner tomorrow."
> = Mr. Hong told me that _____.

① you could come to my house for dinner the following day
② he could come to my house for dinner the following day
③ I could come to his house for dinner the following day
④ I could come to his house for dinner the previous day
⑤ you could come to my house for dinner the previous day

18 다음 직접화법 문장들을 간접화법으로 바꿀 때 잘못된 곳을 바르게 고치시오.

(1) He asked her what she was doing there.
   ➡ He said to her, "What you are doing here?"

   ➡ _____

(2) She told him that she had met her sister the day before.

➡ She said to him, "I meet my sister yesterday."

➡ _____

(3) She said that she was very happy then.

➡ She said, "I am very happy then."

➡ _____

21 위 글의 밑줄 친 (B)의 우리말에 맞게 주어진 어휘를 알맞게 배열하시오.

> to attack / no / clowns / offered / trying / really / students / hard evidence / they / were / that

➡ _____
_____

Reading

[19~21] 다음 글을 읽고 물음에 답하시오.

In October 2016, stories about scary clowns shook schools across the Washington area, but Danina Garcia-Fuller's students didn't believe them a bit.

"Some people were getting scared because they saw things on social media," said Patricia Visoso, one of Garcia-Fuller's students. "But they never checked up on who was saying (A)this." The stories were actually made by teenagers, not by major newspapers or TV stations. (B)그들은 광대들이 정말로 학생들을 공격하려고 한다는 명백한 증거를 하나도 제공하지 않았다. The story turned out to be ⓐ .

[22~24] 다음 글을 읽고 물음에 답하시오.

"I think a lot of people just look at one thing and believe it's true," Patricia's classmate Ivy-Brooks said. "It's really important to look at the right sources and to pay attention to what is real and what is fake."

Like Garcia-Fuller's students, many teenagers in America are learning to think critically about information they're seeing in the news and on the Internet. This skill is getting more important these days ⓐas stories can spread very fast, and anyone can make a website full of false information.

19 위 글의 빈칸 ⓐ에 들어갈 알맞은 말을 고르시오.

① a reliable rumor ② a complete lie
③ a valid story ④ a complete truth
⑤ a suspicious column

20 위 글의 밑줄 친 (A)가 가리키는 것을 우리말로 쓰시오.

➡ _____

22 위 글의 밑줄 친 ⓐas와 문법적 쓰임이 같은 것을 고르시오.

① Leave the papers as they are.
② As you know, Julia is leaving soon.
③ As we go up, the air grows colder.
④ As I was tired, I soon fell asleep.
⑤ He came up to me as I was speaking.

23 위 글의 주제로 알맞은 것을 고르시오.

① the situation where people look at just one thing and believe it's true
② the importance of thinking critically about information you're seeing in the news and on the Internet

③ how to look at the right sources

④ the way you can pay attention to what is real and what is fake

⑤ the skill to make a website full of false information

24 According to the passage, which is NOT true?

① Ivy-Brooks thinks many people just look at one thing and believe it's true.

② Ivy-Brooks said that it was really important to look at the right sources.

③ Many teenagers in America are learning to think critically about information they're seeing only on the SNS.

④ These days, stories can spread very fast.

⑤ These days, it is possible for anyone to make a website full of false information.

[25~26] 다음 글을 읽고 물음에 답하시오.

　Garcia-Fuller also said sometimes it can be very hard to be a smart news reader. She tests her students with a website that appears to provide information on an animal called a tree octopus. The site is full of information on this animal, along with a few unclear photos of octopuses in trees. But like the story of scary clowns, it's totally ⓐmade up.

　The lesson, Garcia-Fuller tells her students, is to "check the information you're seeing once more carefully" and to "question everything, even things that I say."

25 위 글의 밑줄 친 ⓐmade up과 같은 뜻을 가지는 단어를 철자 i로 시작하여 쓰시오.

➡ _____

26 위 글의 제목으로 알맞은 것을 고르시오.

① Who Is a Smart News Reader?

② To Test Students with a Website

③ Information on an Animal Called a Tree Octopus

④ Can You Believe the Information on the Tree Octopus?

⑤ To Check the Information Carefully and to Question Everything

[27~28] 다음 글을 읽고 물음에 답하시오.

　The reporter says the ducks jumped down on the road by themselves. 　ⓐ　, it's not a fact. ⓑA man took the ducks and put down them safely on the road one by one. I wonder if the reporter saw the scene himself.

27 위 글의 빈칸 ⓐ에 들어갈 알맞은 말을 고르시오.

① For example　② In addition

③ In other words　④ However

⑤ Therefore

28 위 글의 밑줄 친 ⓑ에서 어법상 틀린 부분을 찾아 고치시오.

_____ ➡ _____

01 다음 짝지어진 단어의 관계가 같도록 빈칸에 알맞은 말을 쓰시오.

information – inform : performance – _____

02 다음 영영풀이에 해당하는 단어는?

very important and serious

① minor   ② noisy   ③ false
④ total   ⑤ major

[03~04] 다음 대화를 읽고 물음에 답하시오.

G: How do you feel about the teddy bears?
B: They are cute. (A)뭔가 특별한 점이 있니?
G: They were made out of a police officer's uniform.
B: Oh, I see.
G: This police officer made them for the kids. Their dad was a police officer, and he passed away recently.
B: That's very touching.

03 위 대화의 'Teddy Bears'에 관한 내용 중에서 'Fact'에 해당하는 문장을 모두 찾아 그대로 쓰시오.

➡ _____

_____

04 위 대화의 우리말 (A)에 맞게 주어진 단어를 알맞은 순서로 배열하시오.

(special / there / anything / them / about / is / ?)

➡ _____

05 다음 대화의 빈칸에 들어갈 말로 알맞은 것은?

G: There's no monkey like this in the world. Its nose is too big. I think it's fake.
B: _____ I saw that kind of monkey on TV. It's real.

① I think so, too.
② I don't agree.
③ I agree with you.
④ You can say that again.
⑤ I couldn't agree with you more.

[06~07] 다음 대화를 읽고 물음에 답하시오.

G: How do you feel about this kid here?
B: (A) I think she is very pretty. ___(a)___ , why did she cut her hair? (B)
G: Can you guess?
B: Well, girls these days prefer short hair. (C)
G: I don't agree with that. (D) And this kid here is not a girl. ___(b)___ , he is a boy. (E)
B: Really?
G: Yes. He grew his hair to help sick children.

06 위 대화의 (A)~(E) 중 주어진 문장이 들어갈 위치로 알맞은 것은?

Most girls like long hair better than short hair.

① (A)   ② (B)   ③ (C)   ④ (D)   ⑤ (E)

07 위 대화의 빈칸 (a)와 (b)에 들어갈 말로 알맞은 것은?

① By the way – Moreover
② In addition – On the other hand
③ By the way – In fact
④ However – Actually
⑤ Therefore – For example

출제율 90%

08 다음 빈칸에 들어갈 말로 적절한 것을 <u>모두</u> 고르시오.

> Team A and Team B will debate _____ teenagers should work part-time job.

① that   ② if   ③ what
④ though   ⑤ whether

출제율 90%

09 다음 화법 전환 문장들에서 빈칸에 알맞은 말을 쓰시오.

(1) She said to me, "How do you know the answer of this question?"
   ➡ She asked me how I knew _____
      _____ .

(2) He said, "I was in trouble."
   ➡ He said that he _____ .

(3) Eric told me that he was happy with his new house then.
   ➡ Eric said to me, "I'm happy with
      _____ .

(4) He told me he liked the job.
   ➡ He _____ me, "I like the job."

(5) He asked me if I was hungry then.
   ➡ He said to me, "_____ ?"

출제율 95%

10 다음 우리말을 참고하여 괄호 안에 주어진 단어로 빈칸에 알맞은 말을 써 넣으시오.

> 선생님은 학생들에게 수업 중에 밖에 나가지 말라고 말씀하셨다. (go out, during)

(1) The teacher said to students, "_____
      _____ ."

(2) The teacher _____
      _____ .

출제율 95%

11 주어진 어휘를 이용하여 다음 우리말을 영어로 쓰시오.

> 나는 그들이 우리에게 부채춤을 보여 줄 것인지 궁금해. (wonder, the fan dance)

➡ _____
   _____

출제율 95%

12 다음 대화의 빈칸에 밑줄 친 문장을 알맞은 형태로 바꾸어 써 넣으시오.

(1) A: She said, "_____ ."
    B: She said what?
    A: She said that <u>she was so tired then</u>.

(2) A: He said to me, "<u>You are right.</u>"
    B: What did he say?
    A: He told me that _____ .

[13~15] 다음 글을 읽고 물음에 답하시오.

In October 2016, stories about scary clowns shook schools across the Washington area, but Danina Garcia-Fuller's students didn't believe them a bit.

"Some people were getting scared because they saw things on social media," said Patricia Visoso, one of Garcia-Fuller's students. "But they never checked up on who was saying this." The stories were actually made by teenagers, not by major newspapers or TV stations. They offered no ⓐhard evidence that clowns really were trying to attack students. The story ⓑturned out to be a complete lie.

출제율 95%

13 위 글의 밑줄 친 ⓐhard와 같은 의미로 쓰인 것을 고르시오.

① Wait for the concrete to go hard.
② You must try hard.
③ It is hard to believe that she's only nine.
④ The newspaper story is based on hard facts.
⑤ She's a very hard worker.

출제율 90%

14 위 글의 밑줄 친 ⓑturned out과 바꿔 쓸 수 있는 한 단어를 쓰시오.

➡ _____

출제율 95%

15 By whom were the stories about scary clowns made? Answer in English in a full sentence. (5 words)

➡ _____

[16~17] 다음 글을 읽고 물음에 답하시오.

"I think a lot of people just look at one thing and believe it's true," Patricia's classmate Ivy-Brooks said. "It's really important to look at the right sources and ⓐto pay attention to what is real and what is fake."

Like Garcia-Fuller's students, many teenagers in America are learning to think critically about information ⓑthey're seeing in the news and on the Internet. This skill is getting more important these days as stories can spread very fast, and anyone can make a website full of false information.

출제율 100%

16 아래 〈보기〉에서 위 글의 밑줄 친 ⓐto pay와 to부정사의 용법이 같은 것의 개수를 고르시오.

┌─── 보기 ───┐
① I turned on the computer to surf the Internet.
② I don't know where to go.
③ Do you have something interesting to read?
④ Everybody was surprised to see him.
⑤ His wish is to have good eyesight.
└──────────┘

① 1개   ② 2개   ③ 3개   ④ 4개   ⑤ 5개

출제율 90%

17 위 글의 밑줄 친 ⓑthey가 가리키는 것을 본문에서 찾아 쓰시오.

➡ _____

[18~20] 다음 글을 읽고 물음에 답하시오.

Garcia-Fuller said she was teaching her students how to tell fake news from real news.
"(①) If a story or a photo seems too good to be true, stop and think: Is there any evidence that supports what the writer says? (②) And where is this coming from? (③)"
Garcia-Fuller's students also learn how to tell fact from opinion in the news. (④)
"Opinions are good ⓐto read," said 15-year-old McKenzie Campbell, "but you also have to check if they are based on facts." (⑤)

출제율 95%

18 위 글의 흐름으로 보아, 주어진 문장이 들어가기에 가장 적절한 곳은?

> One of the first steps is to slow down.

①   ②   ③   ④   ⑤

출제율 95%

19 위 글의 밑줄 친 ⓐto read와 to부정사의 용법이 다른 것을 모두 고르시오.

① I'm sorry to hear the bad news.
② It's about time to go for a walk.
③ I think it wrong to tell a lie.
④ Jenny grew up to be a pianist.
⑤ Mom told me to stop watching TV.

출제율 100%

20 According to the passage, which is NOT true?

① Garcia-Fuller was teaching her students how to tell fake news from real news.
② One of the first steps to tell fake news from real news is to slow down.
③ Garcia-Fuller's students also learn how to distinguish fact from opinion in the news.
④ 15-year-old McKenzie Campbell said that opinions are good to speak.
⑤ 15-year-old McKenzie Campbell said that we also had to check if the opinions were based on facts.

[21~23] 다음 글을 읽고 물음에 답하시오.

> ⓐTeam NW danced on the stage while the school festival. They wondered ⓑif the students and teachers would like their dancing. ⓒBut they performed much better than any other team. A lot of students stood up and cheered loudly when the team danced. Ms. Yu, the P.E. teacher, said it was the performance of the year.

출제율 90%

21 위 글의 밑줄 친 ⓐ에서 어법상 틀린 부분을 찾아 고치시오.

_____ ➡ _____

출제율 95%

22 위 글의 밑줄 친 ⓑif와 문법적 쓰임이 같은 것을 모두 고르시오.

① I asked her if she knew Mr. White.
② If you see him, give him this note.
③ I'll work here if you offer me more money.
④ He couldn't tell if she was laughing or crying.
⑤ If necessary, I can come at once.

출제율 95%

23 위 글의 밑줄 친 ⓒ를 다음과 같이 바꿔 쓸 때 빈칸에 들어갈 알맞은 한 단어를 쓰시오.

> But they performed _____ of all the teams.

01 다음 대화를 읽고 질문에 영어로 답하시오.

> **Alex:** Big Mouth's show is really cool. How do you feel about it?
>
> **Somi:** Well, I don't think it's that great.
>
> **Alex:** Come on. I love Mr. Big Mouth. He always makes me laugh out loud.
>
> **Somi:** He's funny, but don't believe everything he says.
>
> **Alex:** All right. Oh, look at his photo of an octopus. He said it lives in a tree.
>
> **Somi:** It doesn't make sense
>
> **Alex:** He took the photo when it was climbing the tree. I don't think he's lying. It's a great photo.
>
> **Somi:** I don't agree with you. It's a fake photo. An octopus can't live out of the sea.

Q: Why did Somi say it was a fake photo?

➡ _____

02 접속사 'if', 'that', 'whether' 중 적절한 것을 한 번씩만 골라 주어진 단어와 함께 알맞게 배열하시오.

(1) I am wondering (fit, these, feet, shoes, his).

➡ _____

(2) I am sure (is, the, crying, baby, now).

➡ _____

(3) (a boy, kid, this, is, a girl, or) doesn't matter to me at all.

➡ _____

03 다음 주어진 문장들을 간접화법으로 바꿔 쓰시오.

(1) She said, "I like Tony."

➡ She said that _____.

(2) The old man said, "I want some water."

➡ The old man said that _____
_____.

(3) Bob said, "My sister looks happy."

➡ Bob said that _____.

04 대화의 흐름에 맞게 빈칸에 들어갈 말을 영어로 쓰시오.

> (1) **A:** She said to me, "Where are you living now?"
>
> **B:** Pardon me? Can you repeat that again?
>
> **A:** She asked me where _____.
>
> (2) **A:** He said to me, "Do you like to study in this library?"
>
> **B:** I can't hear what you are saying.
>
> **A:** He asked me _____
> _____.

05 다음 그림 속 내용을 다른 사람에게 전달하는 문장으로 완성하시오.

The boy said _____
_____ and he wondered
_____.

"I think a lot of people just look at one thing and believe it's true," Patricia's classmate Ivy-Brooks said. "It's really important to look at the right sources and to pay attention to what is real and what is fake."

Like Garcia-Fuller's students, many teenagers in America are learning to think critically ⓐ뉴스에서 그리고 인터넷상에서 보고 있는 정보에 관해. This skill is getting more important these days as stories can spread very fast, and anyone can make a website full of false information.

06 위 글의 밑줄 친 ⓐ의 우리말에 맞게 주어진 어휘를 이용하여 11 단어로 영작하시오.

> about, seeing

➡ _____

_____

07 주어진 영영풀이에 해당하는 단어를 본문에서 찾아 쓰시오.

> not genuine or real; being an imitation of the genuine article

➡ _____

08 본문의 내용과 일치하도록 다음 빈칸 (A)와 (B)에 알맞은 단어를 쓰시오.

> According to Patricia's classmate Ivy-Brooks, looking at (A)_____ _____ _____ and paying attention to (B)_____ _____ _____ and what is fake are really important.

Garcia-Fuller said she was teaching her students how to tell fake news from real news.

"One of the first steps is to slow down. ⓐIf a story or a photo seems too good to be true, stop and think: Is there any evidence that supports what the writer says? And where is this coming from?"

Garcia-Fuller's students also learn how to tell fact from opinion in the news. "Opinions are good to read," said 15-year-old McKenzie Campbell, "ⓑbut you also have to check that they are based on facts."

09 위 글의 밑줄 친 ⓐ를 다음과 같이 바꿔 쓸 때 빈칸에 들어갈 알맞은 단어를 쓰시오.

> If a story or a photo seems _____ good _____ it _____ be true

10 위 글의 밑줄 친 ⓑ에서 어법상 틀린 부분을 찾아 고치시오.

_____ ➡ _____

11 According to McKenzie Campbell, when we read opinions in the news, what do we have to check? Answer in English in a full sentence.

➡ _____

01 아래 표의 (A)의 과일이나 야채에 대해 (B)는 좋아하거나 싫어하는 것을 나타낸 것이다. 〈보기〉처럼 상대방의 의견을 묻는 말과 그 대답을 쓰시오.

> ─ 보기 ─
>
> A: How do you feel about apples?
> B: I really love them.

(A)	(B)
• apples • persimmons • cucumbers • pears	• I really love them. • I like them. • I hate them. • I don't like them.

02 다음은 야구선수 Kelly와의 인터뷰를 정리한 내용이다. 인터뷰를 읽고, 조건에 맞게 정리한 내용의 빈칸에 알맞은 말을 쓰시오. (The reporter is a woman and Kelly is a man. Complete the sentence using pronouns.)

> ─ 보기 ─
>
> Reporter: Kelly, our readers want to know all about you. (1)Can you tell me about your day?
> Kelly: (2)I always get up at 6 and go to the stadium at 7.
> Reporter: You get up so early. (3)How long were your training hours today?
> Kelly: (4)It took 5 hours and was really hard.
> Reporter: (5)What will you do in your spare time today?
> Kelly: (6)After this interview, I will go swimming or watch a movie.
> Reporter: It's been really nice talking to you. Thank you for letting us take time for the interview.

(1) The reporter asked Kelly _____.
(2) Kelly said that _____.
(3) The reporter asked Kelly _____.
(4) Kelly said that _____.
(5) The reporter asked Kelly _____.
(6) Kelly said that _____.

단원별 모의고사

01 다음 단어에 대한 영어 설명이 <u>어색한</u> 것은?

① false: incorrect, untrue, or mistaken

② fact: what you think or believe about something

③ lie: an untrue statement

④ totally: completely, absolutely

⑤ octopus: a soft sea creature with eight long arms

02 다음 짝지어진 단어의 관계가 같도록 빈칸에 알맞은 말을 주어진 글자로 시작하여 쓰시오.

search – investigate : supply – p_____

03 다음 영영풀이에 해당하는 단어를 고르시오.

a particular part of a town, a country, or the world

① clown   ② social media

③ evidence   ④ source

⑤ area

04 다음 중 짝지어진 대화가 <u>어색한</u> 것은?

① A: What did the woman say to her brother?
　 B: She told him that she was very happy to meet him.

② A: How do you feel about the girl?
　 B: I think she's pretty.

③ A: How do you feel about the dog?
　 B: I think it's cute.

④ A: How do you feel about the ducks?
　 B: I don't agree with you.

⑤ A: How do you feel about this ad?
　 B: I think it's great. It shows the phone is strong.

[05~06] 다음 대화를 읽고 물음에 답하시오.

G: How do you feel about this drama?

B: _____(A)_____ The boy gave up his life to save his sister. It's the best drama of this year.

G: I don't agree. It's not a good drama.

B: Come on. Why do you think so?

G: It doesn't seem real. And it's a little boring.

05 위 대화의 빈칸 (A)에 들어갈 말로 알맞은 것은?

① I think it's very boring.

② That's a good idea.

③ I think it's very touching.

④ I don't believe it.

⑤ It's not a good drama.

06 위 대화를 읽고 다음 물음에 대한 대답을 완성하시오.

> G: Why doesn't the girl think it's a good drama?

> Because _____ and _____ .

07 다음 대화의 흐름상 밑줄 친 (1)~(5) 중 어색한 것은?

> G: How do you feel about this kid here?
> B: (1)I think she is very pretty. By the way, why did she cut her hair?
> G: (2)Can you guess?
> B: Well, girls these days prefer short hair.
> G: (3)I agree with that. Most girls like long hair better than short hair. And this kid here is not a girl. (4)In fact, he is a boy.
> B: Really?
> G: Yes. (5)He grew his hair to help sick children.

① (1) ② (2) ③ (3) ④ (4) ⑤ (5)

08 다음 대화의 밑줄 친 우리말에 맞게 주어진 단어를 알맞은 순서로 배열하시오.

> G: 저 여자애가 신고 있는 신발 좀 봐. (the girl / those / is / look / wearing / at / shoes) I think they're great. How do you feel about them?
> B: I think they look light and comfortable.
> G: Right. I want to buy them for the school field trip.

➡ _____

09 다음 대화를 읽고, 아래의 〈Criticism〉에 해당하는 문장의 빈 칸을 완성하시오.

> G: How do you feel about the teddy bears?
> B: They are cute. Is there anything special about them?
> G: They were made out of a police officer's uniform.
> B: Oh, I see.
> G: This police officer made them for the kids. Their dad was a police officer, and he passed away recently.
> B: That's very touching.

> The reporter says the police officer bought teddy bears for the kids. However, it's not a (1)_____. The police officer made them out of the kids' dad's (2)_____. for the kids. I wonder (3)_____ the reporter met them himself.

[10~11] 다음 대화를 읽고 물음에 답하시오.

> Alex: Big Mouth's show is really cool. How do you feel about it?
> Somi: Well, I don't think it's (A)that great.
> Alex: Come on. I love Mr. Big Mouth. He always makes me laugh out loud.
> Somi: He's funny, but don't believe everything he says.
> Alex: All right. Oh, look at his photo of an octopus. He said it lives in a tree.
> Somi: It doesn't make sense.
> Alex: He took the photo when it was climbing the tree. I don't think he's lying. It's a great photo.
> Somi: I don't agree with you. It's a fake photo. An octopus can't live out of the sea.

10 위 대화를 읽고 다음 질문에 영어로 답하시오.

> G: What is the octopus in the photo doing?

➡ _____

11 위 대화의 밑줄 친 (A)that과 같은 의미로 사용된 것은?

① This book is much thicker than that one.
② My arm doesn't reach that far.
③ The point is that you are still responsible.
④ It was yesterday that the accident happened.
⑤ That was the best time.

12 다음 중 밑줄 친 if의 의미가 다른 하나를 고르시오.

① We will discuss if this has a positive impact on our society.
② I will help you if you are busy now.
③ Any student will fail if he or she cheats on the test.
④ You can't come on board if you don't have your passport.
⑤ I will be angry if you tell a lie.

13 다음 문장을 간접화법으로 바꿔 쓰시오.

> Mr. Kim said to his daughter, "Can I ask you a few questions?"

➡ _____
_____

14 다음 각 문장에서 어법상 틀린 부분을 찾아 바르게 고쳐 쓰시오.

(1) He says her, "Where do you work now?"

➡ _____

(2) She told me that she hasn't been at school the day before.

➡ _____
_____

15 다음 두 문장을 한 문장으로 바르게 옮긴 것은?

> • Was this song composed by him?
> • That is unknown.

① Whether was this song composed by him is unknown.
② If was this song composed by him is unknown.
③ Whether this song was composed by him is unknown.
④ If this song was composed by him is unknown.
⑤ It is unknown that this song was composed by him

16 다음 우리말을 주어진 단어를 사용하여 영어로 옮기시오.

> (1) 나는 그녀가 내 선물을 좋아할지 궁금해. (if, present)
> (2) 너는 그녀가 결혼했는지 알고 있니? (if, is)

(1) _____
(2) _____

[17~18] 다음 글을 읽고 물음에 답하시오.

In October 2016, stories about (A)[scared / scary] clowns shook schools across the Washington area, but Danina Garcia-Fuller's students didn't believe ⓐthem a bit.

"Some people were getting (B)[scared / scary] because they saw things on social media," said Patricia Visoso, one of Garcia-Fuller's students. "But they never checked up on who was saying this." The stories were actually made by teenagers, not by major newspapers or TV stations. They (C)[offered / were offered] no hard evidence that clowns really were trying to attack students. The story turned out to be a complete lie.

17 위 글의 괄호 (A)~(C)에서 문맥이나 어법상 알맞은 낱말을 골라 쓰시오.

➡ (A) _____ (B) _____ (C) _____

18 위 글의 밑줄 친 ⓐthem이 가리키는 것을 본문에서 찾아 쓰시오.

➡ _____

[19~20] 다음 글을 읽고 물음에 답하시오.

"I think a lot of people just look at one thing and believe it's true," Patricia's classmate Ivy-Brooks said. "It's really important to look at the right sources and to pay attention ⓐ ___ what is real and what is fake."

(A)Like Garcia-Fuller's students, many teenagers in America are learning to think critically about information they're seeing in the news and ⓑ ___ the Internet. This skill is getting more important these days as stories can spread very fast, and anyone can make a website full of false information.

19 위 글의 빈칸 ⓐ와 ⓑ에 들어갈 전치사가 바르게 짝지어진 것은?

ⓐ	ⓑ		ⓐ	ⓑ
① for – to			② to – by	
③ to – on			④ for – on	
⑤ on – to				

20 위 글의 밑줄 친 (A)Like와 같은 의미로 쓰인 것을 고르시오.

① I had a chance to meet people of like mind.

② There are many hobbies like photography or painting.

③ At weekends I like to sleep late.

④ He likes jazz, rock and the like.

⑤ Students were angry at being treated like children.

[21~22] 다음 글을 읽고 물음에 답하시오.

Garcia-Fuller said she was teaching her students how to tell fake news from real news.

"One of the first steps is to slow down. If a story or a photo seems too good to be true, stop and think: Is there any evidence that supports what the writer says? And where is this coming from?"

Garcia-Fuller's students also learn how to tell fact from opinion in the news. "Opinions are good to read," said 15-year-old McKenzie Campbell, "but you also have to check if they are based on facts."

21 다음 문장에서 위 글의 내용과 <u>다른</u> 부분을 찾아서 고치시오.

> Garcia-Fuller was teaching her students how to tell fake news from opinion in the news.

➡ _____

22 만약 어떤 이야기나 어떤 사진이 진짜라고 하기엔 너무 좋아 보일 때 생각해 보아야 할 두 가지를 우리말로 쓰시오.

① _____

_____

② _____

[23~24] 다음 글을 읽고 물음에 답하시오.

(①) Garcia-Fuller also said sometimes it can be very hard to be a smart news reader. (②) She tests her students with a website that appears to provide information on an animal called a tree octopus. (③) But like the story of scary clowns, it's totally made up. (④)

The lesson, Garcia-Fuller tells her students, is to "check the information you're seeing once more carefully" and to "question everything, even things that I say." (⑤)

23 위 글의 흐름으로 보아, 주어진 문장이 들어가기에 가장 적절한 곳은?

> The site is full of information on this animal, along with a few unclear photos of octopuses in trees.

① ② ③ ④ ⑤

24 According to the passage, which is NOT true?

① According to Garcia-Fuller, sometimes it can be very hard to be a smart news reader.

② Garcia-Fuller tests her students with a website that appears to provide information on a tree octopus.

③ The website is full of information on a tree octopus, together with a few unclear photos of octopuses in trees.

④ Unlike the story of scary clowns, the information on a tree octopus is true.

⑤ Garcia-Fuller tells her students to check the information carefully and to question everything.

MEMO

INSIGHT
on the textbook

교과서 파헤치기

※ 다음 영어를 우리말로 쓰시오.

01	awesome		22	seriously
02	battle		23	loudly
03	ground		24	seem
04	toward		25	enemy
05	traffic		26	seat
06	chimney		27	soldier
07	ad(= advertisement)		28	exactly
08	powerful		29	vote
09	close		30	border
10	translate		31	Braille
11	prepare		32	expression
12	curious		33	hire
13	rather		34	product
14	reply		35	get over
15	husband		36	look after
16	dead		37	be covered with
17	knock		38	at a price of
18	discover		39	except for
19	hidden		40	vote for
20	hug		41	be careful with
21	misunderstanding		42	right away
			43	instead of

※ 다음 우리말을 영어로 쓰시오.

01	교통	22	국경, 경계
02	근사한, 멋진, 엄청난, 어마어마한	23	상품, 제품
03	글자, 문자	24	수화
04	전쟁, 전투	25	고용하다
05	번역하다, 해석하다	26	오해
06	죽은, 쓸모없는	27	포옹; 포옹하다
07	적군, 적대자	28	치다, 두드리다
08	발견하다	29	좌석, 의석
09	불을 붙이다, 불을 밝히다	30	연못
10	큰 소리로, 시끄럽게	31	외국의
11	정확히게	32	몸짓, 몸동작
12	호기심이 많은, 궁금한	33	끌다, 잡아당기다
13	표현	34	투표하다, 선출하다
14	남편	35	~ 대신에
15	~을 향하여	36	~을 제외하고
16	굴뚝	37	~을 돌보다
17	진지하게, 심각하게	38	~에 조심하다
18	다소, 약간	39	물러서다
19	준비하다	40	즉시, 당장
20	숨은, 숨겨진	41	~로 덮이다
21	군인	42	~의 가격으로
		43	이겨내다, 극복하다

※ 다음 영영풀이에 알맞은 단어를 <보기>에서 골라 쓴 후, 우리말 뜻을 쓰시오.

1 _____ : no longer alive: _____

2 _____ : in the direction of: _____

3 _____ : an answer to a letter: _____

4 _____ : from another country: _____

5 _____ : the surface of the Earth: _____

6 _____ : to pay someone to work for you: _____

7 _____ : the man that a woman is married to: _____

8 _____ : suffering from an illness or disease:: _____

9 _____ : to make something ready for use: _____

10 _____ : a position as a member of a committee, court, etc.: _____

11 _____ : to express one's preference for a candidate: _____

12 _____ : a thick liquid made from plants or animals that is used in cooking:
_____

13 _____ : a piece of jewelry in the form of a circle that you wear on a finger:
_____

14 _____ : to change spoken or written words into another language: _____

15 _____ : to find out something that you did not know before: _____

16 _____ : the action of putting your arms around someone to show your love or
friendship: _____

보기			
oil	vote	hire	foreign
hug	translate	dead	ill
seat	prepare	toward	reply
discover	ring	husband	ground

※ 다음 우리말과 일치하도록 빈칸에 알맞은 말을 쓰시오.

Get Ready 2

(1) G: I'm _____ _____ that robot. Why _____ _____ there?

B: It's _____ _____ _____ ad. It _____ people their _____ are very _____.

(2) G: What's this? I'_____ _____ _____ it.

B: It's a _____ _____. It _____ "Do not _____."

G: Oh, I see.

(3) G: What are these _____ _____? I'_____ _____ _____ them.

B: Oh, they are _____. They are for _____ people.

G: I see. Now I can _____ _____ they _____.

(4) G: I'm _____ about that _____. Why is it _____ there?

B: Oh, that. It's an _____. It says the _____ is very _____.

Start Off – Listen & Talk A

1. B: What are the _____ doing _____ the five _____ on TV?

G: They are sending _____ to the king _____ _____ the _____.

B: Really? I'_____ _____ _____ the _____. Can you tell me more?

G: Well, do you see the two _____ _____?

B: Yes. _____ do they _____?

G: They mean they just _____ an _____.

2. B: If there's no _____, they don't _____ _____ _____, _____ they?

G: Yes, they do. _____ from one _____ means "No _____."

B: Now smoke is _____ from three chimneys. _____ _____ that _____?

G: _____ _____ an enemy is coming _____ to the _____.

Start Off B

B: Now the enemy _____ _____ the _____ in the _____. What are the _____ _____ _____ _____ to send _____? I'm _____ _____ that.

G: They will _____ four _____.

B: When they _____ all five of the _____, what does that mean?

G: _____ _____ the _____ has _____.

(1) G: 나는 저 로봇에 대해 알고 싶어. 그건 왜 저기에 서 있는 거니?

B: 그건 일종의 광고야. 그것은 그들의 건전지가 매우 강력하다는 것을 사람들에게 말하고 있어.

(2) G: 이것은 뭐지? 난 그게 궁금해.

B: 그것은 교통 표지판이야. 그것은 "들어오지 마시오."를 의미해.

G: 오, 알겠어.

(3) G: 이 점들은 무엇을 위한 거니? 난 그것들에 대해 알고 싶어.

B: 오, 그것들은 점자야. 그것들은 시각장애인을 위한 것이야.

G: 알겠어. 이제 그것들이 무엇을 의미하는지 추측할 수 있어.

(4) G: 나는 저 풍선이 궁금해. 그건 왜 저기에 매달려 있니?

B: 오, 저것. 그건 광고야. 그것은 그 상품이 매우 강력하다는 것을 말하고 있어.

1. B: TV에서 병사들이 5개의 굴뚝으로 무엇을 하고 있니?

G: 그들은 그 굴뚝을 이용하여 왕에게 메시지를 보내고 있어.

B: 정말? 난 그 체계가 궁금해. 좀 더 말해 줄 수 있어?

G: 음, 연기 나는 굴뚝 두 개가 보이지?

B: 그래. 그것들은 무엇을 의미하니?

G: 그것들은 그들이 방금 적을 봤다는 것을 의미해.

2. B: 만약 적이 없다면, 그들은 연기를 전혀 피우지 않아, 그렇지?

G: 아니, 연기를 피워. 굴뚝 한 곳에서 연기가 나오면 "적이 없음"을 의미해.

B: 이제 연기가 굴뚝 세 개에서 올라가고 있어. 그것은 무엇을 의미하니?

G: 그것은 적이 국경 가까이 접근하고 있음을 의미해.

B: 이제 적이 어둠 속에서 국경을 침입하고 있어. 메시지를 보내기 위해서 병사들은 무슨 일을 할까? 나는 그것이 궁금해.

G: 그들은 굴뚝 4개에 불을 붙일 거야.

B: 그들이 5개 굴뚝 모두에 불을 붙였을 때, 그것은 무엇을 의미하니?

G: 그것은 전투가 시작되었음을 의미해.

Start Off – Speak Up

B: I'_____ _____ _____ sign _____.

G: Are you? _____ me _____ you one _____. Look.

B: _____ does it _____?

G: _____ _____ "Hello."

Step Up – Real-life Scene

B: This painting has some _____ _____ in it.

G: Really? I'm _____ _____ them. Where are the _____?

B: _____ one _____.

G: _____ _____. ... Oh, I see some _____ here.

B: You found _____! It _____ "Jan van Eyck was here. 1434." It's _____.

G: That's _____! _____ _____ _____?

B: Okay. This dog _____ us the man here was very _____.

G: I don't _____.

B: They had to _____ _____ _____ money _____ _____ a dog of that _____ _____ _____ _____ _____.

G: I see. Only _____ _____ could have _____ _____ of dog, _____?

B: _____. Pictures _____ _____ _____ words, you know.

Express Yourself A

1. W: What does this woman's _____ mean? I'm _____ _____ it.

   M: I think _____ _____ "Jump _____ the _____."

   W: _____ do you _____ _____?

   M: The boy has _____ _____ _____ on his head. And the woman is _____ at the _____.

2. W: This woman doesn't want a dollar. _____ what does her _____ _____?

   M: _____ _____ she wants a _____.

   W: Then the boy _____ _____ a chicken _____ _____ the fruit, _____?

   M: _____ _____ _____ _____.

3. W: _____ does this man's _____ _____? I'm _____ _____ it.

   M: It means "_____ _____ _____."

   W: Really? _____ _____ you think _____?

   M: _____ _____ _____ there is coming _____ to an animal.

   W: Oh, I _____.

B: 난 수화가 궁금해.

G: 그러니? 내가 표현 하나를 알려줄게. 봐.

B: 그것은 무엇을 의미하니?

G: 그것은 "안녕하세요."를 의미해.

B: 이 그림은 그 안에 숨겨진 비밀이 몇 개 있어.

G: 정말? 난 그것들이 궁금해. 그 비밀들은 어디에 있니?

B: 너 스스로 하나 찾아봐.

G: 어디 보자. … 오, 여기 글자들이 몇 개 보여.

B: 너 하나 찾았구나! 그것은 "Jan van Eyck가 여기 있었다. 1434."를 의미해. 그것은 라틴어야.

G: 멋지! 다른 비밀들은?

B: 좋아. 이 개는 여기 있는 이 남자가 매우 부자였다는 것을 우리에게 말해주지.

G: 나는 이해가 안 돼.

B: 당시에 저런 종류의 개를 사려면 많은 돈을 써야 했어.

G: 알겠다. 단지 부자들만 저런 종류의 개를 살 수 있었어, 맞지?

B: 정확해. 알다시피, 그림이 천 마디 말을 하지.

1. W: 이 여자의 몸짓은 무엇을 의미하니? 난 그것이 궁금해.

   M: 내 생각에 그것은 "연못으로 뛰어들어."를 의미해.

   W: 왜 그렇게 생각하니?

   M: 그 소년은 머리 위에 많은 벌이 있어. 그리고 그 여자는 연못을 가리키고 있어.

2. W: 이 여자는 1달러를 원하지 않아. 그렇다면 그녀의 몸짓은 무엇을 의미하니?

   M: 그것은 그녀가 닭 한 마리를 원한다는 것을 의미해.

   W: 그럼 그 소년은 과일을 얻기 위해 닭을 한 마리 가져와야 하는구나, 맞지?

   M: 난 그렇게 생각해.

3. W: 이 남자의 몸짓은 무엇을 의미하니? 난 그것이 궁금해.

   M: 그것은 "그것을 꺼."를 의미해.

   W: 정말? 왜 그렇게 생각하니?

   M: 거기 있는 나머지 다른 사냥꾼이 어떤 동물 가까이 접근하고 있어.

   W: 오, 알겠어.

※ 다음 우리말에 맞도록 대화를 영어로 쓰시오.

Get Ready 2

(1) G: _____
    B: _____

(2) G: _____
    B: _____
    G: _____

(3) G: _____
    B: _____
    G: _____

(4) G: _____
    B: _____

(1) G: 나는 저 로봇에 대해 알고 싶어. 그건 왜 저기에 서 있는 거니?
   B: 그건 일종의 광고야. 그것은 그들의 건전지가 매우 강력하다는 것을 사람들에게 말하고 있어.
(2) G: 이것은 뭐지? 난 그게 궁금해.
   B: 그것은 교통 표지판이야. 그것은 "들어오지 마시오."를 의미해.
   G: 오, 알겠어.
(3) G: 이 점들은 무엇을 위한 거니? 난 그것들에 대해 알고 싶어.
   B: 오, 그것들은 점자야. 그것들은 시각장애인을 위한 것이야.
   G: 알겠어. 이제 그것들이 무엇을 의미하는지 추측할 수 있어.
(4) G: 나는 저 풍선이 궁금해. 그건 왜 저기에 매달려 있니?
   B: 오, 저것. 그건 광고야. 그것은 그 상품이 매우 강력하다는 것을 말하고 있어.

Start Off – Listen & Talk A

1. B: _____
   G: _____
   B: _____
   G: _____
   B: _____
   G: _____

2. B: _____
   G: _____
   B: _____
   G: _____

1. B: TV에서 병사들이 5개의 굴뚝으로 무엇을 하고 있니?
   G: 그들은 그 굴뚝을 이용하여 왕에게 메시지를 보내고 있어.
   B: 정말? 난 그 체계가 궁금해. 좀 더 말해 줄 수 있어?
   G: 음, 연기 나는 굴뚝 두 개가 보이지?
   B: 그래. 그것들은 무엇을 의미하니?
   G: 그것들은 그들이 방금 적을 봤다는 것을 의미해.
2. B: 만약 적이 없다면, 그들은 연기를 전혀 피우지 않아, 그렇지?
   G: 아니, 연기를 피워. 굴뚝 한 곳에서 연기가 나오면 "적이 없음"을 의미해.
   B: 이제 연기가 굴뚝 세 개에서 올라가고 있어. 그것은 무엇을 의미하니?
   G: 그것은 적이 국경 가까이 접근하고 있음을 의미해.

Start Off B

B: _____
   _____

G: _____

B: _____

G: _____

B: 이제 적이 어둠 속에서 국경을 침입하고 있어. 메시지를 보내기 위해서 병사들은 무슨 일을 할까? 나는 그것이 궁금해.
G: 그들은 굴뚝 4개에 불을 붙일 거야.
B: 그들이 5개 굴뚝 모두에 불을 붙였을 때, 그것은 무엇을 의미하니?
G: 그것은 전투가 시작되었음을 의미해.

Start Off – Speak Up

B: _____

G: _____

B: _____

G: _____

Step Up – Real-life Scene

B: _____

G: _____

B: _____

G: _____

B: _____

G: _____

B: _____

G: _____

B: _____

G: _____

B: _____

Express Yourself A

1. W: _____

   M: _____

   W: _____

   M: _____

2. W: _____

   M: _____

   W: _____

   M: _____

3. W: _____

   M: _____

   W: _____

   M: _____

   W: _____

B: 난 수화가 궁금해.

G: 그러니? 내가 표현 하나를 알려줄게. 봐.

B: 그것은 무엇을 의미하니?

G: 그것은 "안녕하세요."를 의미해.

B: 이 그림은 그 안에 숨겨진 비밀이 몇 개 있어.

G: 정말? 난 그것들이 궁금해. 그 비밀들은 어디에 있니?

B: 너 스스로 하나 찾아봐.

G: 어디 보자. … 오, 여기 글자들이 몇 개 보여.

B: 너 하나 찾았구나! 그것은 "Jan van Eyck가 여기 있었다. 1434."를 의미해. 그것은 라틴어야.

G: 멋지다! 다른 비밀들은?

B: 좋아. 이 개는 여기 있는 이 남자가 매우 부자였다는 것을 우리에게 말해주지.

G: 나는 이해가 안 돼.

B: 당시에 저런 종류의 개를 사려면 많은 돈을 써야 했어.

G: 알겠다. 단지 부자들만 저런 종류의 개를 살 수 있었어, 맞지?

B: 정확해. 알다시피, 그림이 천 마디 말을 하지.

1. W: 이 여자의 몸짓은 무엇을 의미하니? 난 그것이 궁금해.

   M: 내 생각에 그것은 "연못으로 뛰어들어."를 의미해.

   W: 왜 그렇게 생각하니?

   M: 그 소년은 머리 위에 많은 벌이 있어. 그리고 그 여자는 연못을 가리키고 있어.

2. W: 이 여자는 1달러를 원하지 않아. 그렇다면 그녀의 몸짓은 무엇을 의미하니?

   M: 그것은 그녀가 닭 한 마리를 원한다는 것을 의미해.

   W: 그럼 그 소년은 과일을 얻기 위해 닭을 한 마리 가져와야 하는구나, 맞지?

   M: 난 그렇게 생각해.

3. W: 이 남자의 몸짓은 무엇을 의미하니? 난 그것이 궁금해.

   M: 그것은 "그것을 꺼."를 의미해.

   W: 정말? 왜 그렇게 생각하니?

   M: 거기 있는 나머지 다른 사냥꾼이 어떤 동물 가까이 접근하고 있어.

   W: 오, 알겠어.

※ 다음 우리말과 일치하도록 빈칸에 알맞은 것을 골라 쓰시오.

1 A _____ _____ _____ a Mother _____ Three
A. from   B. Picture   C. Letter   D. of

2 _____ to family members or friends in a _____ country is _____ easy and _____ today.
A. rather   B. speaking   C. simple   D. foreign

3 But _____ the _____ of phones and the Internet, it was not _____ _____.
A. easy   B. before   C. that   D. days

4 People just _____ a letter and _____ _____ a _____ for weeks.
A. reply   B. for   C. sent   D. waited

5 And it was a _____ _____ if they _____ read or _____.
A. harder   B. write   C. lot   D. couldn't

6 This letter shows _____ people _____ _____ these _____.
A. difficulties   B. got   C. how   D. over

7 It was written in 1973 _____ a woman _____ husband was _____ _____ _____.
A. away   B. by   C. whose   D. far

8 She lived in Sicily, an Italian _____, _____ her husband _____ _____ Germany.
A. while   B. in   C. island   D. worked

9 At the time, _____ _____ 5% of the people in Italy could not read or write, and she was _____ _____ them.
A. than   B. one   C. more   D. of

10 This letter _____ _____ _____ _____ Sicilian _____ Gesualdo Bufalino.
A. by   B. discovered   C. was   D. writer

11 Here's _____ he _____ the pictures _____ _____.
A. into   B. how   C. translated   D. words

12 My dear love, I _____ you so much, and I _____ my arms _____ _____ you, together with our three kids.
A. toward   B. out   C. reach   D. miss

13 We are all _____ good health _____ _____ the _____ one.
A. for   B. little   C. except   D. in

14 He's a _____ _____, but _____ _____.
A. little   B. seriously   C. not   D. sick

15 I already _____ you a letter, but _____ was no _____, _____ I am sad about it.
A. reply   B. sent   C. there   D. so

16 If I _____ a letter _____ you, I _____ very happy.
A. be   B. got   C. would   D. from

1 세 아이의 엄마가 보낸 그림 편지

2 오늘날 외국에 있는 가족이나 친구와 대화하는 것은 다소 쉽고 간단하다.

3 하지만 전화와 인터넷 시대 이전에는 그것이 그렇게 쉽지 않았다.

4 사람들은 단지 편지를 보내고 답장을 몇 주 동안 기다렸다.

5 그리고 그들이 읽거나 쓸 수 없었다면 그건 훨씬 더 힘들었다.

6 이 편지는 사람들이 이런 어려움을 어떻게 극복했는지 보여준다.

7 그것은 남편이 멀리 떨어져 살았던 한 여자에 의해 1973년에 쓰여졌다.

8 그녀의 남편은 독일에서 일한 반면, 그녀는 이탈리아의 섬인 시실리에서 살았다.

9 그 당시에는 5% 이상의 이탈리아 사람들이 읽거나 쓸 수 없었고, 그녀도 그들 중 한 명이었다.

10 이 편지는 시실리의 작가 *Gesualdo Bufalino*가 발견하였다.

11 그가 그림들을 어떻게 글로 번역했는지는 다음과 같다.

12 사랑하는 여보, 난 당신이 정말 그립고, 우리 세 아이와 함께 당신을 향해 내 팔을 쭉 뻗고 있어요.

13 막내를 제외하고는 우리 모두 건강해요.

14 그 아이는 약간 아프지만 심각하진 않아요.

15 난 당신에게 이미 편지를 보냈지만, 답장이 없어서 그것 때문에 나는 슬퍼요.

16 당신에게서 편지를 받는다면, 나는 정말 행복할 거예요.

17 Your mother _____ _____, and I'm _____ to visit her in the hospital _____ some money and food.

    A. ill   B. with   C. fell   D. going

18 I'll go there _____ our middle son _____ the oldest _____ after the _____.

    A. looks   B. while   C. with   D. youngest

19 I _____ two workers _____ our field and _____ for 150,000 lire.

    A. plant   B. had   C. seeds   D. prepare

20 I _____ _____ the DC.

    A. for   B. voted

21 The PCI lost _____ many seats _____ it _____ dead.

    A. that   B. seems   C. almost   D. so

22 But _____ one or the _____ _____, it's the _____.

    A. other   B. whether   C. same   D. wins

23 _____ _____ for us _____ people.

    A. changes   B. poor   C. nothing

24 We _____ yesterday, and we _____ _____ _____ tomorrow.

    A. will   B. again   C. worked   D. work

25 We _____ _____ of olives _____ our olive trees _____ year.

    A. this   B. lots   C. from   D. picked

26 I _____ a man _____ sons are good _____.

    A. workers   B. whose   C. hired

27 He _____ the olives _____, and his two sons helped him, _____ them _____ from the ground.

    A. up   B. down   C. picking   D. knocked

28 I _____ him 27,000 lire _____ the _____.

    A. for   B. paid   C. work

29 I _____ 12,000 more _____ the olive _____.

    A. for   B. press   C. spent

30 I got _____ oil _____ _____ a large _____ and a small one.

    A. fill   B. enough   C. to   D. pot

31 I can _____ it _____ a _____ of 1,300 _____ a liter.

    A. lire   B. sell   C. at   D. price

32 My love, my _____ thinks _____ you _____ Christmas is _____.

    A. as   B. heart   C. coming   D. of

33 I _____ so happy _____ you _____ with me.

    A. if   B. be   C. were   D. would

34 We _____ _____ you _____ much.

    A. miss   B. all   C. so

35 I'm _____ you a _____ _____ from me and our three _____ kids.

    A. hug   B. sending   C. little   D. big

36 Goodbye, _____.

    A. love   B. dear

37 My _____ is _____, _____ to you _____ our two rings are.

    A. as   B. yours   C. joined   D. heart

---

17 당신의 어머니께서는 병이 드셨고, 나는 약간의 돈과 음식을 가지고 병원에 있는 어머니를 방문할 예정이에요.

18 큰애가 막내를 돌보는 동안 둘째와 함께 그곳에 갈 거예요.

19 나는 150,000리라에 두 일꾼을 시켜 우리 밭을 준비하고 씨앗을 심게 했어요.

20 나는 DC에 투표했어요.

21 PCI는 매우 많은 의석을 잃어서 거의 죽은 것처럼 보여요.

22 하지만 이쪽이 이기건 저쪽이 이기건, 상황은 똑같아요.

23 우리 가난한 사람들에게는 아무 것도 바뀌지 않지요.

24 우리는 어제도 일했고, 내일도 다시 일할 거예요.

25 우리는 올해 올리브나무에서 올리브를 많이 땄어요.

26 나는 아들들이 훌륭한 일꾼인 한 남자를 고용했어요.

27 그가 올리브를 쳐서 떨어뜨리면 그의 두 아들이 땅에서 올리브를 주우면서 그를 도왔어요.

28 나는 그 일을 위해 그에게 27,000리라를 지급했어요.

29 올리브 압착을 위해 12,000리라를 더 썼어요.

30 나는 큰 항아리 하나와 작은 항아리 하나를 채울 만큼 충분한 기름을 얻었어요.

31 리터당 1,300리라의 가격으로 팔 수 있을 것 같아요.

32 여보, 크리스마스가 다가오면서 내 마음은 당신을 떠올려요.

33 당신이 나와 함께 있다면 난 정말 행복할 거예요.

34 우리는 모두 당신을 매우 많이 그리워해요.

35 나와 우리 세 아이의 큰 포옹을 보내요.

36 잘 있어요, 여보.

37 내 마음은 당신의 것이에요. 우리들의 두 반지처럼 당신과 연결된 채로요.

※ 다음 우리말과 일치하도록 빈칸에 알맞은 것을 골라 쓰시오.

1 _____ _____ _____ from a Mother of Three

2 _____ to family members or friends in a _____ _____ _____ _____ easy and _____ today.

3 But _____ the days of phones and the Internet, it was not _____ _____.

4 People just _____ a letter and _____ _____ a reply _____ _____.

5 And it was _____ _____ _____ if they _____ _____ _____ _____.

6 This letter shows how people _____ _____ these difficulties.

7 It _____ _____ _____ 1973 by a woman _____ husband was _____ _____.

8 She lived in Sicily, an Italian island, _____ her husband _____ _____ _____.

9 At the time, _____ _____ _____ of the people in Italy could not read or write, and she was _____ _____ _____.

10 This letter _____ _____ _____ Sicilian _____ Gesualdo Bufalino.

11 Here's _____ he _____ the pictures _____ words.

12 My dear love, I _____ you so much, and I _____ my arms _____ _____ you, together with our three kids.

13 We are _____ _____ _____ _____ _____ _____ the little _____.

14 He's _____ _____ sick, but _____ _____.

15 I _____ sent you a letter, but _____ _____ _____, so I am sad about it.

16 If I _____ a letter from you, I _____ _____ very happy.

1 세 아이의 엄마가 보낸 그림 편지

2 오늘날 외국에 있는 가족이나 친구와 대화하는 것은 다소 쉽 고 간단하다.

3 하지만 전화와 인터넷 시대 이 전에는 그것이 그렇게 쉽지 않 았다.

4 사람들은 단지 편지를 보내고 답장을 몇 주 동안 기다렸다.

5 그리고 그들이 읽거나 쓸 수 없 었다면 그건 훨씬 더 힘들었다.

6 이 편지는 사람들이 이런 어려 움을 어떻게 극복했는지 보여 준다.

7 그것은 남편이 멀리 떨어져 살 았던 한 여자에 의해 1973년에 쓰여졌다.

8 그녀의 남편은 독일에서 일한 반면, 그녀는 이탈리아의 섬인 시실리에서 살았다.

9 그 당시에는 5% 이상의 이탈리 아 사람들이 읽거나 쓸 수 없 고, 그녀도 그들 중 한 명이었다.

10 이 편지는 시실리의 작가 Gesualdo Bufalino가 발견하였다.

11 그가 그림들을 어떻게 글로 번 역했는지는 다음과 같다.

12 사랑하는 여보, 난 당신이 정말 그 립고, 우리 세 아이와 함께 당신을 향해 내 팔을 쭉 뻗고 있어요.

13 막내를 제외하고는 우리 모두 건강해요.

14 그 아이는 약간 아프지만 심각 하진 않아요.

15 난 당신에게 이미 편지를 보냈 지만, 답장이 없어서 그것 때문 에 나는 슬퍼요.

16 당신에게서 편지를 받는다면, 나는 정말 행복할 거예요.

17 Your mother _____ _____, and I'm going to visit her in the hospital _____ some money and food.

18 I'll go there with our middle son _____ the oldest _____ _____ the _____.

19 I _____ two workers _____ our field and _____ _____ for 150,000 lire.

20 I _____ _____ the DC.

21 The PCI lost _____ many seats _____ it almost seems dead.

22 But _____ _____ _____ _____ _____ wins, it's _____ _____.

23 _____ _____ for us poor people.

24 We worked yesterday, and we _____ _____ _____ tomorrow.

25 We _____ lots of olives _____ our olive trees this year.

26 I _____ a man _____ sons are good _____.

27 He _____ the olives _____, and his two sons helped him, _____ them _____ _____ the ground.

28 I _____ him 27,000 lire _____ the work.

29 I _____ 12,000 more _____ the olive _____.

30 I got _____ oil _____ _____ a large pot and a small _____.

31 I can sell it _____ _____ _____ _____ 1,300 lire a liter.

32 My love, my heart thinks of you _____ Christmas is coming.

33 I _____ _____ so happy if you _____ _____ me.

34 We all _____ you so much.

35 I'm sending you _____ _____ _____ from me and our three _____ _____.

36 Goodbye, _____ _____.

37 My heart is yours, _____ to you _____ our two rings are.

17 당신의 어머니께서는 병이 드셨고, 나는 약간의 돈과 음식을 가지고 병원에 있는 어머니를 방문할 예정이에요.

18 큰애가 막내를 돌보는 동안 둘째와 함께 그곳에 갈 거예요.

19 나는 150,000리라에 두 일꾼을 시켜 우리 밭을 준비하고 씨앗을 심게 했어요.

20 나는 DC에 투표했어요.

21 PCI는 매우 많은 의석을 잃어서 거의 죽은 것처럼 보여요.

22 하지만 이쪽이 이기건 저쪽이 이기건, 상황은 똑같아요.

23 우리 가난한 사람들에게는 아무것도 바뀌지 않지요.

24 우리는 어제도 일했고, 내일도 다시 일할 거예요.

25 우리는 올해 올리브나무에서 올리브를 많이 땄어요.

26 나는 아들들이 훌륭한 일꾼인 한 남자를 고용했어요.

27 그가 올리브를 쳐서 떨어뜨리면 그의 두 아들이 땅에서 올리브를 주우면서 그를 도왔어요.

28 나는 그 일을 위해 그에게 27,000리라를 지급했어요.

29 올리브 압착을 위해 12,000리라를 더 썼어요.

30 나는 큰 항아리 하나와 작은 항아리 하나를 채울 만큼 충분한 기름을 얻었어요.

31 리터당 1,300리라의 가격으로 팔 수 있을 것 같아요.

32 여보, 크리스마스가 다가오면서 내 마음은 당신을 떠올려요.

33 당신이 나와 함께 있다면 난 정말 행복할 거예요.

34 우리는 모두 당신을 매우 많이 그리워해요.

35 나와 우리 세 아이의 큰 포옹을 보내요.

36 잘 있어요, 여보.

37 내 마음은 당신의 것이에요. 우리들의 두 반지처럼 당신과 연결된 채로요.

※ 다음 문장을 우리말로 쓰시오.

1 A Picture Letter from a Mother of Three

➡ _____

2 Speaking to family members or friends in a foreign country is rather easy and simple today.

➡ _____

3 But before the days of phones and the Internet, it was not that easy.

➡ _____

4 People just sent a letter and waited for a reply for weeks.

➡ _____

5 And it was a lot harder if they couldn't read or write.

➡ _____

6 This letter shows how people got over these difficulties.

➡ _____

7 It was written in 1973 by a woman whose husband was far away.

➡ _____

8 She lived in Sicily, an Italian island, while her husband worked in Germany.

➡ _____

9 At the time, more than 5% of the people in Italy could not read or write, and she was one of them.

➡ _____

10 This letter was discovered by Sicilian writer Gesualdo Bufalino.

➡ _____

11 Here's how he translated the pictures into words.

➡ _____

12 My dear love, I miss you so much, and I reach my arms out toward you, together with our three kids.

➡ _____

13 We are all in good health except for the little one.

➡ _____

14 He's a little sick, but not seriously.

➡ _____

15 I already sent you a letter, but there was no reply, so I am sad about it.

➡ _____

16 If I got a letter from you, I would be very happy.

➡ _____

17 Your mother fell ill, and I'm going to visit her in the hospital with some money and food.

➡ _____

18 ▶ I'll go there with our middle son while the oldest looks after the youngest.
➡ _____

19 ▶ I had two workers prepare our field and plant seeds for 150,000 lire.
➡ _____

20 ▶ I voted for the DC.
➡ _____

21 ▶ The PCI lost so many seats that it almost seems dead.
➡ _____

22 ▶ But whether one or the other wins, it's the same.
➡ _____

23 ▶ Nothing changes for us poor people.
➡ _____

24 ▶ We worked yesterday, and we will work again tomorrow.
➡ _____

25 ▶ We picked lots of olives from our olive trees this year.
➡ _____

26 ▶ I hired a man whose sons are good workers.
➡ _____

27 ▶ He knocked the olives down, and his two sons helped him, picking them up from the ground.
➡ _____

28 ▶ I paid him 27,000 lire for the work.
➡ _____

29 ▶ I spent 12,000 more for the olive press.
➡ _____

30 ▶ I got enough oil to fill a large pot and a small one.
➡ _____

31 ▶ I can sell it at a price of 1,300 lire a liter.
➡ _____

32 ▶ My love, my heart thinks of you as Christmas is coming.
➡ _____

33 ▶ I would be so happy if you were with me.
➡ _____

34 ▶ We all miss you so much.
➡ _____

35 ▶ I'm sending you a big hug from me and our three little kids.
➡ _____

36 ▶ Goodbye, dear love.
➡ _____

37 ▶ My heart is yours, joined to you as our two rings are.
➡ _____

※ 다음 괄호 안의 단어들을 우리말에 맞도록 바르게 배열하시오.

1 (Picture / A / from / Letter / a / Three / of / Mother)
➡ _____

2 (to / speaking / members / family / or / in / friends / a / country / foreign / easy / is / rather / and / today. / simple)
➡ _____

3 (before / but / days / the / phones / of / and / Internet, / the / was / it / that / not / easy.)
➡ _____

4 (just / people / sent / letter / a / and / for / waited / reply / a / weeks. / for)
➡ _____

5 (it / and / was / lot / a / harder / they / if / read / couldn't / write. / or)
➡ _____

6 (letter / this / shows / people / how / over / got / difficulties. / these)
➡ _____

7 (was / it / in / written / 1973 / a / by / whose / woman / was / husband / away. / far)
➡ _____

8 (lived / she / Sicily, / in / Italian / an / island, / her / while / worked / husband / Germany. / in)
➡ _____

9 (the / at / time, / than / more / 5% / the / of / people / Italy / in / not / could / write, / or / read / and / was / she / of / one / them.)
➡ _____

10 (letter / this / discovered / was / Sicilian / by / writer / Bufalino. / Gesualdo)
➡ _____

11 (how / here's / translated / he / pictures / the / words. / into)
➡ _____

12 (dear / my / love, / miss / I / so / you / much, / and / reach / I / arms / my / toward / out / you, / with / together / three / our / kids.)
➡ _____

13 (are / we / in / all / health / good / for / except / little / the / one.)
➡ _____

14 (a / he's / little / sick, / not / but / seriously.)
➡ _____

15 (already / I / sent / a / you / letter, / there / but / no / was / reply, / I / so / am / about / sad / it.)
➡ _____

16 (I / if / got / letter / a / you, / from / would / I / very / be / happy.)
➡ _____

17 (mother / your / ill, / fell / and / going / I'm / visit / to / in / her / hospital / the / with / money / some / food. / and)
➡ _____

18 (go / I'll / with / there / our / son / middle / the / while / looks / oldest / the / after / youngest.)
➡ _____

1 세 아이의 엄마가 보낸 그림 편지

2 오늘날 외국에 있는 가족이나 친구와 대화하는 것은 다소 쉽고 간단하다.

3 하지만 전화와 인터넷 시대 이전에는 그것이 그렇게 쉽지 않았다.

4 사람들은 단지 편지를 보내고 답장을 몇 주 동안 기다렸다.

5 그리고 그들이 읽거나 쓸 수 없었다면 그건 훨씬 더 힘들었다.

6 이 편지는 사람들이 이런 어려움을 어떻게 극복했는지 보여준다.

7 그것은 남편이 멀리 떨어져 살았던 한 여자에 의해 1973년에 쓰여졌다.

8 그녀의 남편은 독일에서 일한 반면, 그녀는 이탈리아의 섬인 시실리에서 살았다.

9 그 당시에는 5% 이상의 이탈리아 사람들이 읽거나 쓸 수 없었고, 그녀도 그들 중 한 명이었디.

10 이 편지는 시실리의 작가 Gesualdo Bufalino가 발견하였다.

11 그가 그림들을 어떻게 글로 번역했는지는 다음과 같다.

12 사랑하는 여보, 난 당신이 정말 그립고, 우리 세 아이와 함께 당신을 향해 내 팔을 쭉 뻗고 있어요.

13 막내를 제외하고는 우리 모두 건강해요.

14 그 아이는 약간 아프지만 심각하진 않아요.

15 난 당신에게 이미 편지를 보냈지만, 답장이 없어서 그것 때문에 나는 슬퍼요.

16 당신에게서 편지를 받는다면, 나는 정말 행복할 거예요.

17 당신의 어머니께서는 병이 드셨고, 나는 약간의 돈과 음식을 가지고 병원에 있는 어머니를 방문할 예정이에요.

18 큰애가 막내를 돌보는 동안 둘째와 함께 그곳에 갈 거예요.

19 (had / I / two / prepare / workers / field / our / and / seeds / plant / for / lire. / 150,000)
➡ _____

20 (voted / I / the / for / DC.)
➡ _____

21 (PCI / the / so / lost / seats / many / that / almost / it / dead. / seems)
➡ _____

22 (whether / but / or / one / other / the / wins, / the / it's / same.)
➡ _____

23 (changes / nothing / us / for / people. / poor)
➡ _____

24 (worked / we / yesterday, / we / and / will / again / work / tomorrow.)
➡ _____

25 (picked / we / of / lots / olives / our / from / olive / this / trees / year.)
➡ _____

26 (hired / I / man / a / whose / are / sons / workers. / good)
➡ _____

27 (knocked / he / olives / the / down, / and / two / his / helped / sons / him, / them / picking / up / the / from / ground.)
➡ _____

28 (paid / I / him / lire / 27,000 / for / work. / the)
➡ _____

29 (spent / I / 12,000 / for / more / olive / the / press.)
➡ _____

30 (got / I / enough / to / oil / fill / large / a / pot / and / a / one. / small)
➡ _____

31 (can / I / sell / at / it / price / a / of / lire / 1,300 / liter. / a)
➡ _____

32 (love, / my / heart / my / thinks / of / as / you / is / Christmas / coming.)
➡ _____

33 (would / I / so / be / happy / you / if / with / were / me.)
➡ _____

34 (all / we / you / miss / much. / so)
➡ _____

35 (sending / I'm / a / you / big / from / hug / and / me / our / little / three / kids.)
➡ _____

36 (dear / goodbye, / love.)
➡ _____

37 (heart / my / yours, / is / to / joined / you / our / as / rings / two / are.)
➡ _____

19 나는 150,000리라에 두 일꾼을 시켜 우리 밭을 준비하고 씨앗을 심게 했어요.

20 나는 DC에 투표했어요.

21 PCI는 매우 많은 의석을 잃어서 거의 죽은 것처럼 보여요.

22 하지만 이쪽이 이기건 저쪽이 이기건, 상황은 똑같아요.

23 우리 가난한 사람들에게는 아무것도 바뀌지 않지요.

24 우리는 어제도 일했고, 내일도 다시 일할 거예요.

25 우리는 올해 올리브나무에서 올리브를 많이 땄어요.

26 나는 아들들이 훌륭한 일꾼인 한 남자를 고용했어요.

27 그가 올리브를 쳐서 떨어뜨리면 그의 두 아들이 땅에서 올리브를 주우면서 그를 도왔어요.

28 나는 그 일을 위해 그에게 27,000리라를 지급했어요.

29 올리브 압착을 위해 12,000리라를 더 썼어요.

30 나는 큰 항아리 하나와 작은 항아리 하나를 채울 만큼 충분한 기름을 얻었어요.

31 리터당 1,300리라의 가격으로 팔 수 있을 것 같아요.

32 여보, 크리스마스가 다가오면서 내 마음은 당신을 떠올려요.

33 당신이 나와 함께 있다면 난 정말 행복할 거예요.

34 우리는 모두 당신을 매우 많이 그리워해요.

35 나와 우리 세 아이의 큰 포옹을 보내요.

36 잘 있어요, 여보.

37 내 마음은 당신의 것이에요. 우리들의 두 반지처럼 당신과 연결된 채로요.

※ 다음 우리말을 영어로 쓰시오.

1 세 아이의 엄마가 보낸 그림 편지
➡ _____

2 오늘날 외국에 있는 가족이나 친구와 대화하는 것은 다소 쉽고 간단하다.
➡ _____

3 하지만 전화와 인터넷 시대 이전에는 그것이 그렇게 쉽지 않았다.
➡ _____

4 사람들은 단지 편지를 보내고 답장을 몇 주 동안 기다렸다.
➡ _____

5 그리고 그들이 읽거나 쓸 수 없었다면 그건 훨씬 더 힘들었다.
➡ _____

6 이 편지는 사람들이 이런 어려움을 어떻게 극복했는지 보여 준다.
➡ _____

7 그것은 남편이 멀리 떨어져 살았던 한 여자에 의해 1973년에 쓰여졌다.
➡ _____

8 그녀의 남편은 독일에서 일한 반면, 그녀는 이탈리아의 섬인 시실리에서 살았다.
➡ _____

9 그 당시에는 5% 이상의 이탈리아 사람들이 읽거나 쓸 수 없었고, 그녀도 그들 중 한 명이었다.
➡ _____

10 이 편지는 시실리의 작가 Gesualdo Bufalino가 발견하였다.
➡ _____

11 그가 그림들을 어떻게 글로 번역했는지는 다음과 같다.
➡ _____

12 사랑하는 여보, 난 당신이 정말 그립고, 우리 세 아이와 함께 당신을 향해 내 팔을 쭉 뻗고 있어요.
➡ _____

13 막내를 제외하고는 우리 모두 건강해요.
➡ _____

14 그 아이는 약간 아프지만 심각하진 않아요.
➡ _____

15 난 당신에게 이미 편지를 보냈지만, 답장이 없어서 그것 때문에 나는 슬퍼요.
➡ _____

16 당신에게서 편지를 받는다면, 나는 정말 행복할 거예요.
➡ _____

17 당신의 어머니께서는 병이 드셨고, 나는 약간의 돈과 음식을 가지고 병원에 있는 어머니를 방문할 예정이에요.
➡ _____

18 큰애가 막내를 돌보는 동안 둘째와 함께 그곳에 갈 거예요.
➡ _____

19 나는 150,000리라에 두 일꾼을 시켜 우리 밭을 준비하고 씨앗을 심게 했어요.
➡ _____

20 나는 DC에 투표했어요.
➡ _____

21 PCI는 매우 많은 의석을 잃어서 거의 죽은 것처럼 보여요.
➡ _____

22 하지만 이쪽이 이기건 저쪽이 이기건, 상황은 똑같아요.
➡ _____

23 우리 가난한 사람들에게는 아무 것도 바뀌지 않지요.
➡ _____

24 우리는 어제도 일했고, 내일도 다시 일할 거예요.
➡ _____

25 우리는 올해 올리브나무에서 올리브를 많이 땄어요.
➡ _____

26 나는 아들들이 훌륭한 일꾼인 한 남자를 고용했어요.
➡ _____

27 그가 올리브를 쳐서 떨어뜨리면 그의 두 아들이 땅에서 올리브를 주우면서 그를 도왔어요.
➡ _____

28 나는 그 일을 위해 그에게 27,000리라를 지급했어요.
➡ _____

29 올리브 압착을 위해 12,000리라를 더 썼어요.
➡ _____

30 나는 큰 항아리 하나와 작은 항아리 하나를 채울 만큼 충분한 기름을 얻었어요.
➡ _____

31 리터당 1,300리라의 가격으로 팔 수 있을 것 같아요.
➡ _____

32 여보, 크리스마스가 다가오면서 내 마음은 당신을 떠올려요.
➡ _____

33 당신이 나와 함께 있다면 난 정말 행복할 거예요.
➡ _____

34 우리는 모두 당신을 매우 많이 그리워해요.
➡ _____

35 나와 우리 세 아이의 큰 포옹을 보내요.
➡ _____

36 잘 있어요, 여보.
➡ _____

37 내 마음은 당신의 것이에요, 우리들의 두 반지처럼 당신과 연결된 채로요.
➡ _____

※ 다음 우리말과 일치하도록 빈칸에 알맞은 말을 쓰시오.

Express Yourself C1

1. The boy _____ head _____ _____ _____ bees _____
_____ the woman's gesture.

2. I think it _____ "_____ _____ the pond."

3. If I _____ the boy, I _____ _____ _____ the pond
_____ _____.

1. 머리가 벌로 덮인 소년은 그 여자의 몸
짓을 이해하지 못합니다.
2. 제 생각에 그것은 "연못으로 뛰어들
어."를 의미합니다.
3. 제가 그 소년이라면, 저는 당장 연못
으로 뛰어들겠습니다.

Project Do It Yourself

1. "_____ _____ the mountain."

2. If I _____ soldiers to lead, I _____ _____ _____ _____
_____ my messages.

3. For example, I _____ _____ a kite _____ face _____
_____ a mountain to _____ _____ _____ _____ up
the mountain.

1. "산 위로 올라가라."
2. 내가 병사를 지휘한다면, 나는 나의 메
시지를 보내기 위해 연을 사용하겠다.
3. 예를 들어, 나는 병사들이 산 위로 올
라가게 하려고 앞면이 산처럼 보이는
연을 날리겠다.

Link to the World

1. Hangeul _____ _____ _____ King Sejong.

2. _____ _____, many people _____ _____ _____
_____ this new _____ _____.

3. _____, King Sejong _____ _____ _____ _____ people
_____ Hangeul.

4. _____ _____ him, we _____ _____ _____ _____
Hangeul now.

5. If we _____ _____ Hangeul, we _____ _____ _____
_____ easily.

1. 한글은 세종대왕에 의해 창제되었다.
2. 처음에는 많은 사람이 이 새로운 문자
체계를 사용하는 것을 원하지 않았다.
3. 하지만, 세종대왕은 사람들이 한글을 사
용하도록 돕기 위해 열심히 노력했다.
4. 그분 덕택에, 우리는 지금 한글로 무
엇이든 표현할 수 있다.
5. 우리가 한글을 모른다면, 우리 자신을
쉽게 표현할 수 없을 것이다.

※ 다음 우리말을 영어로 쓰시오.

Express Yourself C1

1. 머리가 벌로 덮인 소년은 그 여자의 몸짓을 이해하지 못합니다.

   ➡ _____

2. 제 생각에 그것은 "연못으로 뛰어들어."를 의미합니다.

   ➡ _____

3. 제가 그 소년이라면, 저는 당장 연못으로 뛰어들겠습니다.

   ➡ _____

Project Do It Yourself

1. "산 위로 올라가라."

   ➡ _____

2. 내가 병사를 지휘한다면, 나는 나의 메시지를 보내기 위해 연을 사용하겠다.

   ➡ _____

3. 예를 들어, 나는 병사들이 산 위로 올라가게 하려고 앞면이 산처럼 보이는 연을 날리겠다.

   ➡ _____

   _____

Link to the World

1. 한글은 세종대왕에 의해 창제되었다.

   ➡ _____

2. 처음에는 많은 사람이 이 새로운 문자 체계를 사용하는 것을 원하지 않았다.

   ➡ _____

3. 하지만, 세종대왕은 사람들이 한글을 사용하도록 돕기 위해 열심히 노력했다.

   ➡ _____

4. 그분 덕택에, 우리는 지금 한글로 무엇이든 표현할 수 있다.

   ➡ _____

5. 우리가 한글을 모른다면, 우리 자신을 쉽게 표현할 수 없을 것이다.

   ➡ _____

Step1

※ 다음 영어를 우리말로 쓰시오.

01 produce

02 available

03 filter

04 disease

05 facial

06 artwork

07 public

08 potter

09 connect

10 publisher

11 artistic

12 register

13 actually

14 relax

15 3D print

16 collect

17 traditional

18 provide

19 weight

20 colorful

21 company

22 seed

23 length

24 tear

25 tiny

26 cheerful

27 display

28 drinkable

29 proud

30 beat

31 figure

32 impossible

33 necessary

34 object

35 by hand

36 tear out

37 pick up

38 take a bath

39 find out

40 both A and B

41 give away

42 not ~ anymore

43 think of … as ~

※ 다음 우리말을 영어로 쓰시오.

01 전통적인	_____	22 ~을 거르다, 여과하다	_____
02 이용할 수 있는	_____	23 얼굴의	_____
03 생산하다, 산출하다	_____	24 예술품, 공예품	_____
04 예술적인	_____	25 가능한	_____
05 물리치다	_____	26 붓다, 따르다	_____
06 모으다	_____	27 출판업자, 출판사	_____
07 ~을 찢다, 뜯어내다	_____	28 등록하다	_____
08 (마음의) 긴장을 풀다	_____	29 필요한	_____
09 화려한	_____	30 물체	_____
10 자랑으로 여기는	_____	31 길이	_____
11 연결하다	_____	32 씨앗	_____
12 질병, 질환	_____	33 3차원 인쇄를 하다	_____
13 회사	_____	34 아주 작은	_____
14 무게, 중량	_____	35 알아내다	_____
15 제공하다	_____	36 집어들다	_____
16 사실, 실제로	_____	37 찢다	_____
17 유쾌한, 기분 좋은	_____	38 손으로	_____
18 전시, 진열	_____	39 목욕하다	_____
19 공공의, 공중의	_____	40 …을 ~으로 생각하다	_____
20 마실 수 있는	_____	41 A와 B 둘 다	_____
21 (사람, 동물의) 상, 모양	_____	42 남에게 주다, 나누어 주다	_____
		43 더 이상 ~ 않다	_____

※ 다음 영영풀이에 알맞은 단어를 <보기>에서 골라 쓴 후, 우리말 뜻을 쓰시오.

1 _____ : extremely small: _____

2 _____ : a store that sells books: _____

3 _____ : clean and safe to drink: _____

4 _____ : relating to people in general: _____

5 _____ : a measurement of how long something is: _____

6 _____ : to make a liquid flow out of a container: _____

7 _____ : to pull apart or to pull pieces off: _____

8 _____ : to remove unwanted substances from liquids or gases: _____

9 _____ : a person or company that prints books: _____

10 _____ : a person who makes pottery by hand: _____

11 _____ : to put someone's or something's name on an official list: _____

12 _____ : a measurement that indicates how heavy a person or thing is: _____

13 _____ : to put something somewhere, especially in a place where it will stay: _____

14 _____ : to put something in a place where people can see it easily: _____

15 _____ : the small hard part produced by a plant, from which a new plant can grow: _____

16 _____ : to produce words, numbers, pictures, etc. on paper by using a machine: _____

보기

print	pour	seed	filter
weight	drinkable	publisher	bookstore
leave	length	display	tear
register	tiny	potter	public

※ 다음 우리말과 일치하도록 빈칸에 알맞은 말을 쓰시오.

해석

Get Ready 2

(1) G: _____ do you like _____, _____ dolls or digital _____?
   B: I like digital artwork _____. _____, I don't like dolls much.

(2) G: _____ _____ _____ _____, paper _____ or _____ block _____?
   B: I _____ wood block _____.
   G: Me, too. _____ go to look at _____ _____ _____.

(3) G: _____ do you _____, _____ paper or making _____?
   B: I _____ _____ _____. It's fun and a great _____ _____ _____.

(1) G: 너는 헝겊 인형과 디지털 예술품 중에서 어떤 것을 더 좋아하니?
   B: 나는 디지털 예술품이 더 좋아. 사실, 나는 인형을 별로 좋아하지 않아.
(2) G: 너는 회화 작품과 나무 블록으로 만든 모형 중에서 어떤 것을 더 좋아하니?
   B: 나는 나무 블록으로 만든 모형이 더 좋아.
   G: 나도 그래. 그것 중에서 몇 개를 보러 가자.
(3) G: 너는 종이접기와 옷 만들기 중에서 어떤 것을 더 좋아하니?
   B: 나는 종이접기가 더 좋아. 재미있고 긴장을 풀 수 있는 좋은 방법이야.

Start Off - Listen & Talk A

1. G: _____ _____ _____ make something with jean _____?
   B: Great! _____ _____ _____ make?
   G: _____ do you prefer, a pocket _____ or a cell phone _____?
   B: I _____ a cell phone _____. It'll be easier _____ _____. And I _____ _____ too much time _____ things.
   G: Okay. _____ make a cute cell phone holder _____.

2. B: _____ _____ _____ make a bag _____ old jeans?
   G: Great! _____ _____ of bag are we going _____ _____ _____?
   B: _____ do you _____, a shoulder bag or a hand bag?
   G: I prefer a shoulder bag. _____, I _____ _____ things _____ my hands.
   B: Okay. _____ _____ a shoulder bag _____.

1. G: 청바지 주머니로 뭔가 만들어 보는 게 어떨까?
   B: 좋아! 뭘 만들까?
   G: 너는 주머니를 붙인 판과 휴대 전화 주머니 중에서 어떤 것을 더 좋아하니?
   B: 나는 휴대 전화 주머니가 더 좋아. 만들기가 더 쉬울 거야. 그리고 나는 뭔가를 만드는 데 시간을 너무 많이 들이는 걸 몹시 싫어해.
   G: 좋아. 귀여운 휴대 전화 주머니를 함께 만들자.
2. B: 우리 낡은 청바지로 가방을 하나 만드는 게 어떨까?
   G: 좋아! 어떤 종류의 가방을 만들 건데?
   B: 너는 어깨에 메는 가방과 손에 드는 가방 중에서 어떤 것을 더 좋아하니?
   G: 나는 어깨에 메는 가방이 더 좋아. 사실, 나는 손에 물건을 드는 것을 몹시 싫어해.
   B: 좋아. 어깨에 메는 가방을 함께 만들자.

Start Off - Listen & Talk B

G: Junha, what are you doing _____ _____?
B: I'm making a _____ _____ _____ you.
G: That's great! What are you _____ _____ _____ on it?
B: _____ _____ _____ _____, pandas or cats?
G: I _____ cats. They're _____.
B: Okay. Let me _____ a _____ cat on this pencil case.
G: Thanks! _____ _____ _____ _____ it!

G: 준하야, 청바지로 뭐 해?
B: 너에게 줄 필통을 만들고 있어.
G: 멋지다! 그 위에 뭘 그릴 거야?
B: 너는 판다랑 고양이 중에서 어떤 것을 더 좋아하니?
G: 나는 고양이를 더 좋아해. 고양이는 사랑스러워.
B: 좋아. 내가 이 필통 위에 사랑스러운 고양이를 그려 줄게.
G: 고마워! 몹시 기다려진다!

Start Off - Speak Up

A: Can I _____ your book-making project?

B: _____. _____ do you _____, paper books _____ digital books?

A: I _____ digital books. Actually, I hate _____ paper books.

B: Okay. _____ me _____ you _____ the digital book team.

Start Off - Your Turn

A: _____ do you prefer, _____ the bus or _____ the subway?

B: I _____ _____ _____ _____. Actually, I _____ _____ the bus.

Step Up - Real-life Scene

Minji: Seho, the book club day is _____ one week _____.

Seho: Right, Minji. I'm _____ _____ we've _____ so many _____ books _____ _____ _____.

Minji: Now, _____ _____ some gifts for visitors. Do you have _____ good ideas?

Seho: How about _____ _____?

Minji: Great idea! _____ write cheerful messages on them, too.

Seho: Okay. _____ do you _____, making the bookmarks or _____ the messages?

Minji: _____, I hate _____. I'd like to make the bookmarks.

Seho: _____ _____. I'll write the _____ _____.

Minji: I'm _____ they will love our _____.

Express Yourself A

1. G: Which do you prefer, _____ kites or _____ _____?
   B: I _____ _____ kites.
   G: Why is that?
   B: I hate _____ with _____.

2. B: _____ do you prefer, _____ masks or _____ food art?
   G: I like _____, but _____ is _____ food art _____ I _____.
   B: Why is that?
   G: I love making _____ _____.

A: 너희 책 만들기 프로젝트에 내가 함께 해도 될까?
B: 물론이지. 너는 종이책과 전자책 중에서 어떤 것을 더 좋아하니?
A: 나는 전자책을 더 좋아해. 사실, 나는 종이책 만들기를 몹시 싫어해.
B: 알았어. 전자책 팀에 너를 소개할게.

A: 너는 버스 타기와 지하철 타기 중에서 어떤 것을 더 좋아하니?
B: 나는 지하철 타기를 더 좋아해. 사실, 나는 버스 타기를 몹시 싫어해.

민지: 세호야, 독서 동아리의 날이 겨우 한 주 남았어.
세호: 맞아, 민지야. 나는 우리가 나눠 줄 재미있는 책을 많이 모아서 자랑스러워.
민지: 이제, 방문객들에게 줄 선물을 준비하자. 좋은 생각 있어?
세호: 책갈피를 만드는 게 어떨까?
민지: 좋은 생각이야! 거기에 기분 좋은 메시지도 쓰자.
세호: 그래. 너는 책갈피 만들기와 메시지 쓰기 중에서 어떤 것을 더 좋아하니?
민지: 사실, 나는 글쓰기를 몹시 싫어해. 나는 책갈피를 만들고 싶어.
세호: 문제없어. 내가 기분 좋은 메시지를 쓸게.
민지: 틀림없이 사람들이 우리가 만든 책갈피를 좋아할 거야.

1. G: 너는 연날리기와 드론 날리기 중에서 어떤 것을 더 좋아하니?
   B: 나는 연날리기를 더 좋아해.
   G: 왜 그런데?
   B: 나는 기계를 작동하는 것을 몹시 싫어해.
2. B: 너는 가면 만들기와 푸드 아트 만들기 중에서 어떤 것을 더 좋아하니?
   G: 나는 둘 다 좋지만, 내가 더 좋아하는 것은 푸드 아트 만들기야.
   B: 왜 그런데?
   G: 나는 맛있는 것을 만들기를 좋아해.

※ 다음 우리말에 맞도록 대화를 영어로 쓰시오.

Get Ready 2

(1) G: _____

    B: _____

(2) G: _____

    B: _____

    G: _____

(3) G: _____

    B: _____

Start Off - Listen & Talk A

1. G: _____

    B: _____

    G: _____

    B: _____

    _____

    G: _____

2. B: _____

    G: _____

    B: _____

    G: _____

    B: _____

Start Off - Listen & Talk B

G: _____

B: _____

G: _____

B: _____

G: _____

B: _____

G: _____

(1) G: 너는 헝겊 인형과 디지털 예술품 중에서 어떤 것을 더 좋아하니?
    B: 나는 디지털 예술품이 더 좋아. 사실, 나는 인형을 별로 좋아하지 않아.
(2) G: 너는 회화 작품과 나무 블록으로 만든 모형 중에서 어떤 것을 더 좋아하니?
    B: 나는 나무 블록으로 만든 모형이 더 좋아.
    G: 나도 그래. 그것 중에서 몇 개를 보러 가자.
(3) G: 너는 종이접기와 옷 만들기 중에서 어떤 것을 더 좋아하니?
    B: 나는 종이접기가 더 좋아. 재미있고 긴장을 풀 수 있는 좋은 방법이야.

1. G: 청바지 주머니로 뭔가 만들어 보는 게 어떨까?
    B: 좋아! 뭘 만들까?
    G: 너는 주머니를 붙인 판과 휴대 전화 주머니 중에서 어떤 것을 더 좋아하니?
    B: 나는 휴대 전화 주머니가 더 좋아. 만들기가 더 쉬울 거야. 그리고 나는 뭔가를 만드는 데 시간을 너무 많이 들이는 걸 몹시 싫어해.
    G: 좋아. 귀여운 휴대 전화 주머니를 함께 만들자.
2. B: 우리 낡은 청바지로 가방을 하나 만드는 게 어떨까?
    G: 좋아! 어떤 종류의 가방을 만들 건데?
    B: 너는 어깨에 메는 가방과 손에 드는 가방 중에서 어떤 것을 더 좋아하니?
    G: 나는 어깨에 메는 가방이 더 좋아. 사실, 나는 손에 물건을 드는 것을 몹시 싫어해.
    B: 좋아. 어깨에 메는 가방을 함께 만들자.

G: 준하야, 청바지로 뭐 해?
B: 너에게 줄 필통을 만들고 있어.
G: 멋지다! 그 위에 뭘 그릴 거야?
B: 너는 판다랑 고양이 중에서 어떤 것을 더 좋아하니?
G: 나는 고양이를 더 좋아해. 고양이는 사랑스러워.
B: 좋아. 내가 이 필통 위에 사랑스러운 고양이를 그려 줄게.
G: 고마워! 몹시 기다려진다!

Start Off - Speak Up

A: _____

B: _____

A: _____

B: _____

Start Off - Your Turn

A: _____

B: _____

Step Up - Real-life Scene

Minji: _____

Seho: _____

_____

Minji: _____

Seho: _____

Minji: _____

Seho: _____

Minji: _____

Seho: _____

Minji: _____

Express Yourself A

1. G: _____

   B: _____

   G: _____

   B: _____

2. B: _____

   G: _____

   B: _____

   G: _____

A: 너희 책 만들기 프로젝트에 내가 함께 해도 될까?

B: 물론이지. 너는 종이책과 전자책 중에서 어떤 것을 더 좋아하니?

A: 나는 전자책을 더 좋아해. 사실, 나는 종이책 만들기를 몹시 싫어해.

B: 알았어. 전자책 팀에 너를 소개할게.

A: 너는 버스 타기와 지하철 타기 중에서 어떤 것을 더 좋아하니?

B: 나는 지하철 타기를 더 좋아해. 사실, 나는 버스 타기를 몹시 싫어해.

민지: 세호야, 독서 동아리의 날이 겨우 한 주 남았어.

세호: 맞아, 민지야. 나는 우리가 나눠 줄 재미있는 책을 많이 모아서 자랑스러워.

민지: 이제, 방문객들에게 줄 선물을 준비하자. 좋은 생각 있어?

세호: 책갈피를 만드는 게 어떨까?

민지: 좋은 생각이야! 거기에 기분 좋은 메시지도 쓰자.

세호: 그래. 너는 책갈피 만들기와 메시지 쓰기 중에서 어떤 것을 더 좋아하니?

민지: 사실, 나는 글쓰기를 몹시 싫어해. 나는 책갈피를 만들고 싶어.

세호: 문제없어. 내가 기분 좋은 메시지를 쓸게.

민지: 틀림없이 사람들이 우리가 만든 책갈피를 좋아할 거야.

1. G: 너는 연날리기와 드론 날리기 중에서 어떤 것을 더 좋아하니?

   B: 나는 연날리기를 더 좋아해.

   G: 왜 그런데?

   B: 나는 기계를 작동하는 것을 몹시 싫어해.

2. B: 너는 가면 만들기와 푸드 아트 만들기 중에서 어떤 것을 더 좋아하니?

   G: 나는 둘 다 좋지만, 내가 더 좋아하는 것은 푸드 아트 만들기야.

   B: 왜 그런데?

   G: 나는 맛있는 것을 만들기를 좋아해.

※ 다음 우리말과 일치하도록 빈칸에 알맞은 것을 골라 쓰시오.

1 _____ Book Is _____!
A. Amazing   B. This

2 Most people _____ of books as _____ paper _____ to _____.
A. read   B. think   C. books   D. traditional

3 _____, _____ are many _____ books _____ you.
A. around   B. there   C. unique   D. however

4 _____ _____ about _____ _____ of these books.
A. few   B. let's   C. a   D. learn

5 _____ _____!
A. Travel   B. Books

6 I _____ this _____ book _____ a park bench yesterday.
A. on   B. found   C. old

7 A _____ on the cover _____, " _____ Book!
A. read   B. free   C. note

8 _____ _____ _____ and read me!"
A. home   B. take   C. me

9 _____, this book _____ an ID number and _____ _____ on a website.
A. registered   B. actually   C. had   D. was

10 When I entered the number online, I found _____ that the book had _____ to many countries and that a _____ of readers in _____ countries had read it before me.
A. different   B. out   C. traveled   D. number

11 _____ was _____ _____?
A. that   B. how   C. possible

12 _____ is a _____ _____.
A. project   B. there   C. book-sharing

13 First, _____ your book _____ and _____ an ID number.
A. register   B. get   C. online

14 Next, _____ it in a _____ _____.
A. public   B. leave   C. place

---

1 이 책은 놀라워요!

2 대부분의 사람은 책을 읽기 위한 전통적인 종이책으로 생각합니다.

3 하지만, 여러분 주변에는 독특한 책이 많이 있습니다.

4 이러한 책 중 몇 가지에 대해 배워 봅시다.

5 책이 여행합니다!

6 저는 어제 공원 벤치에서 이 낡은 책을 발견했습니다.

7 표지 위의 쪽지에 "공짜 책이에요!

8 저를 집으로 데려가서 읽어 주세요!"라고 쓰여 있었습니다.

9 사실, 이 책은 ID 번호가 있고 웹사이트에 등록되어 있었어요.

10 제가 온라인으로 그 번호를 입력했을 때, 저는 그 책이 많은 나라를 여행하고 다른 나라의 많은 독자가 저보다 앞서 이 책을 읽었다는 것을 알아냈습니다.

11 그게 어떻게 가능했을까요?

12 책을 공유하는 프로젝트가 있습니다.

13 우선, 온라인에 여러분의 책을 등록하고 ID 번호를 얻으세요.

14 그다음, 그것을 공공장소에 놓아두세요.

15 When the next _____ finds your book and _____ _____ to the website, you can _____ where your book is.

    A. back   B. check   C. reports   D. reader

16 This _____, the _____ world can _____ a big _____.

    A. whole   B. become   C. way   D. library

17 The _____ books we _____, _____ more we _____.

    A. share   B. more   C. learn   D. the

18 The _____ _____

    A. Book   B. Drinkable

19 This _____ book is really _____ to people _____ my _____.

    A. tiny   B. town   C. important   D. in

20 It _____ _____ the _____ and the _____ necessary to make clean drinking water.

    A. both   B. tools   C. information   D. provides

21 It _____ _____ the _____ Book.

    A. called   B. is   C. Drinkable

22 You cannot _____ drink the book, but you can _____ it _____ a _____.

    A. filter   B. actually   C. as   D. use

23 Simply _____ _____ a page and _____ dirty water _____ it.

    A. pour   B. tear   C. on   D. out

24 _____ the water goes _____ the page, it _____ clean drinking water.

    A. into   B. as   C. through   D. changes

25 _____ is this _____ water _____ you can _____.

    A. filtered   B. drink   C. that   D. it

26 This is _____ _____ the book is _____ of _____ filter paper.

    A. because   B. made   C. special   D. possible

27 This _____ book _____ the lives of many children _____ that come from dirty water.

    A. diseases   B. saves   C. from   D. amazing

---

15 다음 독자가 여러분의 책을 발견해서 그 웹사이트에 다시 알릴 때, 여러분은 책이 어디 있는지 확인할 수 있습니다.

16 이런 식으로, 전 세계가 하나의 큰 도서관이 될 수 있습니다.

17 우리가 더 많은 책을 공유할수록, 우리는 더 많이 배웁니다.

18 마실 수 있는 책

19 이 작은 책은 우리 마을 사람들에게는 정말로 중요합니다.

20 그것은 깨끗한 마실 물을 만드는 데 필요한 정보와 도구 둘 다를 제공합니다.

21 그것은 '마실 수 있는 책'이라고 불립니다.

22 여러분은 실제로 그 책을 마실 수는 없지만, 그것을 필터로 사용할 수 있습니다.

23 그냥 한 페이지를 떼어 내서 그 위에 더러운 물을 부으세요.

24 물이 그 페이지를 통과하면서, 깨끗한 마실 물로 바뀝니다.

25 여러분이 마실 수 있는 것은 이 여과된 물입니다.

26 책이 특별한 여과지로 만들어졌기 때문에 이것이 가능합니다.

27 이 놀라운 책은 더러운 물로 생기는 질병으로부터 많은 어린이의 생명을 구합니다.

28 The _____ _____
    A. Project   B. Tree-Book-Tree

29 This is the _____ _____ book that I _____ ever _____.
    A. seen   B. amazing   C. have   D. most

30 After you _____ _____ this book, _____ it and _____ it.
    A. plant   B. water   C. reading   D. finish

31 You will _____ _____ _____ _____ on the book.
    A. growing   B. new   C. see   D. leaves

32 In _____ bookstores in my town, you can see a _____ of this book _____ new _____.
    A. copy   B. leaves   C. producing   D. some

33 The _____ is that the book _____ _____ in _____ page.
    A. each   B. secret   C. seeds   D. has

34 It is these _____ _____ that _____ the book _____ a tree.
    A. into   B. seeds   C. change   D. tiny

35 This book was _____ _____ a small _____ book _____ in Argentina.
    A. publisher   B. by   C. children's   D. made

36 Though the company does _____ print this book _____, this special project makes us _____ about where books come _____.
    A. anymore   B. from   C. not   D. think

37 These are _____ _____ _____ of the _____ books you can find.
    A. unique   B. few   C. a   D. just

38 _____ _____ _____ do you want to make?
    A. unique   B. what   C. books   D. other

39 What special project _____ you _____ _____ _____ with the books?
    A. to   B. would   C. do   D. like

40 The _____ your _____ is, the _____ your books will become.
    A. imagination   B. wonderful   C. bigger   D. more

---

28 나무-책-나무 프로젝트

29 이것은 제가 지금까지 본 것 중에서 가장 놀라운 책입니다.

30 여러분이 이 책을 다 읽은 후에, 그것을 심고 물을 주세요.

31 여러분은 책에서 새잎이 자라는 것을 보게 될 거예요.

32 우리 마을의 몇몇 서점에서, 여러분은 이 책 한 권이 새잎을 내는 것을 볼 수 있습니다.

33 비밀은 책이 각 페이지 안에 씨앗을 갖고 있다는 것입니다.

34 책을 나무로 변화시키는 것은 이 아주 작은 씨앗들이에요.

35 이 책은 아르헨티나에 있는 한 작은 아동 도서 출판사에 의해 만들어졌습니다.

36 그 회사가 더는 이 책을 발행하지는 않지만, 이 특별한 프로젝트는 우리에게 책이 어디에서 오는지에 대해 생각하게 해 줍니다.

37 이것들은 여러분이 찾을 수 있는 독특한 책 중의 단지 몇 가지입니다.

38 여러분은 어떤 다른 독특한 책을 만들기 원하나요?

39 여러분은 책으로 어떤 특별한 프로젝트를 하고 싶나요?

40 여러분의 상상이 크면 클수록, 여러분의 책은 더 훌륭해질 것입니다.

※ 다음 우리말과 일치하도록 빈칸에 알맞은 것을 골라 쓰시오.

1 _____ Book Is _____!

2 Most people _____ _____ books _____ _____ _____ _____ to read.

3 However, there _____ many _____ books _____ you.

4 _____ learn about _____ _____ of these books.

5 Books _____!

6 I _____ this _____ _____ on a park bench yesterday.

7 A _____ on the cover _____, " _____ Book!

8 _____ _____ _____ and read me!"

9 _____, this book had an _____ _____ and _____ _____ on a website.

10 When I entered the number online, I _____ _____ that the book _____ _____ to many countries and that a number of readers in different countries _____ _____ it before me.

11 _____ was that _____?

12 There is a _____ _____.

13 First, _____ your book online and _____ an ID number.

14 Next, _____ _____ in a _____ _____.

1 이 책은 놀라워요!

2 대부분의 사람은 책을 읽기 위한 전통적인 종이책으로 생각합니다.

3 하지만, 여러분 주변에는 독특한 책이 많이 있습니다.

4 이러한 책 중 몇 가지에 대해 배워 봅시다.

5 책이 여행합니다!

6 저는 어제 공원 벤치에서 이 낡은 책을 발견했습니다.

7 표지 위의 쪽지에 "공짜 책이에요!

8 저를 집으로 데려가서 읽어 주세요!"라고 쓰여 있었습니다.

9 사실, 이 책은 ID 번호가 있고 웹사이트에 등록되어 있었어요.

10 제가 온라인으로 그 번호를 입력했을 때, 저는 그 책이 많은 나라를 여행하고 다른 나라의 많은 독자가 저보다 앞서 이 책을 읽었다는 것을 알아냈습니다.

11 그게 어떻게 가능했을까요?

12 책을 공유하는 프로젝트가 있습니다.

13 우선, 온라인에 여러분의 책을 등록하고 ID 번호를 얻으세요.

14 그다음, 그것을 공공장소에 놓아두세요.

15 When the next reader finds your book and _____ _____ to the website, you can check _____ _____ _____ _____.

16 This way, the _____ _____ can become _____ _____ _____.

17 _____ _____ _____ we share, _____ _____ we learn.

18 The _____ Book

19 _____ _____ _____ is really important to people in my town.

20 It provides _____ _____ _____ _____ _____ _____ _____ _____ clean drinking water.

21 It _____ _____ the _____ Book.

22 You cannot actually drink the book, but you can use it _____ _____ _____.

23 Simply _____ _____ a page and _____ dirty water _____ it.

24 _____ the water _____ _____ the page, it _____ _____ clean drinking water.

25 _____ _____ this filtered water _____ you can drink.

26 This is possible because the book _____ _____ _____ _____ _____ _____.

27 This _____ book _____ the lives of many children _____ that _____ _____ dirty water.

15 다음 독자가 여러분의 책을 발견해서 그 웹사이트에 다시 알릴 때, 여러분은 책이 어디 있는지 확인할 수 있습니다.

16 이런 식으로, 전 세계가 하나의 큰 도서관이 될 수 있습니다.

17 우리가 더 많은 책을 공유할수록, 우리는 더 많이 배웁니다.

18 마실 수 있는 책

19 이 작은 책은 우리 마을 사람들에게는 정말로 중요합니다.

20 그것은 깨끗한 마실 물을 만드는 데 필요한 정보와 도구 둘 다를 제공합니다.

21 그것은 '마실 수 있는 책'이라고 불립니다.

22 여러분은 실제로 그 책을 마실 수는 없지만, 그것을 필터로 사용할 수 있습니다.

23 그냥 한 페이지를 떼어 내서 그 위에 더러운 물을 부으세요.

24 물이 그 페이지를 통과하면서, 깨끗한 마실 물로 바뀝니다.

25 여러분이 마실 수 있는 것은 이 여과된 물입니다.

26 책이 특별한 여과지로 만들어졌기 때문에 이것이 가능합니다.

27 이 놀라운 책은 더러운 물로 생기는 질병으로부터 많은 어린이의 생명을 구합니다.

28 The _____ _____

29 This is _____ _____ _____ _____ that I have ever _____.

30 After you finish _____ this book, _____ it and _____ it.

31 You will _____ _____ _____ _____ on the book.

32 In some bookstores in my town, you can see _____ _____ _____ this book _____ _____ _____.

33 The secret is that the book _____ _____ in each page.

34 It is _____ _____ that _____ the book _____ a tree.

35 This book _____ _____ _____ a small children's book _____ in Argentina.

36 _____ the company does _____ print this book _____, this special project _____ us _____ about where books come from.

37 These are _____ _____ _____ of the _____ _____ you can find.

38 _____ _____ _____ _____ do you want to make?

39 What special project _____ you _____ _____ _____ the books?

40 _____ _____ your _____ is, _____ _____ _____ _____ your books will become.

28 나무-책-나무 프로젝트

29 이것은 제가 지금까지 본 것 중에서 가장 놀라운 책입니다.

30 여러분이 이 책을 다 읽은 후에, 그것을 심고 물을 주세요.

31 여러분은 책에서 새잎이 자라는 것을 보게 될 거예요.

32 우리 마을의 몇몇 서점에서, 여러분은 이 책 한 권이 새잎을 내는 것을 볼 수 있습니다.

33 비밀은 책이 각 페이지 안에 씨앗을 갖고 있다는 것입니다.

34 책을 나무로 변화시키는 것은 이 아주 작은 씨앗들이에요.

35 이 책은 아르헨티나에 있는 한 작은 아동 도서 출판사에 의해 만들어졌습니다.

36 그 회사가 더는 이 책을 발행하지는 않지만, 이 특별한 프로젝트는 우리에게 책이 어디에서 오는지에 대해 생각하게 해 줍니다.

37 이것들은 여러분이 찾을 수 있는 독특한 책 중의 단지 몇 가지입니다.

38 여러분은 어떤 다른 독특한 책을 만들기 원하나요?

39 여러분은 책으로 어떤 특별한 프로젝트를 하고 싶나요?

40 여러분의 상상이 크면 클수록, 여러분의 책은 더 훌륭해질 것입니다.

※ 다음 문장을 우리말로 쓰시오.

1 ▸ This Book Is Amazing!

➡ _____

2 ▸ Most people think of books as traditional paper books to read.

➡ _____

3 ▸ However, there are many unique books around you.

➡ _____

4 ▸ Let's learn about a few of these books.

➡ _____

5 ▸ Books Travel!

➡ _____

6 ▸ I found this old book on a park bench yesterday.

➡ _____

7 ▸ A note on the cover read, "Free Book!

➡ _____

8 ▸ Take me home and read me!"

➡ _____

9 ▸ Actually, this book had an ID number and was registered on a website.

➡ _____

10 ▸ When I entered the number online, I found out that the book had traveled to many countries and that a number of readers in different countries had read it before me.

➡ _____

_____

11 ▸ How was that possible?

➡ _____

12 ▸ There is a book-sharing project.

➡ _____

13 ▸ First, register your book online and get an ID number.

➡ _____

14 Next, leave it in a public place.

➡ _____

15 When the next reader finds your book and reports back to the website, you can check where your book is.

➡ _____

16 This way, the whole world can become a big library.

➡ _____

17 The more books we share, the more we learn.

➡ _____

18 The Drinkable Book

➡ _____

19 This tiny book is really important to people in my town.

➡ _____

20 It provides both the information and the tools necessary to make clean drinking water.

➡ _____

21 It is called the Drinkable Book.

➡ _____

22 You cannot actually drink the book, but you can use it as a filter.

➡ _____

23 Simply tear out a page and pour dirty water on it.

➡ _____

24 As the water goes through the page, it changes into clean drinking water.

➡ _____

25 It is this filtered water that you can drink.

➡ _____

26 This is possible because the book is made of special filter paper.

➡ _____

27 This amazing book saves the lives of many children from diseases that come from dirty water.

➡ _____

28 The Tree-Book-Tree Project

➡ _____

29 This is the most amazing book that I have ever seen.

➡ _____

30 After you finish reading this book, plant it and water it.

➡ _____

31 You will see new leaves growing on the book.

➡ _____

32 In some bookstores in my town, you can see a copy of this book producing new leaves.

➡ _____

33 The secret is that the book has seeds in each page.

➡ _____

34 It is these tiny seeds that change the book into a tree.

➡ _____

35 This book was made by a small children's book publisher in Argentina.

➡ _____

36 Though the company does not print this book anymore, this special project makes us think about where books come from.

➡ _____

_____

37 These are just a few of the unique books you can find.

➡ _____

38 What other unique books do you want to make?

➡ _____

39 What special project would you like to do with the books?

➡ _____

40 The bigger your imagination is, the more wonderful your books will become.

➡ _____

※ 다음 괄호 안의 단어들을 우리말에 맞도록 바르게 배열하시오.

1 (Book / This / Amazing! / Is)
➡ _____

2 (people / most / of / think / as / books / paper / traditional / books / read. / to)
➡ _____

3 (there / however, / many / are / books / unique / you. / around)
➡ _____

4 (learn / let's / a / about / few / of / books. / these)
➡ _____

5 (Travel! / Books)
➡ _____

6 (found / I / old / this / book / a / on / park / yesterday. / bench)
➡ _____

7 (note / a / the / on / read, / cover / Book! / "Free)
➡ _____

8 (me / take / and / home / me!" / read)
➡ _____

9 (this / actually, / book / an / had / number / ID / and / registered / was / a / on / website.)
➡ _____

10 (I / when / the / entered / number / I / online, / found / that / out / book / the / traveled / had / many / to / countries / that / and / number / a / of / readers / different / in / countries / read / had / before / it / me.)
➡ _____
_____
_____

11 (was / how / possible? / that)
➡ _____

12 (is / there / a / project. / book-sharing)
➡ _____

13 (register / first, / book / your / and / online / get / ID / an / number.)
➡ _____

14 (leave / next, / in / it / a / place. / public)
➡ _____

1 이 책은 놀라워요!

2 대부분의 사람은 책을 읽기 위한 전통적인 종이책으로 생각합니다.

3 하지만, 여러분 주변에는 독특한 책이 많이 있습니다.

4 이러한 책 중 몇 가지에 대해 배워 봅시다.

5 책이 여행합니다!

6 저는 어제 공원 벤치에서 이 낡은 책을 발견했습니다.

7 표지 위의 쪽지에 "공짜 책이에요!

8 저를 집으로 데려가서 읽어 주세요!"라고 쓰어 있있습니다.

9 사실, 이 책은 ID 번호가 있고 웹사이트에 등록되어 있었어요.

10 제가 온라인으로 그 번호를 입력했을 때, 저는 그 책이 많은 나라를 여행하고 다른 나라의 많은 독자가 저보다 앞서 이 책을 읽었다는 것을 알아냈습니다.

11 그게 어떻게 가능했을까요?

12 책을 공유하는 프로젝트가 있습니다.

13 우선, 온라인에 여러분의 책을 등록하고 ID 번호를 얻으세요.

14 그다음, 그것을 공공장소에 놓아두세요.

15 (the / when / reader / next / your / finds / book / and / back / reports / to / the / website, / can / you / where / check / book / your / is.)

➡ _____

_____

16 (way, / this / whole / the / can / world / a / become / library. / big)

➡ _____

17 (more / the / we / books / share, / more / the / learn. / we)

➡ _____

18 (Book / Drinkable / The)

➡ _____

19 (tiny / this / is / book / important / really / people / to / my / in / town.)

➡ _____

20 (provides / it / the / both / information / and / tools / the / to / necessary / clean / make / water. / drinking)

➡ _____

_____

21 (is / it / the / called / Book. / Drinkable)

➡ _____

22 (cannot / you / drink / actually / book, / the / you / but / use / can / it / a / as / filter.)

➡ _____

23 (tear / simply / a / out / and / page / dirty / pour / on / water / it.)

➡ _____

24 (the / as / goes / water / the / through / page, / changes / it / clean / into / water. / drinking)

➡ _____

25 (is / it / filtered / this / that / water / can / you / drink.)

➡ _____

26 (is / this / because / possible / book / the / is / of / made / filter / special / paper.)

➡ _____

27 (amazing / this / saves / book / lives / the / of / children / many / diseases / from / come / that / dirty / from / water.)

➡ _____

_____

15 다음 독자가 여러분의 책을 발견해서 그 웹사이트에 다시 알릴 때, 여러분은 책이 어디 있는지 확인할 수 있습니다.

16 이런 식으로, 전 세계가 하나의 큰 도서관이 될 수 있습니다.

17 우리가 더 많은 책을 공유할수록, 우리는 더 많이 배웁니다.

18 마실 수 있는 책

19 이 작은 책은 우리 마을 사람들에게는 정말로 중요합니다.

20 그것은 깨끗한 마실 물을 만드는 데 필요한 정보와 도구 둘 다를 제공합니다.

21 그것은 '마실 수 있는 책'이라고 불립니다.

22 여러분은 실제로 그 책을 마실 수는 없지만, 그것을 필터로 사용할 수 있습니다.

23 그냥 한 페이지를 떼어 내서 그 위에 더러운 물을 부으세요.

24 물이 그 페이지를 통과하면서, 깨끗한 마실 물로 바뀝니다.

25 여러분이 마실 수 있는 것은 이 여과된 물입니다.

26 책이 특별한 여과지로 만들어졌기 때문에 이것이 가능합니다.

27 이 놀라운 책은 더러운 물로 생기는 질병으로부터 많은 어린이의 생명을 구합니다.

28 (Project / Tree-Book-Tree / The)

➡ _____

29 (is / this / most / the / book / amazing / I / that / ever / have / seen.)

➡ _____

30 (you / after / reading / finish / book, / this / it / plant / and / it. / water)

➡ _____

31 (will / you / new / see / growing / leaves / the / on / book.)

➡ _____

32 (some / in / bookstores / my / in / town, / can / you / a / see / of / copy / book / this / new / producing / leaves.)

➡ _____

_____

33 (secret / the / that / is / the / has / book / in / seeds / page. / each)

➡ _____

34 (is / it / tiny / these / seeds / change / that / book / the / a / into / tree.)

➡ _____

35 (book / this / made / was / a / by / children's / small / book / publisher / Argentina. / in)

➡ _____

36 (the / though / does / company / print / not / book / this / anymore, / special / this / makes / project / us / think / where / about / come / from. / books)

➡ _____

_____

37 (are / these / a / just / of / few / unique / the / you / books / find. / can)

➡ _____

38 (other / what / books / unique / you / do / want / make? / to)

➡ _____

39 (special / what / would / project / like / you / do / to / the / with / books?)

➡ _____

40 (bigger / the / imagination / your / is, / more / the / your / wonderful / books / become. / will)

➡ _____

_____

28 나무-책-나무 프로젝트

29 이것은 제가 지금까지 본 것 중에서 가장 놀라운 책입니다.

30 여러분이 이 책을 다 읽은 후에, 그것을 심고 물을 주세요.

31 여러분은 책에서 새잎이 자라는 것을 보게 될 거예요.

32 우리 마을의 몇몇 서점에서, 여러분은 이 책 한 권이 새잎을 내는 것을 볼 수 있습니다.

33 비밀은 책이 각 페이지 안에 씨앗을 갖고 있다는 것입니다.

34 책을 나무로 변화시키는 것은 이 아주 작은 씨앗들이에요.

35 이 책은 아르헨티나에 있는 한 작은 아동 도서 출판사에 의해 만들어졌습니다.

36 그 회사가 더는 이 책을 발행하지는 않지만, 이 특별한 프로젝트는 우리에게 책이 어디에서 오는지에 대해 생각하게 해 줍니다.

37 이것들은 여러분이 찾을 수 있는 독특한 책 중의 단지 몇 가지입니다.

38 여러분은 어떤 다른 독특한 책을 만들기 원하나요?

39 여러분은 책으로 어떤 특별한 프로젝트를 하고 싶나요?

40 여러분의 상상이 크면 클수록, 여러분의 책은 더 훌륭해질 것입니다.

※ 다음 우리말을 영어로 쓰시오.

1 이 책은 놀라워요!

➡ _____

2 대부분의 사람은 책을 읽기 위한 전통적인 종이책으로 생각합니다.

➡ _____

3 하지만, 여러분 주변에는 독특한 책이 많이 있습니다.

➡ _____

4 이러한 책 중 몇 가지에 대해 배워 봅시다.

➡ _____

5 책이 여행합니다!

➡ _____

6 저는 어제 공원 벤치에서 이 낡은 책을 발견했습니다.

➡ _____

7 표지 위의 쪽지에 "공짜 책이에요!

➡ _____

8 저를 집으로 데려가서 읽어 주세요!"라고 쓰여 있었습니다.

➡ _____

9 사실, 이 책은 ID 번호가 있고 웹사이트에 등록되어 있었어요.

➡ _____

10 제가 온라인으로 그 번호를 입력했을 때, 저는 그 책이 많은 나라를 여행하고 다른 나라의 많은 독자가 저보다 앞서 이 책을 읽었다는 것을 알아냈습니다.

➡ _____

_____

11 그게 어떻게 가능했을까요?

➡ _____

12 책을 공유하는 프로젝트가 있습니다.

➡ _____

13 우선, 온라인에 여러분의 책을 등록하고 ID 번호를 얻으세요.

➡ _____

14 그다음, 그것을 공공장소에 놓아두세요.

➡ _____

15 다음 독자가 여러분의 책을 발견해서 그 웹사이트에 다시 알릴 때, 여러분은 책이 어디 있는지 확인할 수 있습니다.

➡ _____

_____

16 이런 식으로, 전 세계가 하나의 큰 도서관이 될 수 있습니다.

➡ _____

17 우리가 더 많은 책을 공유할수록, 우리는 더 많이 배웁니다.

➡ _____

18 마실 수 있는 책

➡ _____

19 이 작은 책은 우리 마을 사람들에게는 정말로 중요합니다.

➡ _____

20 그것은 깨끗한 마실 물을 만드는 데 필요한 정보와 도구 둘 다를 제공합니다.

➡ _____

21 그것은 '마실 수 있는 책'이라고 불립니다.

➡ _____

22 여러분은 실제로 그 책을 마실 수는 없지만, 그것을 필터로 사용할 수 있습니다.

➡ _____

23 그냥 한 페이지를 떼어 내서 그 위에 더러운 물을 부으세요.

➡ _____

24 물이 그 페이지를 통과하면서, 깨끗한 마실 물로 바뀝니다.

➡ _____

25 여러분이 마실 수 있는 것은 이 여과된 물입니다.

➡ _____

26 책이 특별한 여과지로 만들어졌기 때문에 이것이 가능합니다.

➡ _____

27 이 놀라운 책은 더러운 물로 생기는 질병으로부터 많은 어린이의 생명을 구합니다.

➡ _____

28 나무-책-나무 프로젝트

➡ _____

29 이것은 제가 지금까지 본 것 중에서 가장 놀라운 책입니다.

➡ _____

30 여러분이 이 책을 다 읽은 후에, 그것을 심고 물을 주세요.

➡ _____

31 여러분은 책에서 새잎이 자라는 것을 보게 될 거예요.

➡ _____

32 우리 마을의 몇몇 서점에서, 여러분은 이 책 한 권이 새잎을 내는 것을 볼 수 있습니다.

➡ _____

33 비밀은 책이 각 페이지 안에 씨앗을 갖고 있다는 것입니다.

➡ _____

34 책을 나무로 변화시키는 것은 이 아주 작은 씨앗들이에요.

➡ _____

35 이 책은 아르헨티나에 있는 한 작은 아동 도서 출판사에 의해 만들어졌습니다.

➡ _____

36 그 회사가 더는 이 책을 발행하지는 않지만, 이 특별한 프로젝트는 우리에게 책이 어디에서 오는지에 대해 생각하게 해 줍니다.

➡ _____

_____

37 이것들은 여러분이 찾을 수 있는 독특한 책 중의 단지 몇 가지입니다.

➡ _____

38 여러분은 어떤 다른 독특한 책을 만들기 원하나요?

➡ _____

39 여러분은 책으로 어떤 특별한 프로젝트를 하고 싶나요?

➡ _____

40 여러분의 상상이 크면 클수록, 여러분의 책은 더 훌륭해질 것입니다.

➡ _____

※ 다음 우리말과 일치하도록 빈칸에 알맞은 말을 쓰시오.

Express Yourself C

1. In _____ and _____ a drone, _____ _____ is important.
2. It is a _____ _____ that has a _____ _____ _____.
3. _____ _____ the drone is, _____ _____ it flies.

1. 드론을 만들어 날릴 때, 그것의 무게가 중요하다.
2. 긴 건전지 수명을 가지는 것은 가벼운 드론이다.
3. 드론이 가벼울수록, 더 오래 난다.

Link to the World

1. This _____ _____ Dalhang-ari, a moon jar, _____ it
   _____ _____ _____ _____ _____.
2. In the past, _____ was _____ _____ _____ this large
   round jar _____ _____.
3. _____ _____ a jar was, ___ _____ _____ it was to
   make.
4. _____ was _____ _____ _____ solved this problem.
5. A smart potter _____ two large bowls together _____ _____
   _____ _____ _____.

1. 이것은 보름달처럼 생겨서 달항아리라고 불린다.
2. 과거에는 손으로 이렇게 크고 둥근 항아리를 만드는 게 불가능했다.
3. 항아리가 클수록, 만들기가 더 어려웠다.
4. 이 문제를 해결한 것은 도공이었다.
5. 현명한 도공은 두 개의 큰 사발을 합쳐서 이 달항아리를 만들었다.

Learning Diary – Listen & Speak 2

1. A: _____ do you _____, going camping _____ going
   swimming?
2. B: I _____ _____ _____. Actually, I _____ _____
   _____. How about you?
3. A: Well, I _____ _____ _____ _____.

1. A: 너는 캠핑 가기와 수영하러 가기 중에서 어떤 것을 더 좋아하니?
2. B: 나는 캠핑 가기를 더 좋아해. 사실, 나는 수영하러 가기를 몹시 싫어해. 너는 어때?
3. A: 음, 나는 수영하러 가기를 더 좋아해.

※ 다음 우리말을 영어로 쓰시오.

Express Yourself C

1. 드론을 만들어 날릴 때, 그것의 무게가 중요하다.

➡ _____

2. 긴 건전지 수명을 가지는 것은 가벼운 드론이다.

➡ _____

3. 드론이 가벼울수록, 더 오래 난다.

➡ _____

Link to the World

1. 이것은 보름달처럼 생겨서 달항아리라고 불린다.

➡ _____

2. 과거에는 손으로 이렇게 크고 둥근 항아리를 만드는 게 불가능했다.

➡ _____

3. 항아리가 클수록, 만들기가 더 어려웠다.

➡ _____

4. 이 문제를 해결한 것은 도공이었다.

➡ _____

5. 현명한 도공은 두 개의 큰 사발을 합쳐서 이 달항아리를 만들었다.

➡ _____

Learning Diary – Listen & Speak 2

1. A: 너는 캠핑 가기와 수영하러 가기 중에서 어떤 것을 더 좋아하니?

➡ _____

2. B: 나는 캠핑 가기를 더 좋아해. 사실, 나는 수영하러 가기를 몹시 싫어해. 너는 어때?

➡ _____

3. A: 음, 나는 수영하러 가기를 더 좋아해.

➡ _____

※ 다음 영어를 우리말로 쓰시오.

01 provide	_____	22 clown	_____
02 recently	_____	23 offer	_____
03 healthy	_____	24 unique	_____
04 search	_____	25 comfortable	_____
05 evidence	_____	26 untrue	_____
06 false	_____	27 cleaner	_____
07 source	_____	28 perfect	_____
08 actually	_____	29 performance	_____
09 artwork	_____	30 spread	_____
10 support	_____	31 unclear	_____
11 seem	_____	32 complete	_____
12 totally	_____	33 snake	_____
13 sink	_____	34 prefer	_____
14 critically	_____	35 turn out	_____
15 funny	_____	36 give up	_____
16 light	_____	37 tell A from B	_____
17 major	_____	38 make sense	_____
18 octopus	_____	39 be based on	_____
19 touching	_____	40 pass away	_____
20 site	_____	41 pay attention to	_____
21 attack	_____	42 made up	_____
		43 laugh out loud	_____

※ 다음 우리말을 영어로 쓰시오.

01 구하다

02 완벽한

03 가라앉다

04 선호하다

05 세제, 청소기

06 비판적으로

07 공격하다

08 최근에

09 거짓의, 잘못된

10 공연, 수행

11 편안한

12 실제로, 사실

13 전적으로

14 근원, 출처

15 증거

16 지지하다, 후원하다

17 완전한

18 제공하다

19 무서운

20 장소

21 광대

22 퍼진; 퍼지다

23 건강한

24 환호하다

25 사실이 아닌

26 가벼운

27 주요한, 주된

28 감동적인

29 문어

30 예술 작품

31 독특한

32 착용하다

33 지루한

34 찾다, 검색하다

35 포기하다

36 돌아가시다

37 ~에 바탕을 두다

38 의미가 통하다

39 큰 소리로 웃다

40 ~로부터 만들어지다

41 판명되다

42 ~에 주의를 기울이다

43 A와 B를 구별하다

※ 다음 영영풀이에 알맞은 단어를 <보기>에서 골라 쓴 후, 우리말 뜻을 쓰시오.

1 _____ : completely, absolutely: _____

2 _____ : an untrue statement: _____

3 _____ : having a strong emotional effect: _____

4 _____ : very important and serious: _____

5 _____ : incorrect, untrue, or mistaken: _____

6 _____ : to shout with joy, approval, or enthusiasm: _____

7 _____ : what you think or believe about something: _____

8 _____ : to supply something that is wanted or needed: _____

9 _____ : in a way that expresses disapproval: _____

10 _____ : to disappear below the surface of the water: _____

11 _____ : a soft sea creature with eight long arms: _____

12 _____ : anything that causes you to believe that something is true: _____

13 _____ : to open it out or arrange it over a place or surface: _____

14 _____ : to try to hurt or damage someone or something using physical violence:
_____

15 _____ : to give assistance, approval, comfort, or encouragement to someone:
_____

16 _____ : a performer in a circus who wears funny clothes and bright make-up,
and does silly things in order to make people laugh: _____

보기

sink	cheer	attack	octopus
clown	touching	opinion	support
critically	false	totally	evidence
provide	lie	major	spread

※ 다음 우리말과 일치하도록 빈칸에 알맞은 말을 쓰시오.

Get Ready 2

(1) **G:** There's no monkey _____ this in the world. Its nose is too big. _____ _____ it's _____.

  B: I don't _____. I saw that _____ of monkey on TV. It's _____.

(2) **G:** This animal has a long nose and two long, _____ _____. _____ _____ _____ it? Is it _____?

  B: Well, _____ _____ the Internet and _____ it together.

  G: That's a good idea.

(3) **B:** _____ do you _____ _____ this animal?

  G: It doesn't have legs, but it doesn't _____ _____ a snake. It's very _____.

  B: I think so, _____.

(4) **B:** _____ monkey is very small. Is it _____?

  G: I don't know. _____ visit some animal _____ _____ and _____ it _____.

  B: That's a good idea.

(1) **G:** 세상에 이런 원숭이는 없어. 코가 너무 크잖아. 나는 그것이 가짜라고 생각해.

  B: 나는 동의하지 않아. 저런 종류의 원숭이를 TV에서 본 적이 있어. 그건 진짜야.

(2) **G:** 이 동물은 긴 코와 두 개의 길고 날카로운 이빨을 가지고 있어. 그것을 어떻게 생각해? 진짜일까?

  B: 음, 인터넷을 찾아보고 함께 확인해 보자.

  G: 좋은 생각이야.

(3) **B:** 이 동물을 어떻게 생각해?

  G: 그것은 다리가 없지만 뱀처럼 보이지는 않아. 정말 이상하네.

  B: 나도 그렇게 생각해.

(4) **B:** 이 원숭이는 정말 작다. 진짜일까?

  G: 모르겠어. 동물 사실 확인 사이트를 방문해서 함께 확인해 보자.

  B: 좋은 생각이야.

Start Off - Listen & Talk A

1. **G:** Look at those shoes the girl is wearing. I think they're great. _____ _____ _____ _____ _____ them?

  B: I think they look _____ and _____.

  G: Right. I want _____ _____ them for the _____ _____.

2. **G:** I like the coat the boy _____ _____. I think it's _____ and _____.

  B: Well, I don't _____ _____ you. _____, I bought one last week. It's not so warm, and it's _____ _____ than it looks.

  G: Really? I don't _____ it.

1. **G:** 저 여자애가 신고 있는 신발 좀 봐. 멋있는 것 같아. 너는 저 신발을 어떻게 생각해?

  B: 가볍고 편안해 보여.

  G: 맞아. 난 학교 체험 학습 때 신으려고 저걸 사고 싶어.

2. **G:** 저 남자애가 입고 있는 코트가 마음에 들어. 따뜻하고 가벼울 것 같아.

  B: 글쎄, 나는 동의하지 않아. 사실 나는 지난주에 저것을 샀어. 그렇게 따뜻하지도 않고 보기보다 훨씬 더 무거워.

  G: 정말로? 믿을 수가 없어.

Start Off - Listen & Talk B

G: _____ do you _____ about this drama?

B: I think it's very _____. The boy _____ _____ his life _____ his sister. It's _____ _____ _____ of this year.

G: I _____ _____. It's not a good drama.

B: Come on. _____ do you _____ _____?

G: It doesn't _____ _____. And it's _____ _____ _____.

G: 이 드라마를 어떻게 생각하니?

B: 난 아주 감동적이라고 생각해. 소년이 그의 여동생을 구하기 위해 자신의 생명을 포기했잖아. 올해 최고의 드라마야.

G: 난 동의하지 않아. 그건 좋은 드라마가 아니야.

B: 이런. 왜 그렇게 생각해?

G: 현실적으로 보이지 않아. 그리고 약간 지루해.

Start Off - Speak Up

A: _____ do you feel _____ this _____?
B: I think it's great. It _____ the phone is strong.
A: I don't agree. We _____ _____ _____ every ad.

A: 이 광고를 어떻게 생각하니?
B: 굉장하다고 생각해. 그건 그 전화기 가 튼튼하다는 것을 보여주고 있어.
A: 나는 동의하지 않아. 우리는 모든 광 고를 믿어서는 안 돼.

Step Up - Real-life Scene

Alex: Big Mouth's show is really _____. _____ _____ _____ _____ _____ it?
Somi: Well, I don't think it's _____ great.
Alex: Come on. I love Mr. Big Mouth. He always _____ me _____ _____ _____.
Somi: He's funny, but don't believe _____ he _____.
Alex: All right. Oh, look at his photo of an _____. He said it lives in a tree.
Somi: It doesn't _____ _____.
Alex: He took the photo _____ it was _____ the tree. I don't think he's _____. It's a great photo.
Somi: I don't _____ _____ you. It's a _____ photo. An octopus can't live _____ _____ the sea.

Alex: Big Mouth 쇼는 정말 굉장해. 너 는 어떻게 생각하니?
소미: 글쎄, 나는 그렇게 대단한 것 같 지 않아.
Alex: 왜 그래. 나는 Big Mouth 씨를 진짜 좋아해. 그는 언제나 나를 큰소리 로 웃게 해 줘.
소미: 웃기긴 하지만, 그가 하는 모든 말을 믿지는 마.
Alex: 알았어. 오, 그가 찍은 문어 사진 을 봐. 그가 말하기를 그건 나무 에 산대.
소미: 말도 안 돼.
Alex: 그는 문어가 나무에 기어 올라갈 때 사진을 찍었대. 그가 거짓말하 고 있는 것 같지는 않아. 대단한 사진이야.
소미: 나는 네 말에 동의하지 않아. 그 건 가짜 사진이야. 문어는 바다 밖에서는 살 수 없다고.

Express Yourself A

1. G: _____ do you _____ _____ these animals?
   B: They are very cute, but I think cats don't _____ _____ well _____ dogs.
   G: I don't agree. And _____ _____ are good friends. They are _____ the trip _____.
2. G: _____ do you _____ about this kid here?
   B: I think she is very pretty. _____ _____ _____, why did she cut her hair?
   G: Can you _____?
   B: Well, girls these days _____ short hair.
   G: I don't agree _____ that. Most girls like long hair _____ _____ short hair. And this kid here is not a girl. _____ _____, he is a boy.
   B: Really?
   G: Yes. He grew his hair _____ _____ sick children.
3. G: How do you _____ _____ the teddy bears?
   B: They are cute. Is there _____ _____ about them?
   G: They _____ _____ of a police officer's _____.
   B: Oh, I see.
   G: This police officer made them for the kids. Their dad was a police officer, and he _____ _____ _____.
   B: That's very _____.

1. G: 이 동물들을 어떻게 생각해?
   B: 아주 귀엽지만, 고양이는 개와 잘 어울리지 못한다고 생각해.
   G: 나는 동의하지 않아. 그리고 이 둘은 좋은 친구야. 그들은 함께 즐겁게 여행하고 있어.
2. G: 여기 이 아이를 어떻게 생각해?
   B: 매우 예쁘다고 생각해. 그런데 그 녀는 왜 머리카락을 잘랐니?
   G: 짐작할 수 있어?
   B: 음, 요새 여자아이들은 짧은 머리 를 더 좋아하더라.
   G: 난 그것에 동의하지 않아. 대부분의 여자아이는 짧은 머리보다 긴 머리 를 좋아해. 그리고 여기 이 아이 는 여자아이가 아니야. 사실, 이 아이 는 남자아이야.
   B: 정말이니?
   G: 응. 그는 아픈 아이들을 돕기 위해 머리를 길렀어.
3. G: 곰 인형들을 어떻게 생각해?
   B: 귀여워. 뭔가 특별한 점이 있니?
   G: 그것들은 한 경찰관의 제복으로 만들어졌어.
   B: 아, 그렇구나.
   G: 이 경찰이 아이들을 위해 그것들을 만들어 줬어. 그들의 아빠는 경찰 관이었고, 최근에 세상을 떠나셨어.
   B: 아주 감동적이야.

※ 다음 우리말에 맞도록 대화를 영어로 쓰시오.

Get Ready 2

(1) G: _____
   _____
   B: _____
(2) G: _____
   _____
   B: _____
   G: _____
(3) B: _____
   G: _____
   _____
   B: _____
(4) B: _____
   G: _____
   _____
   B: _____

(1) G: 세상에 이런 원숭이는 없어. 코가 너무 크잖아. 나는 그것이 가짜라고 생각해.
   B: 나는 동의하지 않아. 저런 종류의 원숭이를 TV에서 본 적이 있어. 그건 진짜야.
(2) G: 이 동물은 긴 코와 두 개의 길고 날카로운 이빨을 가지고 있어. 그것을 어떻게 생각해? 진짜일까?
   B: 음, 인터넷을 찾아보고 함께 확인해 보자.
   G: 좋은 생각이야.
(3) B: 이 동물을 어떻게 생각해?
   G: 그것은 다리가 없지만 뱀처럼 보이지는 않아. 정말 이상하네.
   B: 나도 그렇게 생각해.
(4) B: 이 원숭이는 정말 작다. 진짜일까?
   G: 모르겠어. 동물 사실 확인 사이트를 방문해서 함께 확인해 보자.
   B: 좋은 생각이야.

Start Off - Listen & Talk A

1. G: _____
   _____
   B: _____
   G: _____
2. G: _____
   B: _____
   _____
   G: _____

1. G: 저 여자애가 신고 있는 신발 좀 봐. 멋있는 것 같아. 너는 저 신발을 어떻게 생각해?
   B: 가볍고 편안해 보여.
   G: 맞아. 난 학교 체험 학습 때 신으려고 저걸 사고 싶어.
2. G: 저 남자애가 입고 있는 코트가 마음에 들어. 따뜻하고 가벼울 것 같아.
   B: 글쎄, 나는 동의하지 않아. 사실 나는 지난주에 저것을 샀어. 그렇게 따뜻하지도 않고 보기보다 훨씬 더 무거워.
   G: 정말로? 믿을 수가 없어.

Start Off - Listen & Talk B

G: _____
B: _____
   _____
G: _____
B: _____
G: _____

G: 이 드라마를 어떻게 생각하니?
B: 난 아주 감동적이라고 생각해. 소년이 그의 여동생을 구하기 위해 자신의 생명을 포기했잖아. 올해 최고의 드라마야.
G: 난 동의하지 않아. 그건 좋은 드라마가 아니야.
B: 이런. 왜 그렇게 생각해?
G: 현실적으로 보이지 않아. 그리고 약간 지루해.

Start Off - Speak Up

A: _____

B: _____

A: _____

Step Up - Real-life Scene

Alex: _____

Somi: _____

Alex: _____

Somi: _____

Alex: _____

Somi: _____

Alex: _____

Somi: _____

Express Yourself A

1. G: _____

   B: _____

   G: _____

2. G: _____

   B: _____

   G: _____

   B: _____

   G: _____

   B: _____

   G: _____

3. G: _____

   B: _____

   G: _____

   B: _____

   G: _____

   B: _____

A: 이 광고를 어떻게 생각하니?

B: 굉장하다고 생각해. 그건 그 전화기가 튼튼하다는 것을 보여주고 있어.

A: 나는 동의하지 않아. 우리는 모든 광고를 믿어서는 안 돼.

Alex: Big Mouth 쇼는 정말 굉장해. 너는 어떻게 생각하니?

소미: 글쎄, 나는 그렇게 대단한 것 같지 않아.

Alex: 왜 그래. 나는 Big Mouth 씨를 진짜 좋아해. 그는 언제나 나를 큰 소리로 웃게 해 줘.

소미: 웃기긴 하지만, 그가 하는 모든 말을 믿지는 마.

Alex: 알았어. 오, 그가 찍은 문어 사진을 봐. 그가 말하기를 그건 나무에 산대.

소미: 말도 안 돼.

Alex: 그는 문어가 나무에 기어 올라갈 때 사진을 찍었대. 그가 거짓말하고 있는 것 같지는 않아. 대단한 사진이야.

소미: 나는 네 말에 동의하지 않아. 그건 가짜 사진이야. 문어는 바다 밖에서는 살 수 없다고.

1. G: 이 동물들을 어떻게 생각해?

   B: 아주 귀엽지만, 고양이는 개와 잘 어울리지 못한다고 생각해.

   G: 나는 동의하지 않아. 그리고 이 둘은 좋은 친구야. 그들은 함께 즐겁게 여행하고 있어.

2. G: 여기 이 아이를 어떻게 생각해?

   B: 매우 예쁘다고 생각해. 그런데 그녀는 왜 머리카락을 잘랐니?

   G: 짐작할 수 있어?

   B: 음, 요새 여자아이들은 짧은 머리를 더 좋아하더라.

   G: 난 그것에 동의하지 않아. 대부분의 여자아이는 짧은 머리보다 긴 머리를 좋아해. 그리고 여기 이 아이는 여자아이가 아니야. 사실, 이 아이는 남자아이야.

   B: 정말이니?

   G: 응. 그는 아픈 아이들을 돕기 위해 머리를 길렀어.

3. G: 곰 인형들을 어떻게 생각해?

   B: 귀여워. 뭔가 특별한 점이 있니?

   G: 그것들은 한 경찰관의 제복으로 만들어졌어.

   B: 아, 그렇구나.

   G: 이 경찰이 아이들을 위해 그것들을 만들어 줬어. 그들의 아빠는 경찰관이었고, 최근에 세상을 떠나셨어.

   B: 아주 감동적이야.

※ 다음 우리말과 일치하도록 빈칸에 알맞은 것을 골라 쓰시오.

1 How to Be a _____ _____ _____
   A. News   B. Smart   C. Reader

2 In October 2016, stories about _____ clowns _____ schools _____ the Washington area, but Danina Garcia-Fuller's students didn't believe them a _____.
   A. shook   B. bit   C. scary   D. across

3 "Some people were _____ _____ because they saw _____ on social media," said Patricia Visoso, _____ of Garcia-Fuller's students.
   A. scared   B. one   C. things   D. getting

4 "But they never _____ _____ _____ who was _____ this."
   A. saying   B. checked   C. on   D. up

5 The stories were _____ _____ _____ teenagers, not by major newspapers or TV _____.
   A. by   B. made   C. stations   D. actually

6 They offered no _____ _____ that clowns really were _____ to _____ students.
   A. attack   B. hard   C. trying   D. evidence

7 The story _____ _____ to be a _____ _____.
   A. out   B. turned   C. lie   D. complete

8 "I think a _____ of people just look _____ one _____ and believe it's _____," Patricia's classmate Ivy-Brooks said.
   A. true   B. thing   C. at   D. lot

9 "It's really important to look at the _____ _____ and to pay attention to what is _____ and what is _____."
   A. sources   B. real   C. right   D. fake

10 _____ Garcia-Fuller's students, many _____ in America are learning to _____ _____ about information they're seeing in the news and on the Internet.
   A. critically   B. like   C. teenagers   D. think

11 This skill is _____ more important these days as stories can _____ very fast, and anyone can make a website _____ of _____ information.
   A. spread   B. false   C. getting   D. full

1 현명한 뉴스 독자가 되는 방법

2 2016년 10월, 무서운 광대들에 관한 이야기가 워싱턴 지역 전역의 학교에 충격을 안겼지만, Danina Garcia-Fuller의 학생들은 조금도 그 이야기들을 믿지 않았다.

3 "몇몇 사람들은 그들이 소셜 미디어에 올라온 것들을 봤기 때문에 무서워했어요."라고 Garcia-Fuller의 학생 중 한 명인 Patricia Visoso가 말했다.

4 "하지만 그들은 이것을 누가 말하고 있는지를 전혀 확인하지 않았어요."

5 그 이야기들은 실제로 주요 신문사나 TV 방송국이 아닌 10대들이 지어냈다.

6 그들은 광대들이 정말로 학생들을 공격하려고 한다는 명백한 증거를 하나도 제공하지 않았다.

7 그 이야기는 결국 완벽한 거짓말인 것으로 드러났다.

8 "많은 사람이 단지 한 가지만을 보고 그것이 사실이라고 믿는 것 같아요."라고 Patricia의 반 친구인 Ivy-Brooks가 말했다.

9 올바른 출처를 살펴보고, 무엇이 진짜이고 무엇이 가짜인지에 주의를 기울이는 것은 정말 중요해요."

10 Garcia-Fuller의 학생들처럼, 많은 미국의 10대들은 뉴스 속 그리고 인터넷상에서 보고 있는 정보에 관해 비판적으로 생각하는 것을 배워 나가고 있다.

11 이 기능은 최근 더 중요해지고 있는데, 이야기들은 아주 빠른 속도로 퍼져 나갈 수 있고 누구나 허위 정보로 가득 찬 웹사이트를 만들어 낼 수 있기 때문이다.

12 Garcia-Fuller said she was teaching her students _____
_____ _____ fake news _____ real news.

    A. tell   B. how   C. from   D. to

13 "_____ of the first _____ is to _____ _____.

    A. steps   B. down   C. one   D. slow

14 If a story or a photo seems _____ good _____ be _____,
stop and _____.

    A. to   B. think   C. too   D. true

15 Is there any _____ that _____ _____ the writer _____?

    A. supports   B. evidence   C. what   D. says

16 And _____ is this _____ _____?"

    A. coming   B. where   C. from

17 Garcia-Fuller's students also learn how to _____ _____
_____ _____ in the news.

    A. fact   B. from   C. opinion   D. tell

18 "Opinions are good to read," said 15-year-old McKenzie Campbell,
"but you also have to _____ if they are _____ _____
_____."

    A. based   B. facts   C. check   D. on

19 Garcia-Fuller also said sometimes it can be very _____ to
be a _____ _____ _____.

    A. hard   B. reader   C. smart   D. news

20 She tests her students with a website that _____ to _____
information on an animal _____ a tree _____.

    A. called   B. appears   C. octopus   D. provide

21 The _____ is _____ of information on this animal, _____
with a few _____ photos of octopuses in trees.

    A. unclear   B. full   C. along   D. site

22 But like the story of _____ _____, it's totally _____
_____.

    A. made   B. scary   C. up   D. clowns

23 The lesson, Garcia-Fuller tells her students, is to "check the
information you're seeing _____ more _____" and to
"question _____, _____ things that I say."

    A. carefully   B. even   C. everything   D. once

---

12 Garcia-Fuller는 그녀가 자신의 학생들에게 가짜 뉴스를 진짜 뉴스로부터 구분하는 방법을 가르치고 있다고 말했다.

13 "첫 단계 중 하나는 속도를 늦추는 것(천천히 생각하는 것)입니다.

14 만약 어떤 이야기나 어떤 사진이 진짜라고 하기엔 너무 좋아 보인다면, 멈춰서 생각해 보세요.

15 글쓴이가 말하고 있는 것을 뒷받침하는 어떠한 증거라도 있나요?

16 그리고 이 정보가 어디서 온 것인가요?"

17 Garcia-Fuller의 학생들은 또한 뉴스에서 사실을 의견과 구분하는 방법에 대해서도 배운다.

18 "의견들은 읽을 만한 가치가 있습니다,"라고 15살인 McKenzie Campbell이 말했다. "하지만 여러분은 그것들이 사실에 기반을 둔 것인지를 확인해 보아야 합니다."

19 Garcia-Fuller는 또한 때때로 현명한 뉴스 독자가 되는 것이 아주 어려울 수도 있다고 말했다.

20 그녀는 자신의 학생들을 '나무 문어'라는 이름의 동물에 대한 정보를 제공하는 것처럼 보이는 웹사이트로 시험한다.

21 그 사이트는 나무 위에 있는 문어들의 몇몇 불확실한 사진과 함께, 이 동물에 대한 정보로 가득 차 있다.

22 하지만 무서운 광대들의 이야기와 마찬가지로, 그것은 완전히 꾸며진 것이다.

23 Garcia-Fuller가 그녀의 학생들에게 말하는 교훈은 '당신이 보고 있는 정보를 한 번만 더 신중하게 확인해 보라'는 것과 '모든 것, 심지어 내가 말하는 것에도 의문을 가져 보라'는 것이다.

※ 다음 우리말과 일치하도록 빈칸에 알맞은 것을 골라 쓰시오.

1 _____ _____ Be a _____ _____ _____

2 In October 2016, stories about scary clowns _____ _____ _____ the Washington area, but Danina Garcia-Fuller's students _____ _____ them _____ _____.

3 "Some people were _____ _____ because they saw things on social media," said Patricia Visoso, _____ _____ Garcia-Fuller's students.

4 "But they never _____ _____ _____ who _____ _____ this."

5 The stories _____ _____ _____ _____ teenagers, not by _____ _____ or TV stations.

6 They offered _____ _____ _____ that clowns really were _____ _____ _____ students.

7 The story _____ _____ _____ _____ a _____ _____.

8 "I think a lot of people _____ _____ _____ _____ and believe it's true," Patricia's classmate Ivy-Brooks said.

9 "It's really important _____ _____ _____ _____ _____ _____ and to _____ _____ _____ _____ _____ _____ and _____ _____ _____."

10 _____ Garcia-Fuller's students, many teenagers in America are learning _____ _____ _____ about information they're seeing in the news and _____ _____ _____.

11 This skill is _____ _____ _____ these days as stories can _____ very fast, and anyone can make a website _____ _____ _____ _____.

1 현명한 뉴스 독자가 되는 방법

2 2016년 10월, 무서운 광대들에 관한 이야기가 워싱턴 지역 전역의 학교에 충격을 안겼지만, Danina Garcia-Fuller의 학생들은 조금도 그 이야기들을 믿지 않았다.

3 "몇몇 사람들은 그들이 소셜 미디어에 올라온 것들을 봤기 때문에 무서워했어요."라고 Garcia-Fuller의 학생 중 한 명인 Patricia Visoso가 말했다.

4 "하지만 그들은 이것을 누가 말하고 있는지를 전혀 확인하지 않았어요."

5 그 이야기들은 실제로 주요 신문사나 TV 방송국이 아닌 10대들이 지어냈다.

6 그들은 광대들이 정말로 학생들을 공격하려고 한다는 명백한 증거를 하나도 제공하지 않았다.

7 그 이야기는 결국 완벽한 거짓말인 것으로 드러났다.

8 "많은 사람이 단지 한 가지만을 보고 그것이 사실이라고 믿는 것 같아요."라고 Patricia의 반 친구인 Ivy-Brooks가 말했다.

9 올바른 출처를 살펴보고, 무엇이 진짜이고 무엇이 가짜인지에 주의를 기울이는 것은 정말 중요해요."

10 Garcia-Fuller의 학생들처럼, 많은 미국의 10대들은 뉴스 속 그리고 인터넷상에서 보고 있는 정보에 관해 비판적으로 생각하는 것을 배워 나가고 있다.

11 이 기능은 최근 더 중요해지고 있는데, 이야기들은 아주 빠른 속도로 퍼져 나갈 수 있고 누구나 허위 정보로 가득 찬 웹사이트를 만들어 낼 수 있기 때문이다.

12 Garcia-Fuller said she was teaching her students _____ _____ _____ fake news _____ _____ _____ .

13 "_____ _____ _____ _____ _____ is to _____ _____ .

14 If a story or a photo seems _____ _____ _____ _____ , stop and think.

15 Is there any _____ that supports _____ _____ _____ ?

16 And where is this _____ _____ ?"

17 Garcia-Fuller's students also learn _____ _____ _____ fact _____ opinion in the news.

18 "Opinions are good to read," said 15-year-old McKenzie Campbell, "but you also _____ _____ check _____ they _____ _____ _____ _____ ."

19 Garcia-Fuller also said sometimes it can be very hard to be _____ _____ _____ .

20 She tests her students with a website that _____ _____ _____ information on an animal called a tree octopus.

21 The site _____ _____ _____ information on this animal, _____ _____ a few _____ _____ of octopuses in trees.

22 But _____ the story of _____ _____ , it's totally _____ _____ .

23 The lesson, Garcia-Fuller tells her students, is to "check the information you're seeing _____ _____ _____ " and to "_____ _____ , even things that I say."

12 Garcia-Fuller는 그녀가 자신의 학생들에게 가짜 뉴스를 진짜 뉴스로부터 구분하는 방법을 가르치고 있다고 말했다.

13 "첫 단계 중 하나는 속도를 늦추는 것(천천히 생각하는 것)입니다.

14 만약 어떤 이야기나 어떤 사진이 진짜라고 하기엔 너무 좋아 보인다면, 멈춰서 생각해 보세요.

15 글쓴이가 말하고 있는 것을 뒷받침하는 어떠한 증거라도 있나요?

16 그리고 이 정보가 어디서 온 것인가요?"

17 Garcia-Fuller의 학생들은 또한 뉴스에서 사실을 의견과 구분하는 방법에 대해서도 배운다.

18 "의견들은 읽을 만한 가치가 있습니다."라고 15살인 McKenzie Campbell이 말했다. "하지만 여러분은 그것들이 사실에 기반을 둔 것인지를 확인해 보아야 합니다."

19 Garcia-Fuller는 또한 때때로 현명한 뉴스 독자가 되는 것이 아주 어려울 수도 있다고 말했다.

20 그녀는 자신의 학생들을 '나무 문어'라는 이름의 동물에 대한 정보를 제공하는 것처럼 보이는 웹사이트로 시험한다.

21 그 사이트는 나무 위에 있는 문어들의 몇몇 불확실한 사진과 함께, 이 동물에 대한 정보로 가득 차 있다.

22 하지만 무서운 광대들의 이야기와 마찬가지로, 그것은 완전히 꾸며진 것이다.

23 Garcia-Fuller가 그녀의 학생들에게 말하는 교훈은 '당신이 보고 있는 정보를 한 번만 더 신중하게 확인해 보라'는 것과 '모든 것, 심지어 내가 말하는 것에도 의문을 가져 보라'는 것이다.

※ 다음 문장을 우리말로 쓰시오.

1 How to Be a Smart News Reader

➡ _____

2 In October 2016, stories about scary clowns shook schools across the Washington area, but Danina Garcia-Fuller's students didn't believe them a bit.

➡ _____

_____

3 "Some people were getting scared because they saw things on social media," said Patricia Visoso, one of Garcia-Fuller's students.

➡ _____

_____

4 "But they never checked up on who was saying this."

➡ _____

5 The stories were actually made by teenagers, not by major newspapers or TV stations.

➡ _____

6 They offered no hard evidence that clowns really were trying to attack students.

➡ _____

7 The story turned out to be a complete lie.

➡ _____

8 "I think a lot of people just look at one thing and believe it's true," Patricia's classmate Ivy-Brooks said.

➡ _____

_____

9 "It's really important to look at the right sources and to pay attention to what is real and what is fake."

➡ _____

_____

10 Like Garcia-Fuller's students, many teenagers in America are learning to think critically about information they're seeing in the news and on the Internet.

➡ _____

_____

11 This skill is getting more important these days as stories can spread very fast, and anyone can make a website full of false information.

➡ _____

_____

12 ▶ Garcia-Fuller said she was teaching her students how to tell fake news from real news.

➡ _____ _____

13 ▶ "One of the first steps is to slow down.

➡ _____

14 ▶ If a story or a photo seems too good to be true, stop and think.

➡ _____

15 ▶ Is there any evidence that supports what the writer says?

➡ _____

16 ▶ And where is this coming from?"

➡ _____

17 ▶ Garcia-Fuller's students also learn how to tell fact from opinion in the news.

➡ _____

18 ▶ "Opinions are good to read," said 15-year-old McKenzie Campbell, "but you also have to check if they are based on facts."

➡ _____
_____ _____

19 ▶ Garcia-Fuller also said sometimes it can be very hard to be a smart news reader.

➡ _____

20 ▶ She tests her students with a website that appears to provide information on an animal called a tree octopus.

➡ _____

21 ▶ The site is full of information on this animal, along with a few unclear photos of octopuses in trees.

➡ _____

22 ▶ But like the story of scary clowns, it's totally made up.

➡ _____

23 ▶ The lesson, Garcia-Fuller tells her students, is to "check the information you're seeing once more carefully" and to "question everything, even things that I say."

➡ _____
_____

※ 다음 괄호 안의 단어들을 우리말에 맞도록 바르게 배열하시오.

1 (to / How / a / Be / News / Smart / Reader)
➡ _____

2 (October / in / 2016, / about / stories / clowns / scary / schools / shook / the / across / area, / Washington / but / Garcia-Fuller's / Danina / students / believe / didn't / them / bit. / a)
➡ _____
_____
_____

3 (people / "some / were / scared / getting / because / saw / they / things / social / on / media, / Patricia / said / one / Visoso, / of / students. / Garcia-Fuller's)
➡ _____
_____

4 ("but / never / they / up / checked / who / on / was / this." / saying)
➡ _____

5 (stories / the / actually / were / by / made / teenagers, / by / not / newspapers / major / TV / or / stations.)
➡ _____

6 (offered / they / hard / no / that / evidence / clowns / were / really / trying / were / attack / to / students.)
➡ _____

7 (story / the / out / turned / be / to / a / lie. / complete)
➡ _____

8 (think / "I / lot / a / people / of / look / just / one / at / and / thing / it's / believe / true," / classmate / Paricia's / said. / Ivy-Brooks)
➡ _____

9 (really / "it's / to / important / look / at / right / the / and / sources / to / attention / pay / to / is / what / and / real / is / what / fake.")
➡ _____

10 (Gracia-Fuller's / like / students, / teenagers / many / in / are / America / to / learning / critically / think / information / about / seeing / they're / the / in / and / news / on / Internet. / the)
➡ _____

11 (skill / this / getting / is / important / more / days / these / stories / as / spread / can / fast, / very / anyone / and / make / can / website / a / of / full / information. / false)
➡ _____
_____

1 현명한 뉴스 독자가 되는 방법

2 2016년 10월, 무서운 광대들에 관한 이야기가 워싱턴 지역 전역의 학교에 충격을 안겼지만, Danina Garcia-Fuller의 학생들은 조금도 그 이야기들을 믿지 않았다.

3 "몇몇 사람들은 그들이 소셜 미디어에 올라온 것들을 봤기 때문에 무서워했어요."라고 Garcia-Fuller의 학생 중 한 명인 Patricia Visoso가 말했다.

4 "하지만 그들은 이것을 누가 말하고 있는지를 전혀 확인하지 않았어요."

5 그 이야기들은 실제로 주요 신문사나 TV 방송국이 아닌 10대들이 지어냈다.

6 그들은 광대들이 정말로 학생들을 공격하려고 한다는 명백한 증거를 하나도 제공하지 않았다.

7 그 이야기는 결국 완벽한 거짓말인 것으로 드러났다.

8 "많은 사람이 단지 한 가지만을 보고 그것이 사실이라고 믿는 것 같아요."라고 Patricia의 반 친구인 Ivy-Brooks가 말했다.

9 올바른 출처를 살펴보고, 무엇이 진짜이고 무엇이 가짜인지에 주의를 기울이는 것은 정말 중요해요."

10 Garcia-Fuller의 학생들처럼, 많은 미국의 10대들은 뉴스 속 그리고 인터넷상에서 보고 있는 정보에 관해 비판적으로 생각하는 것을 배워 나가고 있다.

11 이 기능은 최근 더 중요해지고 있는데, 이야기들은 아주 빠른 속도로 퍼져 나갈 수 있고 누구나 허위 정보로 가득 찬 웹사이트를 만들어 낼 수 있기 때문이다.

12 (said / Garcia-Fuller / was / she / her / teaching / how / students / to / fake / tell / news / real / from / news.)

➡ _____

_____

13 (of / "one / first / the / is / steps / slow / to / down.)

➡ _____

14 (a / if / or / story / photo / a / too / seems / to / good / true, / be / and / think. / stop)

➡ _____

15 (there / is / evidence / any / supports / that / the / what / says? / writer)

➡ _____

16 (where / and / this / is / from?" / coming)

➡ _____

17 (students / Garcia-Fuller's / learn / also / to / how / fact / tell / from / in / opinion / news. / the)

➡ _____

_____

18 (are / "opinions / to / good / read," / 15-year-old / said / Campbell, / McKenzie / you / "but / also / you / to / have / if / check / are / they / on / based / facts.")

➡ _____

_____

19 (Garcia-Fuller / said / also / it / sometimes / be / can / hard / very / be / to / a / news / smart / reader.)

➡ _____

_____

20 (tests / she / students / her / a / with / that / website / to / appears / information / provide / an / on / called / animal / tree / octopus. / a)

➡ _____

_____

21 (site / the / full / is / information / of / this / on / animal, / with / along / few / a / photos / unclear / octopuses / of / trees. / in)

➡ _____

_____

22 (like / but / story / the / scary / of / clowns, / totally / it's / up. / made)

➡ _____

23 (lesson, / the / Garcia-Fuller / her / tells / students, / to / is / the / "check / information / seeing / you're / more / once / carefully" / to / and / everything / "question / even / that / things / say." / I)

➡ _____

_____

12 Garcia-Fuller는 그녀가 자신의 학생들에게 가짜 뉴스를 진짜 뉴스로부터 구분하는 방법을 가르치고 있다고 말했다.

13 "첫 단계 중 하나는 속도를 늦추는 것(천천히 생각하는 것)입니다.

14 만약 어떤 이야기나 어떤 사진이 진짜라고 하기엔 너무 좋아 보인다면, 멈춰서 생각해 보세요.

15 글쓴이가 말하고 있는 것을 뒷받침하는 어떠한 증거라도 있나요?

16 그리고 이 정보가 어디서 온 것인가요?"

17 Garcia-Fuller의 학생들은 또한 뉴스에서 사실을 의견과 구분하는 방법에 대해서도 배운다.

18 "의견들은 읽을 만한 가치가 있습니다."라고 15살인 McKenzie Campbell이 말했다. "하지만 여러분은 그것들이 사실에 기반을 둔 것인지를 확인해 보아야 합니다."

19 Garcia-Fuller는 또한 때때로 현명한 뉴스 독자가 되는 것이 아주 어려울 수도 있다고 말했다.

20 그녀는 자신의 학생들을 '나무 문어'라는 이름의 동물에 대한 정보를 제공하는 것처럼 보이는 웹사이트로 시험한다.

21 그 사이트는 나무 위에 있는 문어들의 몇몇 불확실한 사진과 함께, 이 동물에 대한 정보로 가득 차 있다.

22 하지만 무서운 광대들의 이야기와 마찬가지로, 그것은 완전히 꾸며진 것이다.

23 Garcia-Fuller가 그녀의 학생들에게 말하는 교훈은 '당신이 보고 있는 정보를 한 번만 더 신중하게 확인해 보라'는 것과 '모든 것, 심지어 내가 말하는 것에도 의문을 가져 보라'는 것이다.

※ 다음 우리말을 영어로 쓰시오.

1 현명한 뉴스 독자가 되는 방법

➡ _____

2 2016년 10월, 무서운 광대들에 관한 이야기가 워싱턴 지역 전역의 학교에 충격을 안겼지만,
Danina Garcia-Fuller의 학생들은 조금도 그 이야기들을 믿지 않았다.

➡ _____

_____

3 "몇몇 사람들은 그들이 소셜 미디어에 올라온 것들을 봤기 때문에 무서워했어요."라고 Garcia-Fuller의
학생 중 한 명인 Patricia Visoso가 말했다.

➡ _____

_____

4 "하지만 그들은 이것을 누가 말하고 있는지를 전혀 확인하지 않았어요."

➡ _____

5 그 이야기들은 실제로 주요 신문사나 TV 방송국이 아닌 10대들이 지어냈다.

➡ _____

6 그들은 광대들이 정말로 학생들을 공격하려고 한다는 명백한 증거를 하나도 제공하지 않았다.

➡ _____

7 그 이야기는 결국 완벽한 거짓말인 것으로 드러났다.

➡ _____

8 "많은 사람이 단지 한 가지만을 보고 그것이 사실이라고 믿는 것 같아요."라고 Patricia의
반 친구인 Ivy-Brooks가 말했다.

➡ _____

_____

9 "올바른 출처를 살펴보고, 무엇이 진짜이고 무엇이 가짜인지에 주의를 기울이는 것은 정말 중요해요."

➡ _____

10 Garcia-Fuller의 학생들처럼, 많은 미국의 10대들은 뉴스 속 그리고 인터넷상에서 보고 있는 정보에 관해
비판적으로 생각하는 것을 배워 나가고 있다.

➡ _____

_____

11 이 기능은 최근 더 중요해지고 있는데, 이야기들은 아주 빠른 속도로 퍼져 나갈 수 있고 누구나 허위 정보로
가득 찬 웹사이트를 만들어 낼 수 있기 때문이다.

➡ _____

_____

12 Garcia-Fuller는 그녀가 자신의 학생들에게 가짜 뉴스를 진짜 뉴스로부터 구분하는 방법을 가르치고 있다고 말했다.

➡ _____

13 "첫 단계 중 하나는 속도를 늦추는 것(천천히 생각하는 것)입니다.

➡ _____

14 만약 어떤 이야기나 어떤 사진이 진짜라고 하기엔 너무 좋아 보인다면, 멈춰서 생각해 보세요.

➡ _____

15 글쓴이가 말하고 있는 것을 뒷받침하는 어떠한 증거라도 있나요?

➡ _____

16 그리고 이 정보가 어디서 온 것인가요?"

➡ _____

17 Garcia-Fuller의 학생들은 또한 뉴스에서 사실을 의견과 구분하는 방법에 대해서도 배운다.

➡ _____

18 "의견들은 읽을 만한 가치가 있습니다."라고 15살인 McKenzie Campbell이 말했다. "하지만 여러분은 그것들이 사실에 기반을 둔 것인지를 확인해 보아야 합니다."

➡ _____

_____

19 Garcia-Fuller는 또한 때때로 현명한 뉴스 독자가 되는 것이 아주 어려울 수도 있다고 말했다.

➡ _____

20 그녀는 자신의 학생들을 '나무 문어'라는 이름의 동물에 대한 정보를 제공하는 것처럼 보이는 웹사이트로 시험한다.

➡ _____

_____

21 그 사이트는 나무 위에 있는 문어들의 몇몇 불확실한 사진과 함께, 이 동물에 대한 정보로 가득 차 있다.

➡ _____

_____

22 하지만 무서운 광대들의 이야기와 마찬가지로, 그것은 완전히 꾸며진 것이다.

➡ _____

23 Garcia-Fuller가 그녀의 학생들에게 말하는 교훈은 '당신이 보고 있는 정보를 한 번만 더 신중하게 확인해 보라'는 것과 '모든 것, 심지어 내가 말하는 것에도 의문을 가져 보라'는 것이다.

➡ _____

_____

※ 다음 우리말과 일치하도록 빈칸에 알맞은 말을 쓰시오.

After You Read A

1. In October 2016, stories about scary clowns _____ schools
_____ _____ _____ _____.

2. Garcia-Fuller's students also learn _____ _____ _____
_____ _____ _____ in the news.

3. The site _____ _____ _____ information on this animal,
_____ _____ a few _____ _____ _____ _____ in
trees.

1. 2016년 10월, 무서운 광대들에 관한 이야기가 워싱턴 지역 전역의 학교에 충격을 안겼다.
2. Garcia-Fuller의 학생들은 또한 뉴스에서 사실을 의견과 구분하는 방법에 대해서도 배운다.
3. 그 사이트는 나무 위에 있는 문어들의 몇몇 불확실한 사진과 함께, 이 동물에 대한 정보로 가득 차 있다.

Do It Yourself

1. Team NW _____ _____ _____ _____ _____ the
school festival.

2. They _____ _____ the students and teachers _____ _____
_____ _____.

3. But they performed _____ _____ _____ _____ _____
team.

4. A lot of students _____ _____ and _____ _____ when the
team danced.

5. Ms. Yu, the P.E. teacher, said it was _____ _____ _____
_____ _____.

1. NW 팀은 학교 축제 기간에 무대에서 춤을 선보였다.
2. 그들은 학생들과 선생님들이 그들의 춤을 좋아할지 확신이 서지 않았다.
3. 하지만 그들은 다른 어떠한 팀보다 훨씬 더 멋지게 공연을 해냈다.
4. 그 팀이 춤출 때 많은 학생이 일어서서 크게 환호했다.
5. 체육 선생님인 유 선생님은 그해 최고의 공연이라고 말씀하셨다.

Link to the World

Fact

1. This drawing, *Don Quixote*, is _____ _____ _____ _____.

2. Picasso _____ it in 1955 _____ black lines _____ _____
_____ _____.

Opinion

3. I don't know _____ the man on the horse is _____, but he
_____ _____ and _____.

4. I think he _____ _____ _____ and _____.

5. I think this _____ _____ _____ _____ _____ _____
of Cervantes' novel *Don Quixote*.

사실
1. 이 그림 '돈키호테'는 피카소의 작품 중 하나이다.
2. 피카소는 이 그림을 1955년에 흰 배경과 대비를 이루는 검은 선들로 그렸다.
의견
3. 말 위에 올라탄 남자가 용감한지는 잘 모르겠지만, 그는 매우 피곤하고 굶주려 보인다.
4. 내 생각에는 그에게 약간의 음식과 물이 필요한 것 같다.
5. 나는 이 미술품이 세르반테스의 소설인 '돈키호테'의 가장 흥미로운 부분을 보여 주고 있다고 생각한다.

※ 다음 우리말을 영어로 쓰시오.

After You Read A

1. 2016년 10월, 무서운 광대들에 관한 이야기가 워싱턴 지역 전역의 학교에 충격을 안겼다.

➡ _____

2. Garcia-Fuller의 학생들은 또한 뉴스에서 사실을 의견과 구분하는 방법에 대해서도 배운다.

➡ _____

3. 그 사이트는 나무 위에 있는 문어들의 몇몇 불확실한 사진과 함께, 이 동물에 대한 정보로 가득 차 있다.

➡ _____

Do It Yourself

1. NW 팀은 학교 축제 기간에 무대에서 춤을 선보였다.

➡ _____

2. 그들은 학생들과 선생님들이 그들의 춤을 좋아할지 확신이 서지 않았다.

➡ _____

3. 하지만 그들은 다른 어떠한 팀보다 훨씬 더 멋지게 공연을 해냈다.

➡ _____

4. 그 팀이 춤출 때 많은 학생이 일어서서 크게 환호했다.

➡ _____

5. 체육 선생님인 유 선생님은 그해 최고의 공연이라고 말씀하셨다.

➡ _____

Link to the World

사실

1. 이 그림 '돈키호테'는 피카소의 작품 중 하나이다.

➡ _____

2. 피카소는 이 그림을 1955년에 흰 배경과 대비를 이루는 검은 선들로 그렸다.

➡ _____

의견

3. 말 위에 올라탄 남자가 용감한지는 잘 모르겠지만, 그는 매우 피곤하고 굶주려 보인다.

➡ _____

4. 내 생각에는 그에게 약간의 음식과 물이 필요한 것 같다.

➡ _____

5. 나는 이 미술품이 세르반테스의 소설인 '돈키호테'의 가장 흥미로운 부분을 보여 주고 있다고 생각한다.

➡ _____

MEMO

영어 기출 문제집

2학기

정답 및 해설

천재 | 정사열

중 3

적중100

Pictures Speak a Thousand Words

시험대비 실력평가   p.08

01 (c)urious   02 ②   03 ⑤   04 ④
05 be covered with   06 ③   07 close

01 '무언가에 대하여 알거나 배우기를 원하는'의 뜻인 'curious(호기심 많은, 궁금한)'가 적절하다.

02 'letter'는 '편지', '글자, 문자'의 의미를 지닌다. • 전통적인 편지(mail)는 어떤 사람이 손으로 쓴 편지(letter)이기 때문에 특별한 의미를 포함합니다. • 오래 전에, 우리는 우리 자신의 글자(letter)를 가지고 있지 않았습니다.

03 '어떤 후보자에 대하여 선호를 표시하다'라는 의미로 '투표하다(vote)'가 적절하다.

04 '당신의 애정이나 우정을 보여주기 위하여 양팔로 다른 사람을 안는 행위'의 뜻으로 '포옹(hug)'이 적절하다.

05 '~로 덮이다'는 'be covered with'를 사용한다.

06 (A) 나이아가라 폭포는 정말로 멋진 광경이다. (B) 그는 배우로서 그의 숨겨진 재능을 보여주었다.

07 1. crossing 2. lit 3. oil 4. son 5. except

서술형 시험대비   p.09

01 (1) lots of   (2) wait for   (3) except for
    (4) look after
02 Braille
03 (1) hire   (2) misunderstanding   (3) rather
04 (1) ring, 반지   (2) discover, 발견하다   (3) oil, 기름
    (4) translate, 번역하다
05 (A) (f)oreign   (B) (h)unters   (C) (s)oldier

01 (1) 이 가게에는 많은 멋진 신발이 있다. 'lot'을 이용하여 '많은'의 의미를 나타낼 때는 'lots of'가 적절하다. (2) 우리는 식당에서 20분 동안 그를 기다려야 했다. '~를 기다리다'는 'wait for'를 사용한다. (3) 나는 잘 지내고 있고, 미세먼지를 제외하면 날씨도 좋아. '~을 제외하고'는 'except for'를 사용한다. (4) 이웃이 고양이를 돌보아 달라고 부탁했다. '~를 돌보다'는 'look after'가 적절하다.

02 '시각 장애인들이 만져서 읽는 돋우어진 패턴을 사용하는 인쇄 체계'로 '점자(Braille)'가 적절하다.

03 (1) hire: 고용하다 (2) misunderstanding: 오해 (3) rather: 다소

04 (1) 손가락에 끼는 둥근 형태의 보석 (2) 전에 알지 못하던 것을 찾아내다 (3) 요리를 위하여 사용되는 식물이나 동물로부터 만들어진 걸쭉한 액체 (4) 구어 또는 문어를 다른 언어로 바꾸다

05 (A) 한국 사람들은 인구가 더 많은 다른 외국들보다도 더 많은 물을 쓰고 있습니다. (B) 인간은 가장 위대한 사냥꾼이고 항상 고기를 먹어왔다. (C) 그는 제복을 입고 있기 때문에 군인임에 틀림없다.

교과서
Conversation

핵심 Check   p.10~11

1 ②
2 It means an enemy is coming close to the border.

교과서 대화문 익히기

Check(√) True or False   p.12

1 T   2 F   3 T   4 T

교과서 확인학습   p.14~15

Get Ready 2
(1) curious about, is it / a kind of, tells, batteries, powerful
(2) m curious about / traffic sign, means, enter
(3) dots for, m curious about / Braille, blind / guess, mean
(4) curious, balloon, hanging / ad, product, powerful

Start Off – Listen & Talk A
1. soldiers, chimneys / messages, by using, chimneys / m curious about, system / smoking chimneys / What, mean
2. enemy, smoke at all, do / Smoke, chimney / rising, What does, mean / It means, close, border

Start Off B
is crossing, border, dark, soldiers going to do, messages, about / light, chimneys / light, chimneys / It means, battle

m curious about, language / Let, show, expression / What, mean / It means

hidden secrets / curious about, secrets / yourself / Let's see, letters / one, means, Latin / awesome, Any other / tells, rich / understand / spend lots of, to buy, kind / the rich, that kind / Exactly, speak a thousand

1. gesture, curious about / it means, pond / Why, think so / lots of, pointing, pond

2. So, gesture mean / It means, chicken / should bring, to get. right / I think so

3. What, gesture mean / Turn it off / What makes / The other hunter, close / see

---

시험대비 기본평가   p.16

01 It means, not enter   02 ④

03 ③   04 ⑤

---

01 'It means ~.'는 '그것은 ~을 의미한다.'라는 의미로 정의를 내리는 표현이다. 조동사 must의 부정은 뒤에 not을 사용하고 동사원형 enter를 쓴다.

02 궁금증을 표현하는 말로 'I am curious about ~', 'I'm curious if/whether 주어+동사 ~', 'I would like/want to know ~', 'I'd be very interested to know ~', 'Can you tell me about ~?' 등이 있다.

03 'I'm curious ~.' 등으로 상대방이 궁금증을 표현하거나 의미를 물어보면 'This/It means ~.(그것은 ~을 의미한다.)' 또는 'It is ~.(그것은 ~이다.)' 등의 표현을 사용하여 상대방이 궁금해하거나 알고 싶어 하는 것의 의미나 정의를 설명하는 표현을 쓰는 것이 적절하다.

04 'I'm curious about ~'은 '나는 ~이 궁금해'라는 의미로 궁금증을 표현하는 것이다.

시험대비 실력평가   p.17~18

01 ③, ⑤   02 (d) / Other → The other[Another]

03 ④   04 ②   05 ⑤   06 ④

07 batteries   08 ②   09 for   10 ③

11 this painting

---

01 빈칸 앞의 대화가 '그것은 "그것을 꺼."를 의미해.'라고 궁금증을 설명해주는 말을 하고, 그 말에 대해 '정말?'이라고 놀라움을 표현하고 있기 때문에 그 말을 한 이유를 물어보는 것이 타당하다.

02 'other'는 뒤에 복수명사가 온다. 단수명사 'hunter'와 함께 사용될 수 있는 단어는 'the other' 또는 'another'이다.

03 '메시지를 보내기 위해서 병사들은 무슨 일을 할까?'라는 물음 뒤에 그것에 관한 궁금함을 표현하는 말이 오는 것이 자연스럽다.

04 빈칸 (B) 다음의 말이 '그것은 전투가 시작되었음을 의미해.'라는 것으로 보아 빈칸은 의미를 묻는 말이 오는 것이 자연스럽다.

05 적이 없을 때 연기를 피운다고 했으므로 글의 흐름상 굴뚝 한 곳에서 나오는 연기는 'No enemy.(적이 없음.)'을 나타낸다.

06 '그들은 연기를 전혀 피우지 않아, 그렇지?'라는 부정의문문으로 'Yes'는 '아니'로 해석한다.

07 라디오, 장난감, 자동차와 같은 것에 전기를 공급하는 물체

08 나머지는 모두 궁금증을 표현하는 말이고, ②번은 놀라움을 나타낼 때 사용하는 표현이다.

09 (a)는 '~은 무엇을 위한 거니?'라는 의미로 'What ~ for?' 구문이고, (b)는 의미상 '시각장애인을 위한'의 의미로 전치사 'for'가 적절하다.

10 그림에 숨겨진 또 다른 비밀에 관한 말로 보기 (C) 앞의 "Okay."와 뒤의 "I don't understand."가 부자연스럽기 때문에 (C)에 들어가는 것이 적절하다.

11 it은 인칭대명사로 주어인 This painting을 가리킨다.

서술형 시험대비   p.19

01 They mean "Jan van Eyck was here. 1434."

02 (A) I'm curious about them.   (B) It means

03 What makes you think so?

04 They mean they just saw an enemy.

05 They are sending messages to the king by using the chimneys.

---

01 질문: 여자아이가 찾은 글자는 무엇을 의미하는가?

02 (A) 궁금증을 나타내는 표현으로 'be curious about'을 사용하고 'secrets'는 복수형이므로 복수대명사 'them'을 사용한다. (B) 'It means ~.(그것은 ~을 의미한다.)'라는 의미로 정의를 표현하는 말이다.

03 'Why do you think so?'와 같은 의미로 'What makes you think so?'를 사용할 수 있다.

04 'They mean+주어+동사' 어순을 이용한다.

교과서

Grammar

핵심 Check   p.20~21

1 (1) were   (2) would

2 (1) whose   (2) whose   (3) enjoy

시험대비 기본평가 p.22

01 (1) If I were[was] a duck

(2) What would you do

(3) whose dog is carrying a doll

(4) whose dog wants a hot dog

02 (1) If I had wings, I would fly in the sky.

(2) What would you do if you were a fish?

(3) Koko is the boy whose bag is on a big cat.

(4) The girl whose cat is dancing is Didi.

03 (1) If I had a lot of money, I could travel around the world.

(2) If I were[was] tall, I could be a basketball player.

01 (1), (2) 현재 사실에 대한 가정은 'If+주어+동사 과거형, 주어+조동사 과거형(would/should/could/might)+동사원형'의 형태로 쓴다. (3) 'Bubu is the boy.' 문장에서 선행사 the boy 뒤에 소유격 관계대명사 문장을 이어 쓴다. (4) 'Lala is the girl.' 문장에서 선행사 the girl 뒤에 소유격 관계대명사 문장을 이어 쓴다.

02 (1) 가정법 과거 문장은 주절에 조동사의 과거형을 쓴다. (2) 가정법 과거 문장은 If절에 과거동사를 쓴다. (3) 선행사가 사람일 때 소유격 관계대명사는 of which를 쓰지 않고 whose를 쓴다. (4) 사람이 선행사이므로 소유격 관계대명사는 whose를 쓴다.

03 (1), (2) 현재 사실에 대한 가정은 'If+주어+동사 과거형, 주어+조동사 과거형(would/should/could/might)+동사원형'의 형태로 쓴다.

시험대비 실력평가 p.23~25

01 ④   02 ①

03 There was a queen whose daughter was cursed by an evil fairy.

04 ①   05 ③   06 ②

07 Miso is a girl whose dog is jumping rope.

08 If I had a lot of money, I could buy that car.

09 ③, ⑤

10 (1) If I had a monkey, I could play with it.

또는 If I have a monkey, I can play with it.

(2) The boys whose mom is a lawyer live next door.

11 ⑤

12 (1) would build (2) knew (3) whose (4) who

(5) whose

13 ④

14 If I were[was] a bird, I would fly over the mountain.

15 The animal whose name begins with z is a zebra.

16 ④   17 ④   18 ⑤

19 If I met the President, I would shake hands with him[her].

20 (1) would / would (2) were / were[was]

21 she doesn't work with him, is not[isn't] very disappointed with him

01 선행사가 사물일 때 소유격 관계대명사로 whose와 of which 둘 중의 하나를 쓴다. 이때 whose는 무관사의 명사를 써야 하므로 the+명사가 있는 경우는 of which를 쓴다.

02 선행사가 사물일 때 소유격 관계대명사로 whose와 of which 둘 중의 하나를 쓴다. 이때 whose는 무관사의 명사를 써야 하고, the+명사가 있는 경우는 of which를 쓴다.

03 두 문장에서 a queen과 소유격 Her는 동일 인물이므로 소유격 관계사 whose로 연결하여 쓴다.

04 ② drove → drive ③ can → could ④ wins → won ⑤ will → would

05 ③ 건강 상태가 좋아서, 나는 너와 운동할 수 있다. ①, ②, ④, ⑤ 건강 상태가 좋다면, 나는 너와 운동할 텐데. (건강 상태가 좋지 않아서, 나는 너와 운동할 수 없다.)

06 '내가 너라면'이 적절하므로 둘 다 'were'를 쓴다.

07 선행사 a girl 뒤에 소유격 관계대명사를 이어서 쓴다.

08 가정법과거는 현재 사실과 반대되므로 직설법 부정은 가정법 긍정으로 쓰고, 동사는 과거시제로 쓴다.

09 우리는 충분한 시간이 없기 때문에 더 오래 머무를 수 없다. = 우리가 충분한 시간이 있다면, 더 오래 머무를 텐데. (가정법과거) *with: ~이 있다면, without: ~이 없다면 (if절을 대신할 수 있다.)

10 (1) 가정법 과거형 또는 조건절의 형태로 주절과 if절을 맞추어 쓴다. (2) 동사 lives의 주어는 The boys이므로 live로 쓴다. 또는 The boy whose mom is a lawyer lives next door.로 고쳐도 좋다.

11 가정법 과거의 주절은 '조동사의 과거형+동사원형'으로 쓴다. lent → would lend

12 (1) 가정법 과거의 주절은 '조동사의 과거형+동사원형'으로 쓴다. (2) 가정법 과거 문장은 If절에 과거동사를 쓴다. (3) 관계대명사의 선행사 'a friend'가 family를 소유하는 것이 자연스럽다. (4) 관계대명사 다음에 동사가 이어지는 것은 주격 관계대명사 문장이다. (5) 관계대명사의 선행사 animals가 명사 lives를 소유하는 것이 자연스럽다.

13 현재 사실에 대한 가정은 'If+주어+동사 과거형, 주어+조동사 과거형(would/should/could/might)+동사원형'의 형태로 쓴다.

14 현재 사실에 대한 가정은 'If+주어+동사 과거형, 주어+조동사 과거형(would/should/could/might)+동사원형'의 형태로 쓴다.

15 The animal is a zebra 문장에서, 선행사 The animal 뒤에 소유격 관계대명사 whose를 사용하여 문장을 이어 쓰고 술부 is a zebra를 쓴다.

16 현재 사실에 대한 가정은 'If+주어+동사 과거형, 주어+조동사 과거형(would/should/could/might)+동사원형'의 형태로 쓴다.

17 두 문장에서 A girl과 소유격 Her는 동일 인물이므로 소유격 관계사 whose로 연결하여 쓴다.

18 첫 번째 문장은 'They taste like apples.'에서 주어 They로 관계대명사를 만들었기 때문에 which 또는 that을 쓴다. 두 번째 문장은 'Its smell is so sweet.'에서 소유격 Its로 관계대명사를 만들었기 때문에 whose를 쓴다.

19 현재 사실에 대한 가정은 'If+주어+동사 과거형, 주어+조동사 과거형(would/should/could/might)+동사원형'의 형태로 쓴다.

20 (1) 주절에 조동사의 과거형을 쓴다. (2) '네가 오리라면', '내가 오리라면'의 뜻에는 were가 적절하다.

21 가정법과거의 문장은 현재 사실에 대한 반대를 가정한 문장이므로, 가정법 문장이 부정이면 직설법 문장은 긍정으로, 가정법이 과거시제이면 직설법은 현재시제로 쓴다.

서술형 시험대비
p.26~27

01 (1) I have a friend whose brother enjoys skateboarding.
(2) The boy who[that] is dancing on the floor is my brother.
(3) He wants to ride a bike which[that] I bought yesterday.
(4) Do you like the house whose roof looks like a hat? 또는 Do you like the house of which the roof[the roof of which] looks like a hat?
(5) The boy whose cat is spinning a hula hoop is Jeje.

02 (1) If I had strong arms, I could climb trees.
(2) If I had a long nose, I could use it to take a shower.
(3) If I had a beautiful voice, I would sing on the tree.

03 (1) If I were[was] an English teacher, I would play word games every day.
(2) If I were[was] on the moon, I could jump much higher.

04 (1) Were he rich, he could travel to Europe.
(2) The boy who[that] is talking to Mary is my cousin.

(3) He lent me the book which[that] I want to read.
(4) I stayed at the house whose walls are white. 또는 I stayed at the house of which the walls[the walls of which] are white.
(5) If I were you, I would take a swimming lesson.

05 (1) would give (2) would dance with them
(3) would get my feet

06 were[was], could sing and dance

07 (1) he doesn't talk to her. (또는 he won't talk to her)
(2) Were he at home

08 (1) The boy whose cell phone is ringing loudly doesn't understand the man's gesture.
(2) The girl whose feet are in the water doesn't understand the man's gesture.
(3) The boy whose hand the woman is pulling doesn't understand her gesture.
(4) The boy whose bag the monkey is pulling doesn't understand its gesture.

01 (1) 두 문장에서 a friend와 소유격 His는 동일 인물이므로 소유격 관계대명사 whose로 연결하여 쓴다. (2) 두 문장에서 The boy와 주어 He가 동일 인물이므로 주격관계대명사 who 또는 that으로 연결하여 쓴다. (3) 두 문장에서 a bike와 목적어 it이 동일하므로 목적격 관계대명사 which 또는 that으로 연결하여 쓴다. (4) 두 문장에서 a house와 소유격 whose가 동일하므로 소유격 관계대명사 whose로 연결하여 쓴다. (5) 두 문장에서 The boy와 소유격 His는 동일 인물이므로 소유격 관계대명사 whose로 연결하여 쓴다.

02 현재 사실에 대한 가정은 'If+주어+동사 과거형, 주어+조동사 과거형(would/should/could/might)+동사원형'의 형태로 쓴다.

03 가정법 과거는 현재 사실과 반대되므로 직설법 부정은 가정법 긍정으로 쓰고, 동사는 과거시제로 쓴다.

04 (1) rich는 형용사이므로 be동사 were로 가정법 문장을 쓴다. (2) 관계대명사가 주어 역할을 하는 문장이므로 소유격이 아닌 주격 관계대명사를 쓴다. (3) 관계대명사가 목적어 역할을 하는 문장이므로 소유격이 아닌 목적격 관계대명사를 쓴다. (4) 선행사 the house가 walls를 소유하는 문장이므로 소유격 관계대명사 whose나 of which를 쓴다. (5) 가정법 과거의 주절은 '조동사의 과거형+동사원형'으로 쓴다.

05 가정법 과거의 주절은 '조동사의 과거형+동사원형'으로 쓴다.

06 현재 사실에 대한 가정은 'If+주어+동사 과거형, 주어+조동사 과거형(would/should/could/might)+동사원형'의 형태로 쓴다.

07 (1) 가정법 과거는 현재 사실과 반대되므로 직설법 문장으로 표

5

현할 때 긍정은 부정문으로, 과거시제는 현재시제로 쓴다. (2) 'If 주어 were ~'로 표현한 가정법은 if를 생략하고 were를 문두로 도치할 수 있다.

08 (1) 두 문장에서 The boy와 소유격 His는 동일 인물이므로 소유격 관계사 whose로 연결하여 쓴다. (2) 두 문장에서 The girl 과 소유격 Her는 동일 인물이므로 소유격 관계사 whose로 연결하여 쓴다. (3) 두 문장에서 The boy와 소유격 his hand의 his 는 동일 인물이므로 소유격 관계사 whose로 연결하여 쓴다. (4) 두 문장에서 The boy와 소유격 his bag의 his는 동일 인물이므로 소유격 관계사 whose로 연결하여 쓴다.

Reading

확인문제　　　　　　　　　　p.28

1 T　2 F　3 T　4 F　5 T　6 F

확인문제　　　　　　　　　　p.29

1 T　2 F　3 T　4 F　5 T　6 F

교과서 확인학습 A　　　　　p.30~31

01 A Picture Letter
02 Speaking, is rather
03 that easy
04 waited for, for weeks
05 couldn't read or write
06 got over
07 whose, far away
08 in Germany
09 more than 5%, one of them
10 was discovered by
11 translated, into
12 reach, out
13 all in good health, one
14 not seriously
15 there was no reply
16 got, would be
17 fell ill
18 while, looks after
19 had, prepare, plant
20 voted for
21 so, that
22 whether one or the other
23 Nothing changes
24 will work again
25 picked, from
26 hired, whose
27 knocked, down, picking, up
28 paid, for
29 spent, for
30 enough, to fill, one
31 at a price of
32 as
33 would be, were
34 miss
35 a big hug
36 dear love
37 joined, as

교과서 확인학습 B　　　　　p.32~33

1 A Picture Letter from a Mother of Three
2 Speaking to family members or friends in a foreign country is rather easy and simple today.
3 But before the days of phones and the Internet, it was not that easy.
4 People just sent a letter and waited for a reply for weeks.
5 And it was a lot harder if they couldn't read or write.
6 This letter shows how people got over these difficulties.
7 It was written in 1973 by a woman whose husband was far away.
8 She lived in Sicily, an Italian island, while her husband worked in Germany.
9 At the time, more than 5% of the people in Italy could not read or write, and she was one of them.
10 This letter was discovered by Sicilian writer Gesualdo Bufalino.
11 Here's how he translated the pictures into words.
12 My dear love, I miss you so much, and I reach my arms out toward you, together with our three kids.
13 We are all in good health except for the little one.
14 He's a little sick, but not seriously.
15 I already sent you a letter, but there was no reply, so I am sad about it.
16 If I got a letter from you, I would be very happy.
17 Your mother fell ill, and I'm going to visit her in the hospital with some money and food.
18 I'll go there with our middle son while the oldest looks after the youngest.
19 I had two workers prepare our field and plant seeds for 150,000 lire.
20 I voted for the DC.
21 The PCI lost so many seats that it almost seems dead.
22 But whether one or the other wins, it's the same.
23 Nothing changes for us poor people.
24 We worked yesterday, and we will work again tomorrow.
25 We picked lots of olives from our olive trees this year.
26 I hired a man whose sons are good workers.
27 He knocked the olives down, and his two sons helped him, picking them up from the ground.
28 I paid him 27,000 lire for the work.
29 I spent 12,000 more for the olive press.

30 I got enough oil to fill a large pot and a small one.

31 I can sell it at a price of 1,300 lire a liter.

32 My love, my heart thinks of you as Christmas is coming.

33 I would be so happy if you were with me.

34 We all miss you so much.

35 I'm sending you a big hug from me and our three little kids.

36 Goodbye, dear love.

37 My heart is yours, joined to you as our two rings are.

시험대비 실력평가

01 ②, ④, ⑤　　02 ④　　　　03 ⑤　　　　04 hired

05 일꾼이 올리브를 쳐서 떨어뜨리면 그의 두 아들이 땅에서 올리브를 주우면서 그를 도와주는 일

06 per　　　　07 ②　　　　08 ①　　　　09 ⑤

10 ①　　　　11 ⓑ so　ⓒ that

12 one hundred (and) fifty thousand　　13 ④

14 (A) missed　(B) three kids

15 joined　　16 ②　　　　17 joined

18 As[Because, Since] I don't get a letter from you, I'm not very happy. 또는 I don't get a letter from you, so I'm not very happy.

19 ①, ③

20 (A) nothing　(B) worked　(C) will work

21 ②　　　　22 there was no reply

23 If I got a letter from you, I would be very happy.

24 ④　　　　25 ②, ④　　　26 ⑤

01 ⓐ와 ②, ④, ⑤: 동명사, ①, ③: 현재분사

02 이 글은 '전화와 인터넷 시대 이전에 외국에 있는 가족이나 친구와 대화하는 것이 그렇게 쉽지 않았다'는 내용의 글이므로, 제목으로는 ④번 '예전에 해외에 있는 사람들에게 말하는 것의 어려움'이 적절하다.

03 ⑤ 이 글만 읽고서는 읽거나 쓸 수 없는 사람들이 외국에 있는 사람들과 어떻게 대화했는지는 대답할 수 없다. ① No, it is rather easy and simple today. ② No, it was not that easy. ③ They just sent a letter and waited for a reply for weeks. ④ It took weeks.

04 hire: 고용하다

05 일꾼과 그의 두 아들이 한 일을 쓰는 것이 적절하다.

06 ⓒ의 a는 '(가격·양·비율을 나타내어) ~당'이라는 뜻으로, 'per(~당[마다])'로 바꿔 쓸 수 있다.

07 ⓐ by: ~가 한(수동형 문장에서 행위자, 창작자 등을 나타냄), ⓑ translate A into B: A를 B로 번역하다, 해석하다

08 주어진 문장의 It에 주목한다. ①번 앞 문장의 This letter를 받고 있으므로 ①번이 적절하다.

09 Gesualdo Bufalino는 그녀의 '그림들'을 '글'로 번역했다. ② illiterate: 글을 (읽거나 쓸 줄) 모르는, 문맹의

10 have+사람+동사원형

11 so ... that ~ = so ... as to ~: 너무 …해서 ~하다

12 보통 3자리씩 끊어서 읽고, 천의 자리에 thousand를 붙여서 읽는 것이 적절하다. one hundred (and) fifty thousands(X)

13 '세 아이와 함께 당신을 향해 내 팔을 쭉 뻗고 있어요. 막내를 제외하고는 우리 모두 건강해요.'라는 내용을 나타내는 그림으로는 ④번이 적절하다.

14 한 여성이 멀리 떨어져 있는 남편을 '그리워하며' 그녀와 그들의 '세 아이'가 어떻게 지내고 있는지를 알려주는 편지를 썼다.

15 "I join my heart to you"의 수동태 형태로 '(my heart is) joined to you'로 쓰인 것이다. 분사구문의 형태로 볼 수 있다. joined: 연결된 채로

16 '나와 우리 세 아이의 큰 포옹을 보내요. 내 마음은 당신의 것이에요, 우리들의 두 반지처럼 당신과 연결된 채로요'라는 내용을 나타내는 그림으로는 ②번이 적절하다.

17 are 뒤에 'joined'가 생략되었다.

18 가정법 과거 문장은 현재 사실과 반대되는 상상이나 가정을 나타내는 것이므로, 직설법으로 고칠 때는 현재시제를 사용하는 것이 적절하다.

19 look after = take care of = care for: ~을 돌보다, ② ~을 닮다, ④ ~을 찾다, 구하다, ⑤ ~의 안부를 묻다, 문안하다

20 가난한 사람들에게는 '아무 것도 바뀌지 않고' 그들은 어제도 '일했고', 내일도 다시 '일할' 것이기 때문이다.

21 ⓐ와 ②: 그리워[아쉬워]하다, ① (치거나 잡거나 닿지 못하고) 놓치다[빗나가다], ③ (식사 등을) 거르다, ④ (기회를) 놓치다, ⑤ (어디에 참석하지 않아서 그 일을) 놓치다

22 '(편지를 보냈는데) 답장이 없는 것'을 가리킨다.

23 현재 사실과 반대되는 상상이나 가정을 나타내는 가정법 과거 문장으로 쓰는 것이 적절하다.

24 ⓐ [교환] ~에 대하여, ~의 금액[값]으로, ⓑ at a price of: ~의 가격으로

25 ⓒ와 ②, ④: (가격·양·비율을 나타내어) ~당, ① (사람의 이름 앞에 쓰여) ~라는 사람, ③ 단수 명사 앞에 쓰여 그 부류를 통칭함, ⑤ 글 속에 처음 언급되는 단수형 명사 앞에 쓰임.

26 글쓴이가 올리브 기름(올리브유)을 팔아 얼마를 벌었는지는 알 수 없다. ① Yes. ② A man whose sons are good workers. ③ 27,000 lire. ④ The writer got enough oil to fill a large pot and a small one.

01 This letter shows how people got over these difficulties

02 Sicilian writer Gesualdo Bufalino discovered this letter.

03 (A) her husband   (B) in Germany

04 stretch   05 We are all in good health

06 kid   07 (A) 27,000   (B) 12,000   (C) 1,300

08 the olives   09 She spent 39,000 lire.

10 I already sent a letter to you

11 will → would

12 (A) fell ill   (B) some money and food

13 for   14 to prepare   15 as

16 As[Because, Since] you are not with me, I'm not so happy. 또는 You are not with me, so I'm not so happy.

01 shows의 목적어를 간접의문문의 순서(how+주어+동사)로 쓰는 것이 적절하다.

02 Sicilian writer Gesualdo Bufalino를 주어로 해서 능동태로 고치는 것이 적절하다.

03 '독일'에서 일하는 '그녀의 남편'에게 편지를 썼다.

04 reach ~ out = stretch ~ out: (손 등을) 내밀다, 뻗다

05 be in good health: 건강 상태가 좋다

06 세 아이(three kids) 중 막내'아이'를 가리킨다.

07 그림 편지의 '일꾼이 올리브를 쳐서 떨어뜨리면 그의 두 아들이 땅에서 올리브를 주우면서 그를 도와주는 것'을 나타내는 가운데 그림을 참조하여 (A)에는 '27,000'을, '올리브 압착'을 나타내는 오른쪽 그림을 참조하여 (B)에는 '12,000'을, '큰 항아리 하나와 작은 항아리 하나를 채울 만큼의 충분한 기름'을 나타내는 왼쪽 그림을 참조하여 (C)에는 '1,300'을 쓰는 것이 적절하다.

08 '올리브'를 가리킨다.

09 올리브나무에서 올리브를 따는 비용 27,000리라+올리브를 압착하는 비용 12,000리라 = 39,000리라

10 send는 to를 사용하여 3형식으로 고친다.

11 가정법 과거 문장이므로, 주절의 시제를 'would'+동사원형으로 고치는 것이 적절하다.

12 그녀의 시어머니께서 '병이 드셔서' 병원에 계시기 때문에, 그녀는 '약간의 돈과 음식'을 가지고 병원을 방문할 예정이다. mother-in-law: 시어머니

13 ⓐ [교환] ~의 금액[값]으로, ⓑ vote for: ~에 (찬성) 투표를 하다

14 have+사람+동사원형 = get+사람+to부정사

15 ⓐ as Christmas is coming: 크리스마스가 다가오면서, ⓑ ~처럼

16 가정법 과거 문장은 현재 사실과 반대되는 상상이나 가정을 나타내는 것이므로, 직설법으로 고칠 때는 현재시제를 사용하는 것이 적절하다.

01 hug   02 ②   03 ⑤   04 ①

05 expression   06 ③

07 (a) board → border   08 ④   09 ②

10 ③   11 ⑤   12 ⑤

13 (1) I didn't know the singer, I couldn't shake hands with him
   (2) he were[was] smart, he would prepare for the game in advance

14 ①   15 ⓓdon't → didn't   16 ③

17 ③   18 could see, were[was] taller

19 (1) would use kites to send my messages
   (2) whose face looks like a mountain
   (3) whose bag is full of fruit

20 ②

21 more than 5% of the people in Italy who could not read or write

22 ③   23 ⑤   24 reply   25 ③

26 ①   27 picking them up from the ground

28 were[was]   29 its gesture

01 유의어 관계이다. 고용하다 – 포옹하다, 안다

02 (a): 당신은 추위를 극복하기 위한 당신만의 방법을 갖고 있나요? (b): 이것이 존경할 만한 정치인을 뽑는 것이 중요한 이유이다.

03 한 여자가 결혼한 남자

04 '위원회, 법정 등의 구성원으로서의 지위'의 뜻으로 'seat(의석)'이 적절하다.

05 '특별한 의미를 가지는 단어들의 그룹'의 의미를 가지는 'expression(표현)'이 적절하다.

06 'whether'는 부사절 접속사로 사용되면 '~이든 아니든'의 의미가 된다. 명사절 접속사일 때는 '~인지 아닌지'로 해석한다.

07 board: 판, 위원회, border: 국경

08 그 당시의 사람들이 어떤 종류의 개를 기르고 싶어했는지는 알 수가 없다.

09 위 대화는 Jan van Eyck의 그림 속에 숨겨진 비밀을 발견하여 그림을 통해 화가가 전달하고자 하는 메시지를 파악할 수 있는지에 관한 내용이다.

10 (C) '이 점들이 무엇을 위한거니?'라고 궁금증을 표현하는 말이 오고 → (B) 궁금증에 대한 설명이 오고, Braille의 용도를 이야기해 준다. (A) 마지막으로 알았다는 대답이 오는 것이 자연스럽다.

11 '난 수화가 궁금해'라는 A의 말에 대해, B가 '내가 표현 하나를 알려줄게. 봐. 그것은 무엇을 의미하니?'라고 다시 묻는 것은 어색하다.

12 가정법 과거의 문장이 '만일 그가 춤을 잘 춘다면' 이므로 직설법 문장은 '그는 춤을 못 추기 때문에'로 쓰는 것이 적절하다. 'not poor'를 'poor' 또는 'not good'으로 쓴다.

13 가정법 과거는 현재 사실과 반대되므로 직설법 문장을 가정법으로 표현할 때 긍정은 부정문으로, 부정은 긍정문으로 쓰고, 현재 시제는 과거시제로 쓴다.

14 ①은 두 문장을 연결하는 접속사와 주어 역할을 하는 주격 관계대명사가 필요하므로 which 또는 that을 쓴다. ②, ③, ④, ⑤는 소유격 관계대명사 whose를 쓴다.

15 가정법 과거 문장이므로 if절의 동사를 과거시제로 쓴다.

16 ③은 의문사 whose이다. ①, ②, ④, ⑤는 소유격 관계대명사 whose이다.

17 c. have → had d. won't → wouldn't e. will → would

18 현재 사실에 대한 가정은 'If+주어+동사 과거형, 주어+조동사 과거형(would/should/could/might)+동사원형'의 형태로 쓴다.

19 (1) 가정법 과거의 주절은 '조동사의 과거형+동사원형'으로 쓴다. (2) 선행사 a kite가 명사 face를 소유하는 것이 자연스러우므로 whose를 쓴다. (3) 선행사 The boy가 명사 bag을 소유하는 것이 자연스러우므로 whose를 쓴다.

20 선행사가 사물인 경우에는 소유격을 whose나 of which로 쓸 수 있지만, 사람인 경우에는 of which로 쓸 수 없다. ① overcome: 극복하다, ③ over: ~ 이상, ④ the Italians: 이탈리아 사람들, ⑤ 관계부사 'how'를 'the way'로 바꿔 쓸 수 있다. 그러나 'the way how'와 같이 선행사와 관계부사를 함께 쓸 수는 없다.

21 '읽거나 쓸 수 없었던 5% 이상의 이탈리아 사람들'을 가리킨다.

22 글의 마지막에서 '그가 그림들을 어떻게 글로 번역했는지는 다음과 같다.'고 했으므로, 뒤에 올 내용으로는 'Gesualdo Bufalino가 그림 편지들을 글로 번역한 내용'이 가장 적절하다.

23 ⓐ와 ⑤: 가산 명사를 반복하는 것을 피하기 위해 쓰임. ① 하나(의), ② (과거·미래의) 어느 한, ③ 같은, ④ 사람, 누구나

24 ⓑ의 letter는 '편지'를 가리킨다.

25 글쓴이는 남편에게 이미 편지를 보냈지만, 답장이 없어서 슬프다고 했으므로, 처음으로 편지를 보내고 있다는 ③번은 옳지 않다. ④ mother-in-law: 시어머니.

26 ①번 다음 문장의 He에 주목한다. 주어진 문장의 a man을 받고 있으므로 ①번이 적절하다.

27 이어동사 picking: '주우면서'라는 의미로 동시 동작을 표현한다. 이어동사 picking up의 목적어가 인칭대명사 them이므로 picking과 up 사이에 them을 쓰는 것이 적절하다.

28 가정법 과거이므로 'were'로 쓰는 것이 적절하다. if절에 쓰이는 be동사의 과거형은 보통 'were'를 사용하지만, 구어체에서는

주어가 'I' 또는 3인칭 단수인 경우 'was'를 쓰기도 한다.

29 '원숭이의 몸짓'을 가리킨다.

단원별 예상문제 p.46~49

01 (a)live 02 ②
03 It means "Do not[Don't] enter." 또는 It means (that) you must not enter here.
04 (C) - (A) - (B) - (D)
05 They are for sending messages to the king.
06 ③ 07 ② 08 ④ 09 ⑤
10 ③ 11 ①
12 (1) Is there any student whose name was not called?
(2) Mike is the boy whose hair is very short.
(3) The house whose windows are very big is my uncle's.
(4) My sister is the girl whose cat is eating a fish.
(5) Do you know the old man whose shoes are red and blue?
13 (1) I know a boy whose mother grows bananas.
(2) The boy whose dog is barking is my cousin.
(3) The girl whose hat is covered with flowers is a great dancer.
(4) If you were with me(또는 Were you with me), I could show you my painting.
(5) If I were a fish, I could swim in the water.
14 Speaking to family members or friends in a foreign country
15 ② 16 ④ 17 ① 18 out
19 ③ 20 don't → doesn't
21 ②, ③, ⑤

01 반의어 관계다. 아픈-건강한 : 죽은-살아 있는

02 '어떤 것을 사용할 준비가 되도록 하다'라는 의미로 'prepare(준비하다)'가 적절하다.

03 그림은 진입 금지를 나타내는 표지판이다.

04 '병사들이 5개의 굴뚝으로 무엇을 하고 있니?'라는 물음에 → (C) 왕에게 메시지를 보내고 있다는 답을 하고 → (A) '정말?'이라고 놀라움을 표현한 다음, 그 체계에 대한 궁금증을 표현하며, 좀 더 말해달라고 부탁을 하는 말에 대해 → (B) '연기 나는 굴뚝 두 개가 보이지?'라는 물음을 통해 그 체계에 대한 질문을 하고 마지막으로 → (D) 긍정의 답을 하며 그것이 무엇을 의미하는지 묻고, 소녀의 마지막 말이 오는 것이 적절하다.

05 질문: 그 굴뚝들은 무엇을 위한 것이라고 생각하는가?

06 G의 빈칸 다음 말에서 굴뚝 하나에서 연기가 나오면 적이 없다는 것을 의미한다고 했으므로, '만약 적이 없다면, 그들은 연기

9

를 전혀 피우지 않아, 그렇지?'라는 B의 물음에 대해 '아니, 연기를 피워.'라는 대답이 적절하다.

07 주어진 문장은 '그것은 "Jan van Eyck가 여기 있었다. 1434."를 의미해.'라는 뜻으로 (B)에 오는 것이 적절하다.

08 남자의 마지막 말에 '그 여자는 연못을 가리키고 있어.'라고 말하는 것으로 보아 ④번이 자연스럽다.

09 ⑤번은 '이 집은 수 천 개의 비밀을 가진 것으로 유명해.'라는 말에 대해 '정말? 그것은 네가 비밀을 찾아야 하는 것을 의미해.'라고 말하는 것은 자연스럽지 않다.

10 빈칸 다음에 '그럼 그 소년은 과일을 얻기 위해 닭을 한 마리 가져와야 하는구나, 맞지?'라고 말하는 것으로 보아 ③이 적절하다.

11 선행사 The house 뒤에 its doors의 관계이므로 whose doors로 쓴다.

12 (1) 두 문장에서 any student와 소유격 His는 동일 인물이므로 소유격 관계사 whose로 연결하여 쓴다. (2) 두 문장에서 The boy와 소유격 His는 동일 인물이므로 소유격 관계사 whose로 연결하여 쓴다. (3) 두 문장에서 The house와 소유격 Its가 동일하므로 소유격 관계사 whose로 연결하여 쓴다. (4) 두 문장에서 the girl과 소유격 Her는 동일 인물이므로 소유격 관계사 whose로 연결하여 쓴다. (5) 두 문장에서 the old man과 소유격 His는 동일 인물이므로 소유격 관계사 whose로 연결하여 쓴다.

13 (1) 선행사 a boy가 mother를 소유하는 문장이므로 주격이 아닌 소유격 관계대명사 whose를 쓴다. (2) 선행사가 사람일 때는 소유격 관계대명사로 of which가 아닌 whose를 쓴다. (3) 선행사 The girl이 문장의 주어이므로 동사는 are가 아닌 is를 쓴다. (4) 한 문장에 두 개의 절이 있을 때 접속사가 필요하므로 If you were with me, 또는 if를 생략한 도치문장 Were you with me로 쓴다. (5) 가정법 과거의 주절은 '조동사의 과거형+동사원형'으로 쓴다.

14 '외국에 있는 가족이나 친구와 대화하는 것'을 가리킨다.

15 ⓑ와 ①, ⑤: 지시부사('그렇게'), ②, ④: 지시형용사, ③: 접속사

16 ⓓ a lot(much/even/still/far): 비교급을 강조하는 부사('훨씬'), ④ rather: 다소, 약간.

17 주어진 문장의 We에 주목한다. ①번 앞 문장의 'I'와 'our three kids'를 받고 있으므로 ①번이 적절하다.

18 reach ~ out: '(손 등을) 내밀다, 뻗다,' 목적어가 명사일 경우에는 목적어를 out 다음에 쓰는 것도 가능하다.

19 그녀의 남편으로부터 왜 답장이 없었는지는 알 수 없다. ① There were three kids. ② No. ④ She will visit the hospital with her middle son. ⑤ The oldest will look after the youngest.

20 The boy가 주어이므로 don't를 doesn't로 고치는 것이 적절하다.

21 right away = right now = at once = immediately: 즉시, ① 머뭇거리며, 망설이며, ④ 순차적으로

서술형 실전문제 p.50~51

01 It tells people their batteries are very powerful.
02 Pictures speak a thousand words
03 hidden secrets, Latin, means, the rich, rich
04 (1) ㉠ → was created (2) ㉡ → (to) use
    (3) ㉢ → couldn't
05 (1) If I didn't have any money, I couldn't buy the new shoes.
    (2) If Suji were[was] here, I could tell her the story.
06 (1) If I were[was] you, I would set the alarm clock.
    (2) If I were[was] you, I would write it by hand.
    (3) If I were[was] you, I would search it on the Internet.
07 picking up them → picking them up
08 olive oil   09 whose
10 (A) is   (B) while   (C) how
11 it was a lot harder if they couldn't read or write.

01 'tell+간접목적어(people)+직접목적어(their batteries are ~)' 어순으로 쓴다.

02 그림을 통해 여러 가지 숨겨진 사실들을 알 수 있다는 내용이므로 'Pictures speak a thousand words(그림이 천 마디 말을 하지.)'가 적절하다.

04 (1) 주어 Hangeul과 동사 'create'는 수동 관계이므로 수동태를 쓴다. (2) help의 목적보어는 원형부정사 또는 to부정사를 쓴다. (3) 가정법 과거를 써야 하므로 조동사를 과거형으로 쓴다.

05 가정법 과거는 현재 사실과 반대되므로 직설법 문장을 가정법으로 표현할 때, 긍정은 부정문으로, 부정은 긍정문으로 쓰고, 현재시제는 과거시제로 쓴다.

06 현재 사실에 대한 가정은 'If+주어+동사 과거형, 주어+조동사 과거형(would/should/could/might)+동사원형'의 형태로 쓴다.

07 picking up의 목적어가 대명사 them이므로 picking과 up 사이에 them을 쓰는 것이 적절하다.

08 '올리브기름(올리브유)'을 가리킨다.

09 소유격 관계대명사 'whose'가 적절하다.

10 (A) 동명사 Speaking이 문장의 주어이므로 is가 적절하다. (B) 뒤에 '주어+동사'가 있으므로 while이 적절하다. during+기간을 나타내는 명사, while+주어+동사, (C) 뒤에 완전한 문장이 이어지고 있으므로 관계부사 how가 적절하다.

11 'Speaking to family members or friends in a foreign country'를 가리키는 'it'을 주어로 해서 쓰는 것이 적절하다.

|모범답안|

01 (1) A: What does this sign mean?

      B: It means you must not ride a bike here.

  (2) A: What does this sign mean?

      B: It means you must drive slowly here.

02 (1) I would see a doctor

  (2) wouldn't wait for him anymore

  (3) wouldn't hurry

  (4) wouldn't quit the job

03 (A) in the pond   (B) gesture

  (C) Step back from the pond

---

01 ④   02 border   03 ④   04 ⑤

05 ②   06 No enemy   07 ①   08 ③

09 Because only the rich could have that kind of dog at that time.

10 (A) They mean they just saw an enemy.

  (B) Now the enemy is crossing the border in the dark.

  (C) It means the battle has started.

11 ②   12 ⑤   13 ②   14 ②

15 I have a brother whose job is a fire fighter.

16 (1) If I were[was] God   (2) If I traveled to the past

17 ④

18 (A) a foreign country

  (B) phones and the Internet

19 the way how → the way 또는 how   20 ②

21 ⓑ twenty-seven thousand   ⓒ twelve thousand

  ⓓ one thousand three hundred

22 ②   23 ③

24 (A) a letter   (B) the hospital

25 oldest → middle   26 ③   27 pot

01 ④번은 '당신을 걱정하게 만들 만큼 나쁘거나 위험한 방법으로'를 의미하는 'seriously'에 대한 설명이다. 'ill'에 대한 설명은 'suffering from an illness or disease'이다.

02 유의어 관계이다. 궁금한 : 경계, 국경

03 '지구의 표면'의 의미로 'ground(땅, 지면)'가 적절하다.

04 ⑤: 이 글자가 무엇을 의미하는지 묻는 말에 이 편지가 파란 잉크로 쓰였다고 말하는 것은 어색하다.

05 '메시지를 보내기 위해서 병사들은 무슨 일을 할까?'라는 물음에 대한 답으로 ②번이 적절하다.

06 대화의 흐름상 굴뚝 한 곳에서 연기가 나오면 적이 없다는 것을 의미한다.

07 '~에 대해 궁금해 하다'는 'be curious about'을 사용한다.

08 G의 첫 번째 대화에서 '그 비밀들은 어디에 있니?'라고 묻는 것으로 보아 그림 속에 비밀이 숨겨져 있다는 것을 알 수 있다.

09 질문: 왜 사람들은 사진 속의 남자가 매우 부자였다고 생각하는가?

10 봉수대의 연기는 적이 성에 접근하는 위치에 따라 굴뚝의 연기 개수가 많아진다는 것을 알 수 있다.

11 이 남자의 몸짓은 무엇을 의미하는지 묻는 말 다음에 궁금증을 표현하는 말이 적절하다.

12 ①~④: were ⑤ had

13 'The man is good at playing soccer.' 문장에서, 선행사 'The man' 뒤에 소유격 관계대명사 whose를 사용하여 문장을 이어 쓰고 술부 'is good at playing soccer'를 쓴다.

14 현재 사실에 대한 가정은 'If+주어+동사 과거형, 주어+조동사 과거형(would/should/could/might)+동사원형'의 형태로 쓴다. *fall in love with: ~와 사랑에 빠지다 (수동형으로 쓰지 않는다.)

15 'I have a brother.'의 문장을 쓰고, 선행사 a brother 뒤에 소유격 관계대명사 문장을 이어 쓴다.

16 현재 사실에 대한 가정은 'If+주어+동사 과거형'으로 쓴다.

17 이 글은 '읽거나 쓸 줄 모르는 한 여자가 독일에서 일하는 남편에게 그림으로 쓴 편지를 시실리의 작가 Gesualdo Bufalino가 글로 번역했다'는 내용의 글이므로, 주제로는 ④번 '읽거나 쓸 줄 모르는 한 여자가 외국에 있는 남편에게 보낸 그림 편지'가 적절하다. ② illiterate: 글을 (읽거나 쓸 줄) 모르는, 문맹의, ③ illiteracy rate:문맹률

18 사람들, 특히 문맹인 사람들이 '전화와 인터넷' 시대 이전에 '외국'에 있는 가족이나 친구와 대화하려고 노력할 때 겪었던 어려움들을 의미한다.

19 관계부사 'how'를 'the way'로 바꿔 쓸 수 있지만, 'the way how'와 같이 선행사와 관계부사를 함께 쓸 수는 없다.

20 ⓐ와 ①, ②, ④: 현재분사, ③, ⑤: 동명사

21 천의 자리에서 끊어서 읽으면서, 그 자리에 thousand를 붙여서 읽는 것이 적절하다. ⓑ 십 단위와 단 단위 사이에 보통 하이픈으로 연결하는 것이 적절하다. twenty-seven thousands(×), ⓒ twelve thousands(×), ⓓ one thousand three hundreds(×)

22 땅에서 올리브를 주운 것은 '일꾼'이 아니라 그의 '두 아들'이다. 본문의 picking은 분사구문으로 행위자가 his two sons이고, ②번의 pick은 helped의 목적격보어로서 행위자가 목적어인 him이 된다.

23 ⓐ in good health: 건강하여, ⓑ look after: ~을 돌보다

24 그림 편지의 '편지 봉투' 문양을 참조하여 (A)에는 a letter를, '십자가 문양의 병원 표시'를 참조하여 (B)에는 the hospital을 쓰는 것이 적절하다.

25 글쓴이는 '둘째' 아들과 시어머니를 방문할 것이다.

26 ⓐ와 ①, ③, ④: 형용사적 용법, enough+명사+to부정사: 형용사적 용법, enough+형용사/부사+to부정사: 부사적 용법, ②: 부사적 용법, ⑤: 명사적 용법

27 '항아리'를 가리킨다.

We Are All Makers

시험대비 실력평가 p.62

01 cloth	02 ③	03 ⑤	04 ①
05 gave away	06 ④	07 ⑤	08 ②

01 '대부분의 커튼은 천으로 만들어진다. <영어 설명> 옷과 같은 것을 만드는 데 사용되는 재료

02 figure는 '① (사람, 동물의) 상, 모형 ② 모양 ③ 숫자'의 의미를 지닌다. • 그는 말 청동상을 만들었다. • 그 수치는 OECD 평균 6,741 달러보다 낮은 것이다.

03 '공식적인 명단에 누군가 또는 무엇인가의 이름을 올리다'라는 의미로 '등록하다(register)'가 적절하다.

04 '액체나 기체에서 원치 않는 물질을 제거하다'라는 뜻으로 '~을 거르다, 여과하다(filter)'가 적절하다.

05 '남에게 주다, 나누어 주다'는 'give away'를 사용한다.

06 (A) 그는 중병에 걸려 병원에 입원했다. (B) 그녀는 그녀의 엄마를 친구로 생각한다.

07 나머지는 모두 '명사-형용사' 관계이고, ⑤번은 '동사-명사'관계이다.

08 공공의, 대중의: 한 나라의 모든 사람과 관련된. '우리는 밖에 있을 때, 공중 화장실을 사용해야 한다.'

서술형 시험대비 p.63

01 (1) drinkable (2) report (3) necessary (4) tore
02 prefer
03 (1) (c)heerful (2) (a)ctually (3) both (4) (p)rovide
04 (1) bookstore, 서점 (2) leave, 남겨두다
   (3) pour, 붓다, 따르다
05 thought of[looked upon, regard], as

01 (1) 이 물은 마실 수 있나요? be동사 다음에 '마실 수 있는'의 뜻으로 형용사 'drinkable'이 적절하다. (2) 그는 대형 기사를 보도한 최초의 기자였다. (3) 음식과 물은 인간이 살기 위해 필요하다. (4) 내 고양이가 어제 그 책의 페이지를 찢었다. 'tear'의 과거형 'tore'가 적절하다.

02 '또 다른 사람이나 물건보다 어떤 사람이나 물건을 더 좋아하다'라는 의미로 '선호하다(prefer)'가 적절하다.

03 (1) cheerful: 유쾌한 (2) actually: 실제로, 사실상 (3) both: 둘 다 (4) provide: 제공하다

04 (1) 책을 파는 상점 (2) 어떤 것을 어떤 장소 특히 그것이 머무

를 장소에 두다 (3) 용기 밖으로 액체가 흘러가도록 만들다

05 그는 초창기 때부터 이 회사를 위해 일해서, 모든 사람들은 그를 실질적인 사장으로 여기고 있었다. '…을 ~로 생각하다[여기다]'는 'regard A as B = think of A as B = look upon A as B = consider A (as) B' 등으로 표현할 수 있다.

교과서 Conversation

핵심 Check p.64~65

1 Which do you prefer, paper drawings or wood block figures?
2 ④

교과서 대화문 익히기

Check(√) True or False p.66

1 T 2 F 3 F 4 T

교과서 확인학습 p.68~69

Get Ready 2

(1) Which, better, cloth, artwork / better, Actually
(2) Which do you prefer, drawings, wood / prefer, figures / Let's, some of them
(3) Which, prefer, folding, clothes / folding paper, to realx

Start Off – Listen & Talk A

1. Why don't we, pockets / What shall we / Which, board, holder / prefer, holder, to make, spending, making / Let's, together
2. Why don't we / What kind, to make / prefer / hate holding, in / Let's make

Start Off - Listen & Talk B

with jeans / for / draw / Which do you prefer / prefer, lovely / draw / I can't wait for

Start Off – Speak Up

Sure, Which, prefer, or / prefer, making / introduce, to

Start Off - Your Turn

Which, taking, taking / prefer taking, hate taking

Step Up – Real-life Scene

away / proud that, collected, interesting, to give away / prepare, any / making / Let's / Which, prefer, writing / writing / No problem, cheerful messages / sure, bookmarks

Express Yourself A

1. flying, flying drones / flying / working, machines
2. Which, making, making / both, it, that, prefer / something delicious

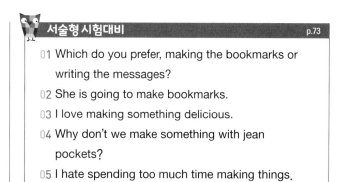

시험대비 기본평가 p.70

01 ④	02 ②	03 ⑤

01 전자책을 더 좋아한다는 말 다음의 Actually는 문장을 강조하는 표현으로 ④번이 어울린다.

02 푸드 아트 만들기를 좋아하는 이유를 묻는 말에 대해 '맛있는 것을 만들기를 좋아해'라는 말이 가장 자연스럽다.

03 'I hate ~(나는 ~하기를 싫어한다)'는 자신이 하기 싫어하는 것을 강하게 표현하는 말이다.

시험대비 실력평가 p.71~72

01 ④	02 to draw → draw	03 ③
04 ②	05 the book club day is just one week	
away	06 prepare	07 ⑤	08 ③
09 ④	10 ①	11 or

01 빈칸은 선호를 묻는 표현이 적절하다. ④번은 판다를 더 좋아하는 이유를 묻는 표현으로 어색하다.

02 'let+목적어+목적보어(동사원형)' 형태가 적절하다.

03 빈칸은 '우리 낡은 청바지로 가방을 하나 만드는 게 어떨까?'라는 제안의 표현이 자연스럽다.

04 어깨에 메는 가방이 더 좋다고 말하고 있기 때문에 빈칸에는 손에 물건을 드는 것을 몹시 싫어한다는 표현이 오는 것이 적절하다.

05 '한 주 남았다'는 의미로 'one week away'를 사용한다.

06 '앞으로 일어날 일에 대한 계획을 하거나 준비를 하다'라는 의미로 '준비하다(prepare)'가 적절하다.

07 밑줄 친 (e) 다음 문장에서 '나는 책갈피를 만들고 싶어.'라고 말하고 있으므로 글쓰기를 좋아한다는 말은 어색하다. 'love'를 'hate'로 바꾸는 것이 적절하다.

08 대화의 흐름상 빈칸에는 무엇을 만들지 물어보는 말이 자연스럽다.

09 빈칸 앞에 '만들기가 더 쉬워'라고 말하고 있으므로 시간이 많이 걸리는 것은 싫어한다는 말이 오는 것이 자연스럽다.

10 빈칸은 둘 중에 무엇을 더 선호하는지를 묻는 표현이 적절하다.

11 A와 B 중에서 선택을 할 때 사용하는 접속사 'or'가 적절하다.

서술형 시험대비 p.73

01 Which do you prefer, making the bookmarks or writing the messages?
02 She is going to make bookmarks.
03 I love making something delicious.
04 Why don't we make something with jean pockets?
05 I hate spending too much time making things.

01 상대방의 선호를 물을 때는 'prefer(더 좋아하다)'를 사용하여 'Which do you prefer, A or B?'를 쓴다.

02 질문: 민지는 방문객들에게 무엇을 만들어 줄 것인가?

03 좋아하는 표현은 'I love+동명사'를 사용하고, something은 형용사가 뒤에서 수식을 한다.

04 'Why don't we+동사원형 ~?'을 이용하여 '~하는 게 어때?'라는 제안의 표현을 쓸 수 있다.

05 hate는 동명사를 목적어로 취할 수 있고, 'spend+시간+-ing' 구문을 이용한다.

교과서

Grammar

핵심 Check p.74~75

1 (1) happier   (2) better
2 (1) was my mother that[who]
  (2) was a chocolate cake that[which]

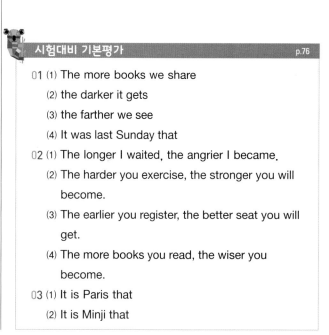

시험대비 기본평가 p.76

01 (1) The more books we share
  (2) the darker it gets
  (3) the farther we see
  (4) It was last Sunday that
02 (1) The longer I waited, the angrier I became.
  (2) The harder you exercise, the stronger you will become.
  (3) The earlier you register, the better seat you will get.
  (4) The more books you read, the wiser you become.
03 (1) It is Paris that
  (2) It is Minji that

01 'the+비교급, the+비교급'은 '…하면 할수록, 더 ~하다'라는
의미이다. (1) many books의 비교급을 the more books
로 쓰고 '주어+동사'의 어순으로 쓴다. (2) dark의 비교급을
the darker로 쓰고 '주어+동사'의 어순으로 쓴다. (3) far의 비
교급으로 farther(더 멀리)와 further(더 나아가)가 있다. 보
통 farther는 거리를 나타내고, further는 정도를 나타내므
로 여기서는 farther를 쓰는 것이 더 좋다. 그러나 further를
써도 틀리는 것은 아니다. (4) 'It is[was]+강조할 부분(last
Sunday)+that+문장의 나머지 부분'으로 쓴다.

02 (1) angry의 비교급은 angrier이다. (2) 'the+비교급, the+비
교급'의 형태로 써야 한다. (3) '더 좋은 자리'의 의미로 형용사
better와 명사 seat을 함께 써야 한다. (4) wiser가 이미 비교
급이므로 more를 쓰지 않는다.(4) 사람이 선행사이므로 소유격
관계대명사는 whose를 쓴다.

03 'It is[was]+강조할 부분(Paris, Minji)+that+문장의 나머지
부분'으로 쓴다.

시험대비 실력평가   p.77~79

01 ⑤   02 ④   03 ①, ④
04 ⑤   05 ④
06 (1) It is Linda that[who] doesn't like cheese cake.
   (2) It is this old computer that gives me a headache.
07 The more mistakes you make   08 ③
09 The higher the wave rose, the faster we swam.
10 The earlier you leave, the sooner you will arrive.
11 (1) shines brighter, I feel happier
   (2) waited longer, I became angrier
   (3) you read more books, you will know more
       things
12 ③
13 It is this beautiful garden that will make people
   feel better.
14 the more birds will come
15 ①   16 ④   17 ⑤   18 ③
19 (1) It was Makers' Camp that[which] we went to.
   (2) It was Chagall that[who] painted *I and the
       Village*.
20 ③

01 'the+비교급, the+비교급'은 '…하면 할수록, 더 ~하다'라는 의미
이다. happy의 비교급을 more happy로 쓰는 것은 옳지 않다.

02 'the+비교급, the+비교급'은 '…하면 할수록, 더 ~하다'라는 의
미이다. the best는 최상급이므로 적절하지 않다.

03 Junha를 강조하는 'It was ~ that' 강조구문이다. 사람을 강조
할 때 that 대신 who를 쓸 수 있다.

04 ⑤의 that은 진주어를 이끄는 접속사 that이다. 해석: 스마트폰이

학생들이 새로운 것을 배우는 것을 도와준다는 것은 분명하다.

05 Canadian team이 Team Kim을 이긴 것이 아니라 Team
Kim이 Canadian team을 이긴 것이므로, It was the
Canadian team that Team Kim beat in Gangneung in
2018.으로 쓰는 것이 적절하다. ③ Team Kim이 경기를 이긴
것은 바로 2점차이다.

06 (1) 'It … that' 강조구문으로 강조하는 부분이 사람이므로 which
가 아닌 that이나 who를 쓴다. (2) 'It is[was]+강조할 부분
+that+문장의 나머지 부분'으로 쓸 때 강조할 부분이 문장의 주어
이면 that 뒤의 동사의 수는 그 주어에 일치시켜야 하므로 give는
gives로 쓰는 것이 적절하다.

07 'the+비교급, the+비교급' 문장을 쓸 때 비교급의 형용사가 명
사를 수식하는 명사면, 'the+비교급 형용사(the more)+명사
(mistakes)'로 쓴다.

08 'the+비교급, the+비교급'은 '…하면 할수록, 더 ~하다'라는 의
미이다. difficult의 비교급은 more difficult이고, hard의 비
교급은 harder이다.

09 '파도가 높아질수록 우리는 더 빨리 수영했다.'의 뜻으로 'the+
비교급+주어+동사, the+비교급+주어+동사'로 완성한다.

10 'the+비교급+주어+동사, the+비교급+주어+동사' 형태로 쓴다.

11 (1), (2), (3) 'the+비교급, the+비교급' 구문은 접속사 'as' 또
는 'if' 등을 사용하여, '접속사+주어+동사+비교급, 주어+동사
+비교급'의 형태로 같은 의미의 문장을 쓸 수 있다.

12 'It … that' 강조구문으로 'It is[was]+강조할 부분+that+문
장의 나머지 부분'으로 쓰며, It was 다음에 강조할 부분인 the
chocolate cake을 쓴 후 ③에 that을 쓰는 것이 적절하다.

13 'It is[was]+강조할 부분(this beautiful garden)+that+문장
의 나머지 부분'으로 쓸 때, make를 사용한 5형식 문장(목적어
+원형부정사) 형태로 쓴다.

14 'the+비교급, the+비교급' 문장을 쓸 때 비교급의 형용사가 명사
를 수식하는 명사면, 'the+비교급 형용사+명사'로 쓴다.

15 disappointed의 비교급은 more disappointed이다. 'The
more you want, the more disappointed you will be.'로
쓴다. 해석: 더 많이 원할수록, 너는 더 실망하게 된다.

16 첫 번째 문장은 'It ~ that' 강조구문이고 강조하는 부분이 사람
이므로 that이나 who를 쓸 수 있다. 두 번째 문장은 주격 관계
대명사를 계속적 용법으로 써야 하므로 who를 쓰는 것이 적절
하다. 그러므로 공통으로 들어갈 단어는 'who'이다.

17 첫 번째의 빈칸은 'It … that' 강조구문으로 강조부분이 주어이
므로 동사는 그에 맞게 makes를 쓰는 것이 적절하다. 두 번째
문장은 'the+비교급, the+비교급' 구문이고, pretty의 비교급
은 prettier이므로 the prettier를 쓰는 것이 적절하다.

18 faster가 이미 비교급의 형태이므로 more를 쓰지 않는 것이 적
절하다.

19 A의 질문에 사용된 단어를 활용하여 'It was+강조할 부분
(Makers' Camp, Chagall)+that+문장의 나머지 부분'으로

쓴다.

20　b. It was on the Internet that she bought her shirts. c. It is Kiyoung that loves to write poems. d. The higher I climbed the mountain, the darker the sky was getting.

01 (1) The harder you practice, the faster you can type.
(2) The more they tried, the better they did.
(3) The colder it gets, the more clothes we need.
(4) The closer he got to the fire, the warmer he felt.
(5) The earlier you get up, the more time you can spend on makeup.

02 (1) the smell of lemons that[which] cats hate
(2) my grandmother that[who] made me banana cakes
(3) It was my grandfather that[who] told me the story.
(4) It is this Friday that[when] we will attend a conference.
(5) It was in front of the MBC building that[where] we saw the statue.

03 (1) It was five copies of the same books that he bought at the bookstore.
(2) It is the class field trip that I won't forget.
(3) It is this experience that deeply connected all of us.

04 (1) a light drone, lighter
(2) the facial design, more

05 (1) It is tomorrow that she will sing the song.
(2) It is Joan that cheers me up all the time.

06 The more worse → The worse

07 (1) It is her teddy bear that Cathy likes the best.
(2) It was from Junsu that I first heard the news.
(3) It was Minji that went to visit her aunt last Thursday.
(4) It is the star watching experience in Yeongwol that Minjun can't forget.
(5) It was at the bookstore that my dad first met my mom.

01 (1), (2), (4) 접속사를 뺀 후 'the+비교급+주어+동사, the+비교급+주어+동사' 형태로 쓴다. (3), (5) 'the+비교급, the+비교급' 문장을 쓸 때 비교급의 형용사가 명사를 수식하는 명사면, 'the 비교급 형용사+명사'로 쓴다. (3) the more clothes, (5)

the more time

02 'It is[was]+강조할 부분(last Sunday)+that+문장의 나머지 부분'으로 쓴다. 이때 문장의 시제에 따라 is와 was를 구분해서 쓴다. 또한 that 대신에 강조하는 것이 사람이면 who, 사물이면 which, 시간이면 when, 장소면 where를 쓸 수 있다.

03 'It is[was]+강조할 부분(five copies of the same books, the class field trip, this experience)+that+문장의 나머지 부분'으로 쓴다.

04 (1), (2) 첫 번째 빈칸은 'It ... that' 강조구문으로 빈칸에 강조하고자 하는 말을 쓴다. 두 번째 빈칸은 'the+비교급, the+비교급'이므로 형용사 light의 비교급인 lighter와 popular의 비교급인 more popular를 쓴다.

05 (1) 과거시제가 현재시제로 바뀌어야 하므로 동사의 시제를 모두 현재로 바꾼다. (2) 'It is[was]+강조할 부분+that+문장의 나머지 부분'으로 쓸 때 강조할 부분이 문장의 주어이면 that 뒤의 동사의 수는 그 주어에 맞추어야 한다. 복수 주어를 단수 주어로 바꾸면서 동사에 -s를 붙이는 것이 적절하다.

06 worse는 bad의 비교급이므로 more를 붙이지 않는다.

07 (1) that절의 시제가 현재이므로 강조구문의 동사를 was가 아닌 is를 쓴다. (2) 강조하는 부분이 사람이 아닌 장소 (from Junsu)이므로 who가 아닌 that을 쓴다. (3) that절의 시제가 과거이므로 강조구문의 동사를 is가 아닌 was를 쓴다. (4) 강조하는 부분이 목적어이므로 that절에 목적어를 쓰지 않는다. (5) that절에 장소가 와야 하므로 강조하는 부분에 전치사를 넣어 장소로 쓴다.

교과서
Reading

확인문제　　　　　　　　p.82
1 T　2 F　3 T　4 F　5 T　6 F

확인문제　　　　　　　　p.83
1 T　2 F　3 T　4 F　5 T　6 F

확인문제　　　　　　　　p.84
1 T　2 F　3 T　4 F　5 T　6 F

01 Amazing
02 traditional paper books
03 unique
04 a few
05 Travel
06 found
07 read, Free
08 Take me home
09 ID number, was registered
10 had traveled, had read
11 How
12 book-sharing project
13 register, get
14 leave it
15 reports back, where your book is
16 a big library
17 The more books, the more
18 Drinkable
19 This tiny book
20 both the information and the tools
21 is called
22 as a filter
23 tear out, pour, on
24 As, changes into
25 It is, that
26 special filter paper
27 amazing, saves, from, diseases
28 Tree-Book-Tree Project
29 the most amazing book
30 reading, plant, water
31 growing
32 a copy of, producing
33 has seeds
34 these tiny seeds
35 was made by
36 not, anymore, think
37 just a few
38 What other unique books
39 would, like to do
40 The bigger, the more wonderful

1 This Book Is Amazing!
2 Most people think of books as traditional paper books to read.
3 However, there are many unique books around you.
4 Let's learn about a few of these books.
5 Books Travel!
6 I found this old book on a park bench yesterday.
7 A note on the cover read, "Free Book!
8 Take me home and read me!"
9 Actually, this book had an ID number and was registered on a website.
10 When I entered the number online, I found out that the book had traveled to many countries and that a number of readers in different countries had read it before me.
11 How was that possible?

12 There is a book-sharing project.
13 First, register your book online and get an ID number.
14 Next, leave it in a public place.
15 When the next reader finds your book and reports back to the website, you can check where your book is.
16 This way, the whole world can become a big library.
17 The more books we share, the more we learn.
18 The Drinkable Book
19 This tiny book is really important to people in my town.
20 It provides both the information and the tools necessary to make clean drinking water.
21 It is called the Drinkable Book.
22 You cannot actually drink the book, but you can use it as a filter.
23 Simply tear out a page and pour dirty water on it.
24 As the water goes through the page, it changes into clean drinking water.
25 It is this filtered water that you can drink.
26 This is possible because the book is made of special filter paper.
27 This amazing book saves the lives of many children from diseases that come from dirty water.
28 The Tree-Book-Tree Project
29 This is the most amazing book that I have ever seen.
30 After you finish reading this book, plant it and water it.
31 You will see new leaves growing on the book.
32 In some bookstores in my town, you can see a copy of this book producing new leaves.
33 The secret is that the book has seeds in each page.
34 It is these tiny seeds that change the book into a tree.
35 This book was made by a small children's book publisher in Argentina.
36 Though the company does not print this book anymore, this special project makes us think about where books come from.
37 These are just a few of the unique books you can find.
38 What other unique books do you want to make?
39 What special project would you like to do with the books?

40 The bigger your imagination is, the more wonderful your books will become.

01 ④   02 ①, ⑤   03 ②   04 ②

05 many   06 ⑤   07 (A) register (B) get

08 private → public   09 ④   10 ④

11 As the water goes through the page, it changes into clean drinking water.

12 ④   13 ①, ③   14 to read → reading

15 ②   16 ⑤   17 ③   18 ④

19 ③   20 ④   21 ⑤   22 ②

23 the (dirty) water   24 ⑤

25 (A) It is (B) think (C) to do   26 ③

27 where books come from 28 ⑤   29 ②

30 the bigger → bigger
the more wonderful → more wonderful

01 앞에 나오는 내용과 상반되는 내용이 뒤에 이어지므로 However가 가장 적절하다. ① 즉[말하자면], ② 그러므로, ③ 그 결과

02 (A)와 ①, ⑤: 형용사적 용법, ②, ④: 부사적 용법, ③: 명사적 용법

03 '여러분 주변에는 독특한 책이 많이 있습니다. 이러한 책 중 몇 가지에 대해 배워 봅시다.'라고 했으므로, 위 글의 뒤에 올 내용으로는 '몇 가지 독특한 책에 대한 설명'이 적절하다.

04 ⓐ on a park bench: 공원 벤치 위에서, ⓑ A note on the cover: 표지 위의 쪽지, ⓒ on a website: 웹사이트에

05 a number of = many

06 글쓴이는 그 책이 많은 나라를 여행하고 '다른 나라의 많은 독자가 자신보다 앞서 이 책을 읽었다'는 것을 알아냈으므로 최초의 독자라는 것은 사실이 아니다.

07 책을 공유하는 프로젝트의 첫 단계는 온라인에 여러분의 책을 '등록하고' ID 번호를 '얻는 것'이다.

08 다음 독자가 여러분의 책을 발견하도록 책을 '공공'장소에 놓아 두라고 하는 것이 적절하므로, private를 public으로 고치는 것이 적절하다. private: 사적인

09 이 글은 '책을 공유하는 프로젝트'에 관한 글이므로, 주제로는 ④번 '책을 공유하기 위한 프로젝트'가 적절하다. ③ report back on something to somebody: (~에 대한 정보를 …에게) 보고하다[알리다]

10 ⓐ와 ①, ②, ③, ⑤: 동명사, 목적, 용도를 나타낼 때: 동명사. ⑤ hearing aid: 보청기, ④ 진행, 상태를 나타낼 때: 현재분사

11 as: ~하면서, go through: ~을 통과하다, change into: ~로 변하다

12 선행사에 형용사의 최상급이 있을 때는 보통 관계대명사 that을 쓴다.

13 ⓑ와 ①, ③: 경험 용법, ②, ⑤: 완료 용법, ④ 계속 용법

14 finish는 동명사를 목적어로 취하는 동사이다.

15 report back to somebody: (…에게) 보고하다[알리다]

16 책을 공유하는 프로젝트를 통해 여러 독자들이 책을 빌려서 읽게 되는 것이므로, 전 세계가 하나의 큰 '도서관'이 될 수 있다고 하는 것이 적절하다. ② 출판사

17 (A)와 ③: 남겨 두다, 놓아두다, ① (관리, 처리 등을) 맡기다, ② (사람, 장소에서) 떠나다[출발하다], ④ (정기 또는 특별 사유에 의한) 휴가(명사), take a month's paid leave: 한 달간의 유급 휴가를 갖다, ⑤ (어떤 상태에 계속) 있게 하다

18 다음 독자가 여러분의 책을 발견하는 데 보통 얼마가 걸리는지는 대답할 수 없다. ① First, we should register our book online and get an ID number. ② We should leave it in a public place. ③ The next reader should report back to the website. ⑤ We can check where our book is when the next reader finds our book and reports back to the website.

19 이 글은 '책이 많은 나라를 여행하고 다른 나라의 많은 독자가 그 책을 읽는다.'는 내용의 글이므로, 제목으로는 ③번 '책이 여행합니다!'가 적절하다.

20 think of A as B = regard A as B = look upon A as B = consider A as B = see A as B = view A as B: A를 B로 생각하다

21 주어진 문장의 that에 주목한다. ⑤번 앞 문장의 내용을 받고 있으므로 ⑤번이 적절하다.

22 ⓐ와 ②: [역할·자격·기능·성질 따위를 나타내어] ~으로(전치사), ① ~일 때(접속사), ③ [비례] ~함에 따라, ~할수록(접속사), ④ [보통 as ~ as ...로 형용사·부사 앞에서] …와 같은 정도로, (as ~ as ...에서, 앞의 as가 지시부사, 뒤의 as는 접속사), ⑤ [상태] ~하는대로 (접속사)

23 '더러운 물'을 가리킨다.

24 이 글은 '특별한 여과지로 만들어진 책(the Drinkable Book: 마실 수 있는 책)을 필터로 사용해서 더러운 물을 깨끗한 마실 물로 바꾸는 것'에 관한 글이므로, 주제로는 '깨끗한 마실 물을 만드는 데 필요한 도구를 제공하는 책'이 적절하다.

25 (A) 'These tiny seeds change the book into a tree.'에서 주어 'These tiny seeds'를 강조하기 위한 'It … that ~' 강조 구문 문장이므로 It is가 적절하다. (B) 사역동사 makes의 목적격보어이므로 think가 적절하다. (C) would like는 to부정사를 목적어로 취한다.

26 이 책이 맨 처음 언제 출판되었는지는 대답할 수 없다. ① It

17

has seeds. ② A small children's book publisher in Argentina did. ④ No, it isn't. ⑤ We can think about where books come from.

27 전치사 'about'의 목적어 역할을 하는 간접의문문(의문사+주어+동사)의 어순으로 쓰는 것이 적절하다.

28 그 출판사는 더 이상 이 책을 발행하지 않는다.

29 글의 첫 부분에 '이것들은 여러분이 찾을 수 있는 독특한 책 중의 단지 몇 가지입니다.'라고 되어 있으므로, 앞에 올 내용으로는 '여러분이 찾을 수 있는 몇 가지 독특한 책에 대한 설명'이 적절하다.

30 The+비교급+주어+동사 …, the+비교급+주어+동사 ~: = As+주어+동사+비교급, 주어+동사+비교급: …하면 할수록, 더 ~하다

서술형 시험대비 p.96~97

01 (A) Most   (B) unique   (C) a
02 the book had traveled to many countries and a number of readers in different countries had read it before the writer
03 (A) an ID number   (B) on a website   (C) free
04 register   05 more books, more
06 (A) an ID number   (B) a public place   (C) the website   (D) where
07 can not only → cannot actually
08 It is this filtered water that you can drink.
09 dirty water
10 producing 또는 produce
11 no more
12 It's that the book has seeds in each page.

01 (A) '대부분의' 사람이라고 해야 하므로 Most가 적절하다. almost: 거의, most: 대부분의, (B) '독특한' 책이 많이 있다고 해야 하므로 unique가 적절하다. ordinary: 보통의, unique: 독특한, (C) '많은' 독자라고 해야 하므로 a가 적절하다. a number of: 많은, the number of: ~의 수

02 '그 책이 많은 나라를 여행하고 다른 나라의 많은 독자가 글쓴이보다 앞서 이 책을 읽었다는 것'을 가리킨다.

03 글쓴이는 어제 공원 벤치에서 발견한 낡은 책은 'ID 번호'가 있고 '웹사이트'에 등록되어 있었다. 그 책은 '공짜' 책이기 때문에, 그 책을 발견한 사람은 누구라도 그것을 집으로 가져가서 읽을 수 있었다.

04 register: 등록하다, 어떤 것을 하기 위해서 혹은 서비스를 받기 위해서 공식적인 목록에 이름을 올리다

05 The+비교급+주어+동사 …, the+비교급+주어+동사 ~: = As+주어+동사+비교급, 주어+동사+비교급: …하면 할수록,

더 ~하다

06 (A) 여러분의 책을 등록하고 'ID 번호'를 얻으세요. (B) 그것을 '공공장소' 어디에라도 놓아두세요. (C) 누군가가 여러분의 책을 집어 들고 '웹사이트'에 알립니다. (D) 여러분의 책이 '어디' 있는지 그리고 누가 그것을 읽는지 확인하십시오.

07 여러분은 '실제로 그 책을 마실 수는 없지만', 그것을 필터로 사용할 수 있습니다.

08 'You can drink this filtered water.'에서 'this filtered water'를 강조하는 강조구문으로 쓰는 것이 적절하다.

09 the Drinkable Book(마실 수 있는 책) 덕분에, 많은 어린이들이 '더러운 물'로 생기는 질병으로부터 스스로를 보호할 수 있다.

10 지각동사 'see'의 목적격보어에 해당하므로 현재분사 producing으로 쓰는 것이 적절하다. produce도 가능하다.

11 not ~ anymore = no more

12 새잎이 자라는 책의 비밀은 '책이 각 페이지 안에 씨앗을 갖고 있다'는 것이다.

영역별 핵심문제 p.99~103

01 provide   02 ②   03 ⑤   04 ①
05 introduce   06 ⑤   07 (b) and → or
08 ③   09 ③   10 ④   11 ②
12 ⑤   13 (a) longer   (b) better
14 ②   15 ⑤
16 (1) The closer we got to the fire, the warmer we felt.
(2) It was the lost key that[which] I found under the bed.
(3) It was on the wall that[where] the baby drew the rabbit.
17 ④   18 ③   19 ④   20 ③
21 ③   22 the Drinkable Book(마실 수 있는 책)의 한 페이지를 떼어 내서 그 위에 더러운 물을 부으면, 물이 그 페이지를 통과하면서 깨끗한 마실 물로 바뀌게 되는 것.
23 ④   24 the more your books will become wonderful → the more wonderful your books will become   25 you can check where your book is
26 ⑤

01 유의어 관계다. 병, 질병 – 제공하다

02 (a) 친구에게 게임의 점수를 알아봐 달라고 부탁할 것이다. (b) 작은 개미들은 잎을 들어올리기 위해 함께 일했다.

03 '기계를 이용해서 종이 위에 단어, 그림, 숫자 등을 생성하다'라는 뜻으로 '인쇄하다(print)'가 적절하다.

04 '잡아 찢거나 작은 조각으로 뜯어내다'라는 뜻으로 '~을 찢다, 뜯어내다(tear)'가 적절하다.

05 처음 만났을 때 누군가에게 또 다른 사람의 이름을 말하다:소개

하다

06 'register'는 '등록하다'라는 뜻이다.

07 'A와 B 중에서 어떤 것을 더 좋아하니?'를 묻는 선택의문문에서는 'Which do you prefer, A or B?'의 형태를 사용한다.

08 (C) 가면 만들기와 푸드 아트 만들기 중에서 어떤 것을 더 좋아하는지 묻고 → (B) 둘 다 좋아하는데 푸드 아트 만들기를 더 좋아한다고 대답하고 → (D) 그 이유를 묻는 말이 온다. 마지막으로 → (A) 이유를 설명하는 말이 온다.

09 등산을 하는 것과 해변에 가는 것 중에서 무엇을 더 좋아하니?'라는 물음에 '등반을 더 좋아해. 사실 해변에 가는 것을 가장 좋아해.'라고 말하는 것은 자연스럽지 못하다.

10 어깨에 메는 가방과 손에 드는 가방 중에서 무엇을 만들지에 대해 나누는 대화로, G가 손에 물건을 드는 것을 싫어한다고 말하고, B가 Okay라고 긍정의 대답을 하는 것으로 보아 어깨에 메는 가방을 만들자는 ④가 가장 적절하다.

11 첫 문장에 독서 동아리의 날이 일주일 남았다고 말하고 있고 이것을 준비하기 위해 할 일에 대해 이야기하고 있으므로 ②가 적절하다.

12 'It is[was]+강조할 부분+that+문장의 나머지 부분'으로 쓸 때 강조할 부분이 문장의 주어이면 that 뒤의 동사의 수는 그 주어에 맞추어야 한다. 그러므로 ⑤의 동사 go는 goes로 쓰는 것이 적절하다.

13 'the+비교급, the+비교급' 문장이므로, (a)는 명사 length의 형용사형인 long의 비교급 longer를, (b)는 부사 well의 비교급인 better를 넣는 것이 길길이다.

14 'the+비교급(the happier)+주어+동사, the+비교급(the more likely+주어+동사'로 쓴다.

15 a. 강조하는 부분이 주어이므로 that절에 주어를 쓰지 말아야 한다. It was Jack that broke the vase. c. 주절의 시제에 맞게 강조구문의 동사를 현재로 쓴다. It is Jessica that likes Korean dramas. d. 'the+비교급, the+비교급'의 형태가 되도록 쓴다. The more information you provide, the better we can help you. e. 비교급의 형용사가 명사를 수식하는 명사면, 'the+비교급 형용사+명사'로 쓴다. The more money you make, the more things you will buy. f. 'the+비교급, the+비교급'의 비교급 자리에는 형용사와 부사 모두 올 수 있고, 뒤에 이어지는 동사에 따라 달라진다. The harder he practiced, the more beautifully he got to dance.

16 (1) 'the+비교급, the+비교급'은 '…하면 할수록, 더 ~하다'라는 의미이다. 뒤에 주어 동사를 쓸 때 시제에 유의한다. (2), (3) 'It … that' 강조구문으로 'It is[was]+강조할 부분(the lost key, on the wall)+that+문장의 나머지 부분'으로 쓰며, '~하는 것은 바로 …이다'라고 해석한다.

17 앞에 나오는 내용과 상반되는 내용을 연결하는 However로 문장이 시작하고 있으므로, 대부분의 사람은 책을 읽기 위한 '전통적인 종이책'으로만 생각하지만 여러분 주변에는 '독특한

(unique) 책'이 많이 있다고 하는 것이 적절하다. ① 보통의, ② 보통의, 정상적인, ③ 일상의, 정기적인, ⑤ 전형적인

18 ⓑ와 ③: (이름·숫자·내용 등을) 적어 넣다[기입하다/입력하다], ① 들어가다[오다], ② (생각 따위가 머리에) 떠오르다 (occur to), ④ (활동·상황 등을[에]) 시작하다[접어들다/진입하다], ⑤ (대회 등에) 출전[참가]하다

19 그 책의 ID 번호는 알 수 없다. ① On a park bench. ② Yesterday. ③ "Free Book! Take me home and read me!" ⑤ The writer found out that the book had traveled to many countries and that a number of readers in different countries had read it before him/her.

20 이 글은 '특별한 여과지로 만들어진 책(the Drinkable Book: 마실 수 있는 책)'을 필터로 사용해서 더러운 물을 깨끗한 마실 물로 바꾸는 것'에 관한 글이므로, 제목으로는 ③번 '마실 수 있는 책'이 적절하다.

21 ⓑ와 ②, ⑤: 부사적 용법, ①, ④: 명사적 용법, ③: 형용사적 용법

22 책이 특별한 여과지로 만들어졌기 때문에 책을 필터로 사용하여 더러운 물을 사람들이 마실 수 있는 깨끗한 마실 물로 바꾸는 것을 가리킨다.

23 수동태의 행위자를 나타내는 'by'가 적절하다.

24 the+비교급+주어+동사 …, the+비교급+주어+동사 ~(…하면 할수록, 더 ~하다) 구문이므로, wonderful의 비교급 more wonderful 앞에 the를 같이 붙여 쓰는 것이 적절하다.

25 check의 목적어로 간접의문문(의문사+주어+동사)의 순서로 쓰는 것이 적절하다.

26 책을 공유하는 프로젝트를 통해 전 세계가 하나의 큰 도서관이 될 수 있고, '우리가 더 많은 책을 공유할수록, 우리는 더 많이 배운다'고 했다. ④ locate: ~의 정확한 위치를 찾아내다

단원별 예상문제
p.104~107

01 connection　　　　　02 ②
03 I hate working with a plan.
04 (C) - (A) - (B) - (D)
05 They are going to make a shoulder bag.　06 ②
07 ③　　　08 ④　　　09 ①　　　10 ⑤
11 ② looks like ③ The larger　　　12 ②
13 (1) It is the size that influences the time of your print
　(2) the longer you will have to wait
14 ②　　　15 (A) seeds　(B) a tree　　　16 ⑤
17 ②　　　18 ③, ④　　　19 ③　　　20 ①
21 special filter paper
22 A small children's book publisher in Argentina

made this book.

23 It makes us think about where books come from.

01 동사-명사의 관계이다. 모으다-수집 : 연결하다-연결

02 '해 놓은 어떤 것이나 갖고 있는 어떤 것에 대해 즐거움을 느끼는'라는 뜻으로 '자랑으로 여기는(proud)'가 적절하다.

03 싫어하는 것을 말할 때는 'I hate+동명사'를 사용한다.

04 낡은 청바지로 가방을 하나 만들자는 제안에 → (C) 어떤 종류의 가방을 만들지 묻자 → (A) 어깨에 메는 가방과 손에 드는 가방 중에서 어떤 것을 더 좋아하는지 묻는다. → (B) 어깨에 메는 가방이 더 좋다는 말을 하고 사실, 손에 물건을 드는 것을 몹시 싫어한다는 강조의 말을 한다. → (D) 어깨에 메는 가방을 함께 만들자는 말이 오는 것이 적절하다.

05 질문: 대화자들은 무엇을 만들 것인가?

06 'Which do you prefer, A or B?(너는 A와 B 중에서 어느 것을 더 좋아하니?)'에서 A와 B는 문법적으로 병렬관계가 되어야 한다. 'taking the bus or taking the subway'가 되어야 한다.

07 둘 중 무엇을 더 좋아하는지 선호를 묻는 표현으로 적절한 것을 묻는 문제다.

08 주어진 문장의 It은 'a cell phone holder'를 가리키고, 물건을 만드는 데 많은 시간이 드는 것을 싫어한다는 말 앞에 오는 것이 적절하다.

09 선택의문문에서 접속사 'or'를 사용한다.

10 빈칸 다음의 말이 '고양이를 더 좋아해.'라고 말하고 있으므로 ⑤번이 적절하다.

11 ② look 다음에 명사가 올 때는 look like로 쓰는 것이 적절하다. ③ 'the+비교급, the+비교급'의 형태로 쓰는 것이 적절하다.

12 ②의 It은 가주어이다. ①, ③, ④, ⑤의 It은 강조구문의 It이다.

13 (1) 'It is[was]+강조할 부분(the size)+that+문장의 나머지 부분'으로 쓴다. (2) 'the+비교급, the+비교급' 문장이므로 형용사 long을 the longer로 쓰고 뒤에 주어와 동사를 쓴다.

14 이 글은 '책을 다 읽은 후에, 그것을 심고 물을 주면 책에서 새 잎이 자라게 되는 프로젝트'에 관한 글이므로, 제목으로는 ②번 '나무-책-나무 프로젝트'가 적절하다.

15 이 책은 각 페이지 안에 '씨앗'을 갖고 있어서, 만약 여러분이 이 책을 심고 물을 주면 이 아주 작은 씨앗들이 책을 '나무'로 변화시키게 된다.

16 ⑤는 '글쓴이'를 가리키고, 나머지는 다 글쓴이가 어제 공원 벤치에서 발견한 '낡은 책'을 가리킨다.

17 ⓐ와 ②: 'read'는 자동사로서 '~라고 쓰여 있다, ~로 해석되다'라는 의미이다. 그 표지판에는 '입장 금지'라고 적혀 있었다. ①, ④: (글,기호 등을) 읽다[판독하다], ③ (계기를) 확인[검침]하다, ⑤ 읽어 주다

18 actually: 사실, 실제로 (= in reality, in fact, as a matter of fact), ③, ④ especially = in particular: 특히

19 ⓐ change into: ~으로 바뀌다, ⓑ save A from B: B로부터 A를 구하다

20 주어진 문장의 the book에 주목한다. ①번 앞 문장의 the Drinkable Book을 받고 있으므로 ①번이 적절하다.

21 the Drinkable Book(마실 수 있는 책)이 '특별한 여과지'로 만들어졌기 때문에, 단지 그 책에서 떼어낸 페이지 위에 더러운 물을 부음으로써 깨끗한 마실 물을 만드는 것이 가능하다.

22 A small children's book publisher in Argentina를 주어로 해서 고치는 것이 적절하다.

23 the Tree-Book-Tree Project(나무-책-나무 프로젝트)는 우리에게 '책이 어디에서 오는지에 대해 생각하게' 해준다.

🦉 서술형 실전문제 p.108~109

01 It's because a cell phone holder will be easier to make. And he hates spending too much time making things.

02 it is making food art that[which] I prefer.

03 He is going to write cheerful messages on the bookmarks.

04 (1) called → is called
   (2) it was difficult → difficult it was
   (3) which → that[who]

05 (1) It was I that waited for him for a long time.
   (2) The bigger my son grew, the more worried I got.

06 (1) it was the *Mona Lisa* that[which] Leonardo da Vinci painted
   (2) the better you can speak

07 Most people think of books as traditional paper books to read.

08 many unique books around you

09 read → had read

10 People call it the Drinkable Book.

11 (A) filtered   (B) of   (C) amazing

12 (A) the tools   (B) tear out   (C) pour   (D) clean

01 소년은 '만들기가 더 쉬울 거야. 그리고 나는 뭔가를 만드는 데 시간을 너무 많이 들이는 걸 몹시 싫어해.'라고 하고 있다.

02 강조구문은 'It is ~ that ...' 구문을 사용하고, 주어인 making food art를 강조하는 말을 쓴다.

03 질문: Seho는 책갈피를 만드는 것에 관해 무엇을 할 것인가?

04 (1) called 다음 목적어가 없고 목적보어만 있으므로 This를 주어로 수동으로 쓰는 것이 적절하다. (2) The larger와 상응하는 the 비교급을 쓸 때, difficult의 비교급은 the more difficult이고 분리해서 쓰지 않는다. (3) potter가 사람이므로 that이나 who로 써야 한다.

20 정답 및 해설

05 (1) 'It was+강조할 부분(I)+that+문장의 나머지 부분'으로 쓴다. (2) '아들이 더 커감에 따라 나는 점점 더 걱정이 되었다'라는 문장이므로 'the+비교급, the+비교급'을 사용하여 문장을 쓴다.

06 (1) 'It … that' 강조구문으로 'It is[was]+강조할 부분(the Mona Lisa)+that+문장의 나머지 부분'으로 쓰며, '~하는 것은 바로 …이다'라고 해석한다. (2) 'the+비교급, the+비교급'은 '…하면 할수록, 더 ~하다'라는 의미이다. 부사 well의 비교급을 the better로 쓰고 '주어(you)+동사(speak)'의 어순으로 쓴다.

07 think of A as B: A를 B로 생각하다, 'to read'가 to부정사의 형용사적 용법으로 앞의 'books'를 수식하도록 쓰는 것이 적절하다.

08 '여러분 주변의 많은 독특한 책들'을 가리킨다.

09 'I'가 '알아냈다'고 한 시점 이전에 사람들이 그 책을 읽었으므로 과거완료 'had read'로 쓰는 것이 적절하다.

10 People를 주어로 해서 고치는 것이 적절하다.

11 (A) '여과된 물'이라고 해야 하므로 filtered가 적절하다. (B) 종이로 책을 만든 것이므로 of가 적절하다. be made of: 물리적 변화, be made from: 화학적 변화, (C) 이 '놀라운' 책이라고 해야 하므로 amazing이 적절하다.

12 the Drinkable Book(마실 수 있는 책)은 깨끗한 마실 물을 만드는 데 필요한 '도구'를 제공합니다. 여러분이 그 책의 한 페이지를 '떼어 내서' 그 위에 더러운 물을 '부을' 때, 그 물이 '깨끗한' 마실 물로 바뀝니다.

창의사고력 서술형 문제
p.110

|모범답안|

01 (1) A: Which do you prefer, working with a plan or working without a plan?
   B: I prefer working without a plan. Actually I hate working with a plan.
(2) A: Which do you prefer, working with numbers and texts or working with pictures and music?
   B: I prefer working with pictures and music. Actually, I hate working with numbers and texts.

02 (1) it is in Pisa that I can visit the Leaning Tower
(2) it was radium that the Curies discovered
(3) it is English that is spoken all over the world

03 (A) a kite (B) the length (C) the better

단원별 모의고사
p.111~114

01 ④   02 (d)islike   03 ③   04 ②
05 It is working with machines that I hate. 06 ③
07 I can't wait for it!
08 (A) Do you have any good ideas?
   (B) Which do you prefer, making the bookmarks or writing the messages?
   (C) I hate writing.
09 They have collected so many interesting books to give away.
10 ④   11 ③   12 ③
13 (1) was in 2017 that[when] he became President
   (2) was Dash that[who] chose what to eat at dinner
14 (1) The less sugar I use, the healthier the cookies are.
   (2) It is these healthy cookies that will make everyone healthy.
15 had traveled   16 ③   17 ②
18 The more books we share, the more we learn.
19 ⑤   20 ⑤   21 amazing   22 ⑤

01 ④번은 '매우 작은'의 의미로 'tiny'를 설명한 말이다.

02 반의어 관계이다. 필요한 - 불필요한 : 좋아하다 - 싫어하다

03 '책을 출판하는 사람 또는 회사'의 의미로 'publisher(출판업자, 출판사)'가 적절하다.

04 지하철 타는 것을 선호한다고 말한 다음 '사실(Actually)'이라고 말하고 있으므로 ②번이 자연스럽다.

05 'It is ~ that …' 강조구문은 강조하고자 하는 말을 It is와 that 사이에 넣어 쓰면 된다.

06 시간이 오래 걸리는 것을 싫어한다고 했기 때문에 만들기에 쉽다는 내용이 오는 것이 적절하다.

07 기대를 나타내는 표현으로 'can't wait for+명사[대명사]'를 사용한다.

09 Seho가 '나는 우리가 나눠 줄 재미있는 책을 많이 모아서 자랑스러워.'라고 하고 있다.

10 ④ 'the+비교급, the+비교급' 비교급 자리에는 형용사, 부사 모두 올 수 있고, 뒤에 이어지는 동사에 따라 달라진다. The more foolish you are, the more easily you believe what others say.

11 접속사를 뺀 후 'the+비교급+주어+동사, the+비교급+주어+동사' 형태로 쓴다.

12 문장의 시제가 과거이므로 'It was+강조할 부분+that+문장의 나머지 부분'으로 문장을 쓴다. 강조하는 부분이 사람이 아니므로 that 대신 who를 쓰지 않는다.

13 'It is[was]+강조할 부분+that+문장의 나머지 부분'으로 쓴다.

14 (1) 'the+비교급, the+비교급'은 '…하면 할수록, 더 ~하다'라는 의미이다. little sugar의 비교급을 the less sugar로 쓰고,

21

healthy의 비교급은 the healthier로 쓴 다음 각각 그 뒤에 '주어+동사'를 쓴다. (2) 'It is[was]+강조할 부분(these healthy cookies)+that+문장의 나머지 부분'으로 쓴다.

15 과거의 특정 시점 이전에 일어난 일은 과거완료(had+과거분사)로 표현한다. 'I'가 '알아냈다(found out)'고 한 시점 이전에 책이 여행하였으므로 과거완료 'had traveled'로 쓰는것이 적절하다.

16 (A)와 ③: 무료의, 공짜의, ① 사용 중이 아닌, ② (유해하거나 불쾌한 것이) 없는, live free from care: 걱정 없는 생활을 하다, ④: 사용 중이 아닌, 이 자리에 사람 없나요? ⑤ 자유로운, 자기 하고 싶은 대로 하는

17 이 글은 'ID 번호가 있고 웹사이트에 등록되어 있어 발견한 사람이 자신의 집으로 가져가 읽을 수 있는 공짜 책'에 관한 글이므로, 주제로는 ②번 '여러분 주변의 독특한 책'이 적절하다. ① typical: 전형적인

18 The+비교급+주어+동사 …, the+비교급+주어+동사 ~: …하면 할수록, 더 ~하다

19 독자가 여러분의 책을 발견한 다음, 독자 자신이 직접 그 웹사이트에 다시 알려야 한다.

20 ⑤는 the Drinkable Book(마실 수 있는 책)에서 떼어낸 한 페이지를 가리키고, 나머지는 다 the Drinkable Book(마실 수 있는 책)을 가리킨다.

21 책이 사람을 놀라게 하는 것이므로 현재분사형의 형용사가 알맞다.

22 ⑤ the Drinkable Book(마실 수 있는 책)은 '더러운 물'로 생기는 질병으로부터 많은 어린이의 생명을 구한다. malnutrition: 영양실조

Fact, Opinion or Fake

시험대비 실력평가 p.118

01 opinion 02 ④ 03 ⑤ 04 ②
05 ③ 06 ① 07 turned out
08 false

01 내 생각에 영어는 가장 어려운 과목이다. <영어 설명> 사물 또는 사람에 대한 생각이나 믿음

02 'appear'는 '~처럼 보이다', '나타나다'의 의미를 가지고 있다. • 이 새로운 추세는 한 동안 계속될 것으로 보인다. • 도쿄의 한 지하철역에 새로운 자판기가 등장할 것이다.

03 (A) 내 숙제가 완벽하지(complete) 않아서 선생님은 화가 나셨다. (B) 우리는 우선 정보의 출처(source)를 찾아야 한다. critical: 비평의, 비판적인, complex: 복잡한, 착잡한, resource: 자원, 역량

04 '물리적인 폭력을 사용하여 어떤 사람이나 어떤 것을 다치게 하거나 손상을 주려고 하다'의 의미로 'attack(공격하다)'이 적절하다.

05 '서커스에서 우스운 옷을 입고 밝은 화장을 하고 사람들을 웃게 하려고 어리석은 행동을 하는 공연자'란 의미로 'clown(광대)'이 적절하다. 'crown'은 '왕관'이다.

06 나머지는 모두 '명사-형용사' 관계이고, ①번은 '동사-명사'관계이다.

07 '~로 밝혀지다'는 'turn out'을 이용하여 과거형 turned를 쓰는 것이 적절하다.

08 유의어 관계다. 증거 : 거짓의

서술형 시험대비 p.119

01 (1) spread (2) critically (3) scared (4) sink
02 touching
03 (1) (c)omfortable (2) (b)oring
   (3) (m)ajor (4) (S)low
04 (1) support, **지지하다** (2) spread, **퍼지다**
   (3) sink, **가라앉다** (4) octopus, **문어**
05 (1) pay attention to (2) tell, from (3) made up

01 (1) '그 이야기는 빠르게 모든 사람에게 퍼졌다.' 'spread'의 과거형은 'spread'다. (2) '노동자들은 문제를 해결하기 위해 비판적으로 생각해야 한다.' 동사를 수식하기 위해 부사 'critically'로 바꾸어야 한다. (3) '그 어린 소년은 괴물을 무서워한다.'

'scare'는 동사로 be동사 뒤에 사용되기 위해 과거분사 형태로 바뀌어야 한다. (4) '만약 배에 구멍이 생기면, 배는 가라앉을 것이다.'

02 '연민, 동정, 슬픔 등을 느끼게 하는'의 의미로 'touching(감동적인)'이 적절하다.

03 (1) comfortable: 편안한 (2) boring: 지루한 (3) major: 주요한 (4) slow down: 속도를 줄이다

04 (1) 어떤 사람에게 도움, 동의, 위로, 격려 등을 주다 (2) 한 장소나 표면 위에 펼치거나 배열하다 (3) 수면 아래로 사라지다 (4) 여덟 개의 긴 다리를 가진 연한 바다 생물

05 (1) 학생들은 선생님에게 집중해야 한다. (2) 그의 부모님은 그에게 옳고 그른 것을 구별하는 법을 가르쳐 주셨다. (3) 분홍 말에 관한 이야기는 꾸며낸 것이었다.

Conversation 교과서

핵심 Check p.120~121

1 How do you feel about them?　　2 ③

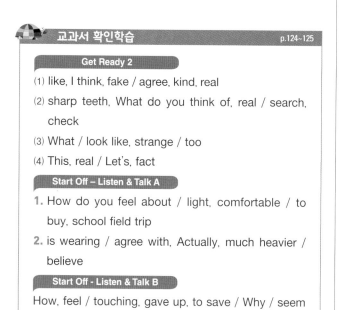

교과서 대화문 익히기

Check(√) True or False　　p.122

1 T　2 F　3 T　4 T

교과서 확인학습　　p.124~125

Get Ready 2

(1) like, I think, fake / agree, kind, real

(2) sharp teeth, What do you think of, real / search, check

(3) What / look like, strange / too

(4) This, real / Let's, fact

Start Off – Listen & Talk A

1. How do you feel about / light, comfortable / to buy, school field trip

2. is wearing / agree with, Actually, much heavier / believe

Start Off - Listen & Talk B

How, feel / touching, gave up, to save / Why / seem

real, a little boring

Start Off – Speak Up

How, about, ad / shows / should not

Step Up – Real-life Scene

cool, How do you feel about / that / makes, laugh, loud / octopus / make sense / when, climbing, lying / agree with, fake, out of

Express Yourself A

1. How, about / get along, with / these two, enjoying, together

2. By the way / guess / prefer / with, better than, In fact / to help

3. feel about / anything special / were made, uniform / passed away / touching

---

p.126

01 What, think of[about]　　02 ④　　03 ③
04 ②

01 'What do you think of[about] ~?'는 '~에 대하여 어떻게 생각하니?'라는 표현이다.

02 상대방에게 어떤 대상에 대한 의견을 물을 때 사용하는 표현으로 'How do you feel about ~?', 'What do you think about ~?(~에 대하여 어떻게 생각하니?)', 'What's your opinion about ~?(~에 대한 의견이 무엇이니?)', 'What do you say about ~?(~에 대하여 어떻게 생각하십니까?)' 등을 사용할 수 있다. ④번의 'What do you know about ~?'은 '~에 대해 무엇을 알고 있어?'라는 뜻으로 특정 대상에 대해 무엇을 알고 있는지 물을 때 사용하는 표현이다.

03 ④번의 'I couldn't agree more.'는 '전적으로 동의해.'라는 표현이다.

04 'I don't agree with you.(나는 동의하지 않아요.)'는 상대와 의견이 달라서 동의하지 않고 상대의 의견에 이의를 제기하는 말이다.

시험대비 실력평가　　p.127~128

01 ④　　　02 (a) touching　(b) boring　03 ⑤
04 ③　　　05 ③　　　06 ②
07 get along, with　　08 ⑤　　　09 ④
10 ①　　　11 ③

01 B의 '이 드라마가 올해 최고의 드라마다.'라는 말에 대해 G가 '그것은 좋은 드라마가 아니다.'라고 말하고 있으므로 ④가 적절하다. 나머지는 모두 동의하는 표현이다.

02 (a)는 '감동적인'의 뜻을 가지는 'touching'이 적절하고, (b)는 '지루한'의 뜻을 가진 'boring'이 적절하다.

03 Alex가 문어에 대해 많이 알고 있는지는 알 수 없다.

04 나머지는 'An octopus'를 가리키고, (c)는 앞 문장의 '문어가 나무에 사는 것'을 가리킨다.

05 빈칸 앞의 동의하지 않는다는 말에 대해 더 구체적으로 '강조, 첨가'하는 표현을 가진 'Actually(사실)'가 적절하다.

06 비교급을 강조하는 말은 'much, even, still, far, a lot'이다. 'very'는 원급(형용사나 부사)을 강조하는 말이다.

07 '사이좋게 지내다'라는 의미로 'get along (well) with'를 사용한다.

08 (A)는 상대방의 의견을 묻는 표현으로 'What do you think about ~?(~에 대하여 어떻게 생각하니?)', 'What's your opinion about ~?(~에 대한 의견이 무엇이니?)', 'What do you say about ~?(~에 대하여 어떻게 생각하십니까?)' 등으로 바꾸어 말할 수 있다.

09 대화에서 Fact에 해당하는 내용은 '아이가 아픈 아이들을 돕기 위해 머리를 잘랐다'는 것이다. 나머지는 '의견'이나 '거짓' 정보에 해당한다. ① 의견 ② 의견 ③ 거짓 정보 ⑤ 거짓 정보

10 상대방에게 어떤 대상에 대한 의견을 물을 때 사용하는 표현으로 '~에 대해 어떻게 생각하니?'라고 묻는 ①이 적절하다.

11 (a)는 이상한 동물을 보고 '진짜일까?' 또는 '가짜일까?'라고 물을 수 있다. (b)는 다리가 없고 뱀처럼 보이지는 않는 동물을 보고 '이것은 매우 이상해.'라고 말하는 것이 자연스럽다.

서술형 시험대비
p.129

01 (A) How do you feel about it?
    (B) I don't agree with you.
02 Because he always makes him laugh out loud.
03 (A) What do you think about
    (B) I think cats don't get along well with dogs
04 I don't agree with you

01 (A) 'How do you feel about ~?'은 '~을[~에 대해] 어떻게 생각해?'라는 의미로 상대방에게 어떤 대상에 대한 의견을 물을 때 사용하는 표현이다. (B) 'I don't agree with you.(나는 동의하지 않아요.)'는 상대와 의견이 달라서 동의하지 않고 상대의 의견에 이의를 제기하는 말이다.

02 질문: 왜 Alex는 Mr. Big Mouth를 좋아하는가?

03 (A) 'What do you think about ~?(~에 대하여 어떻게 생각하니?)', (B) 'I think+주어+동사 ~' 어순으로 쓴다.

04 G가 코트가 따뜻하고 가벼울 것 같아서 마음에 든다는 말에 대해 B가 '그렇게 따뜻하지도 않고 보기보다 훨씬 더 무거워.'라고 말하는 것으로 보아 G의 말에 동의하지 않는 표현이 들어가는 것이 적절하다.

Grammar

핵심 Check
p.130~131

1 (1) told (2) was
2 (1) Whether (2) whether

시험대비 기본평가
p.132

01 (1) he is very tall
    (2) she was very happy to meet him
    (3) she was not crying
    (4) she looked great
02 (1) I wonder if[whether] she will like my present.
    (2) I don't know if he will give me flowers or not.
    (3) I want to know if he will throw the ball.
    (4) The question is whether they believe what I said or not.

01 전달동사가 과거이므로 따옴표 안의 현재시제는 과거시제로 바꾸고 따옴표 속 'I'는 문장의 주어, 따옴표 속 'you'는 듣는 이로 바꾼다. (1)은 키가 큰 것이 현재의 사실이므로 시제의 일치 원칙에 적용되지 않는다.

02 (1) 동사 wonder의 목적절로는 if 또는 whether절이 적절하다. (2) 'if'는 'or not'을 함께 사용할 때 문장 끝에만 사용 가능하며, 'whether'는 바로 다음이나 문장 끝에 'or not'을 붙여 쓸 수도 있다. (3) 접속사 if 다음에 '주어+동사'의 어순으로 쓴다. (4) 'whether'는 주어, 보어, 동사의 목적어, 전치사의 목적어 자리에 모두 쓰일 수 있지만, 'if'는 동사의 목적어 자리에 주로 쓰인다. 이 글에서는 명사절이 보어로 쓰이고 있으므로 if가 아닌 whether를 쓰는 것이 적절하다.

시험대비 실력평가
p.133~135

01 ④   02 I wonder if he will catch my ball.
03 ⑤   04 ④   05 ④
06 (1) I told Amy that I wanted to play with her then.
    (2) Mom asked me if I was finished with my homework.
07 ③   08 ①   09 ③
10 I am not sure if I do well on the test.   11 ③
12 I'm not sure if[whether] they will give me a big hand.
13 My sister doubts if I cheated on the test (or not).
14 ②   15 ⑤   16 ⑤   17 ②
18 ③   19 (1) asked (2) says (3) if (4) felt (5) is

01 ④ 전달동사가 과거일 경우, 시제의 일치 법칙에 맞게 따옴표(" ") 안의 동사가 과거시제라면 과거완료로 바꾸어야 한다. (has eaten → had eaten)

02 wonder가 원형이므로 주절의 주어는 he가 아닌 I로 하고, 동사 wonder의 목적절로 'if+주어+동사+목적어'로 한다.

03 ①~④는 동사의 목적어로 쓰인 명사절의 접속사 if이고, ⑤는 조건을 나타내는 부사절의 접속사이다. 해석: 그 동물이 기분이 좋다면, 너는 그것을 볼 수 있을 거야.

04 ④ 전달동사(said)와 that절의 내용이 과거(would be)이므로, tomorrow를 the next day로 쓰는 것이 적절하다.

05 동사 asked의 목적어 자리에 질문을 나타내는 명사절의 접속사이면서 or not과 함께 쓸 수 있는 접속사는 whether이다.

06 (1) 부사를 전달자의 관점에 맞게 고쳐야 하므로 now는 then으로 쓰는 것이 적절하다. (2) 따옴표 안의 내용이 의문문인 화법전환은 전달동사를 ask로 바꾸어 쓴다.

07 ③은 목적절이 질문이 아닌 주어가 알고 있는 내용이므로, 명사절의 접속사 'that'이 적절하다. ①, ④는 조건을 나타내는 접속사 if가 적절하고 ②, ⑤는 목적어가 되는 명사절의 접속사 if를 쓰는 것이 적절하다.

08 의문문을 간접화법으로 전환할 때 전달동사 say 또는 say to를 ask로 바꿔야 한다.

09 첫 번째 문장은 동사 wonder의 목적절로 내용상 if 또는 whether가 적절하고, 두 번째 문장은 be동사의 보어절로 접속사 if는 쓸 수 없고 whether를 쓰는 것이 적절하다. 단, 두 문장 모두 질문하는 내용이므로 접속사 that의 사용은 어색하다.

10 am not sure(확실하지 않다)의 목적어 자리에 명사절의 접속사 if를 사용하여 목적절을 넣는다.

11 전달동사 said to는 told로 바꾼다. 직접화법을 간접화법으로 바꿀 때 따옴표 속 'I'는 문장의 주어로 바꾸고 따옴표 속 'you'는 듣는 이로 바꾼다. 전달동사가 과거이므로, 시제의 일치 법칙에 맞게 따옴표(" ") 안의 현재시제 동사는 과거시제로 바꾼다.

12 I'm not sure의 목적어 자리에 의문문을 넣어야 하므로, 명사절의 접속사 if 또는 whether를 넣어 연결한다. 이때, 이 의문문은 평서문의 어순으로 바꾸어 쓴다.

13 문장의 주어에 맞게 동사 doubt를 3인칭 단수형으로 쓰고 목적절로 if절을 쓴다. 단, 목적절의 내용이 과거이므로 if절의 동사 cheat는 과거시제로 쓴다.

14 ② 시제의 일치의 법칙에 맞게 My sister told me that she had met Tom by chance the day before.로 쓴다.

15 첫 번째 문장은 주어로 쓰인 명사절의 접속사이면서 or not과 함께 쓸 수 있는 whether가 적절하고, 두 번째 문장에서는 find out의 의미상 단정적 내용의 접속사 that이 아닌, 의문의 내용을 위한 접속사 if 또는 whether가 적절하다.

16 to keep과 함께 쓸 수 있는 전달동사로 made는 사용할 수 없다. 해석: 그 할머니는 나에게 그녀의 개를 지켜보라고 요청했다[말했다, 명령했다].

17 '내가 ~할게'의 의미로 'let me+동사원형'을 쓰고 동사 check의 목적절로 '~인지 아닌지'의 if절을 쓰는 것이 적절하다. 단, 접속사 if 바로 뒤에 or not을 쓰지 않고 문장 맨 끝에 써야 한다.

18 b. 듣는 이가 없으므로 전달동사를 told가 아닌 said로 쓴다. c. 전달동사를 said가 아닌 told로 쓴다. d. 명령문을 간접화법으로 쓸 때 부정명령문은 to not이 아닌 not to 동사원형으로 쓴다.

19 (1) 의문문을 간접화법으로 쓸 때 전달동사는 asked가 적절하다. (2) 듣는 이가 없으므로 전달동사는 says가 적절하다. (3) 목적절에 질문하는 내용이 적절하므로 접속사 if를 쓴다. (4) 전달하는 내용이 과거이므로 felt가 적절하다. (5) 전달동사는 과거이나 명사절의 내용이 과학적 사실이므로 현재시제를 쓴다.

서술형 시험대비

p.136~137

01 (1) I wonder if[whether] the plane arrived on time.
(2) I asked if[whether] she was married.
(3) The question is whether the meeting is ready.
(4) I think that he is very honest.
(5) Whether she will attend the audition depends on her physical condition.

02 (1) He told me (that) he really appreciated my help.
(2) My roommate told me (that) she[he] would be late that night.

03 (1) he knew (2) I want (3) he would help me

04 (1) John said to Mary, "I love you."
(2) She told him that she was sorry.
(3) I told my dad that I would call him later.
(4) Mr. Brown told me that he wanted me to study more.
(5) My mom said that dish tasted good.

05 He asked her what the weather was like in New York that day.

06 (1) I understand that you don't want to talk about it.
(2) Whether you are a boy or a girl makes no difference to me.
(3) Whether you will succeed or not depends on your efforts.
(4) I am not sure if[whether] there is life on other planets.
(5) Tell me if[whether] you have any plans for your future.

07 (1) whether we have enough money to buy the new car
(2) that he had lied to his family
(3) if she would have a garage sale in her backyard

08 (1) was hungry, why she looked angry
(2) was very cute, if she liked that food

01 (1), (2) 의문사가 없는 의문문을 목적절로 만들어야 하므로 접속사 if 또는 whether를 사용한다. (3) 의문문을 보어로 만들어야 하므로 접속사 if는 사용할 수 없고 whether를 사용한다. (4) 평서문을 목적절로 만들 때는 접속사 that을 사용한다. (5) 의문문을 주절로 만들어야 하므로 접속사 if는 사용할 수 없고 whether를 사용한다.

02 (1) 간접화법을 쓸 때 전달동사가 과거라면, 시제의 일치 법칙에 맞게 따옴표(" ") 안의 현재동사를 과거시제로 바꾼다. 또한 따옴표 속 'I'는 문장의 주어로 바꾸고, 따옴표 속 'you'는 듣는 이로 바꾼다. (2) 부사 tonight는 시제에 맞게 that night으로 바꾼다.

03 (1) 직접화법을 간접화법으로 바꿀 때 따옴표 속 'I'는 문장의 주어로 바꾸고, 전달동사가 과거라면, 시제의 일치 법칙에 맞게 따옴표(" ") 안의 동사가 현재시제라면 과거시제로 바꾼다. (2) 주절의 주어와 that절의 주어가 같다면 직접화법에서 'I'가 되고 본동사의 시제와 that절의 시제가 과거로 같으므로 따옴표(" ") 안에서는 현재시제로 쓰는 것이 적절하다. (3) 직접화법을 간접화법으로 바꿀 때 따옴표 속 'I'는 문장의 주어로 바꾸고 따옴표 속 'you'는 듣는 이로 바꾼다.

04 (1) 직접화법의 전달동사는 듣는 이가 있을 때 said to로 쓴다. (2) 전달동사가 과거이므로 that절의 동사 is는 was로 쓴다. (3) 주어가 아버지에게 말한 내용이므로 that절의 you는 him으로 쓴다. (4) 간접화법의 전달동사는 듣는 이가 있을 때 told로 쓴다. (5) 간접화법이므로 지시형용사 this는 that으로 쓴다.

05 의문문을 간접화법으로 전환할 때 전달동사 said to를 asked로 바꿔야 한다. 전달동사가 과거이므로, 시제의 일치 법칙에 맞게 따옴표(" ") 안의 현재동사를 과거시제로 바꾼다. 이때 부사 today는 의미상 적절하게 that day로 쓴다.

06 (1) 동사 understand의 목적어로는 질문을 나타내는 if는 적절하지 않으므로 접속사 that을 쓴다. (2) 명사절이 주어일 때 단수로 취급하므로 동사 make를 makes로 쓴다. (3) if절은 주어로 쓰이지 않으므로 whether를 쓰는 것이 적절하다. (4) I am not sure(나는 확실하지 않다)와 어울리는 접속사는 질문의 의미를 가진 if나 whether가 적절하다. (5) 동사 Tell의 목적어로 if 또는 whether절을 쓰는 것이 적절하다.

07 (1) 문장의 보어 자리이고 내용상 질문이므로 접속사 whether를 쓴다. (2) 동사 admit와 어울리는 접속사는 that이다. (3) 동사 ask의 목적절로 질문을 나타내는 if를 쓰는 것이 적절하다. 해석: 나는 할머니에게 그녀의 뒷마당에서 중고물품 판매를 할 것인지 물었다.

08 (1) 전달동사가 과거이므로 그림 속 대화의 현재는 과거시제로 질문은 간접의문문으로 바꾼다. (2) 지시형용사를 적절히 바꾼다. (this → that)

확인문제   p.138

1 T   2 F   3 T   4 F

확인문제   p.139

1 T   2 F   3 T   4 F

교과서 확인학습 A   p.140~141

01 Smart News Reader
02 shook schools, didn't believe, a bit
03 getting scared   04 checked up on
05 were actually made   06 no hard evidence
07 turned out to be   08 just look at one thing
09 to look at the right sources, what is real, what is fake
10 Like, to think critically, on the Internet
11 getting more important   12 how to tell, from
13 One of the first steps   14 too good to be true
15 what the writer says   16 coming from
17 how to tell, from   18 if, are based on
19 a smart news reader   20 appears to provide
21 along with   22 like, made up
23 once more carefully, question everything

교과서 확인학습 B   p.142~143

1 How to Be a Smart News Reader
2 In October 2016, stories about scary clowns shook schools across the Washington area, but Danina Garcia-Fuller's students didn't believe them a bit.
3 "Some people were getting scared because they saw things on social media," said Patricia Visoso, one of Garcia-Fuller's students.
4 "But they never checked up on who was saying this."
5 The stories were actually made by teenagers, not by major newspapers or TV stations.
6 They offered no hard evidence that clowns really were trying to attack students.
7 The story turned out to be a complete lie.
8 "I think a lot of people just look at one thing and believe it's true," Patricia's classmate Ivy-Brooks

said.

9 "It's really important to look at the right sources and to pay attention to what is real and what is fake."

10 Like Garcia-Fuller's students, many teenagers in America are learning to think critically about information they're seeing in the news and on the Internet.

11 This skill is getting more important these days as stories can spread very fast, and anyone can make a website full of false information.

12 Garcia-Fuller said she was teaching her students how to tell fake news from real news.

13 "One of the first steps is to slow down.

14 If a story or a photo seems too good to be true, stop and think.

15 Is there any evidence that supports what the writer says?

16 And where is this coming from?"

17 Garcia-Fuller's students also learn how to tell fact from opinion in the news.

18 "Opinions are good to read," said 15-year-old McKenzie Campbell, "but you also have to check if they are based on facts."

19 Garcia-Fuller also said sometimes it can be very hard to be a smart news reader.

20 She tests her students with a website that appears to provide information on an animal called a tree octopus.

21 The site is full of information on this animal, along with a few unclear photos of octopuses in trees.

22 But like the story of scary clowns, it's totally made up.

23 The lesson, Garcia-Fuller tells her students, is to "check the information you're seeing once more carefully" and to "question everything, even things that I say."

시험대비 실력평가 p.144~147

01 ⑤   02 The stories 03 ④   04 ④
05 (A) sources (B) Like (C) false
06 look at everything → just look at one thing
07 is appeared → appears 08 together with
09 ⑤   10 ①, ④   11 ②, ⑤   12 ③
13 which[that] is   14 ⑤
15 Is there any evidence that supports what the

---

writer says?
16 opinions 17 ②   18 ①, ③   19 ③
20 called   21 ②

01 ⓐ on social media: 소셜 미디어에 올라온, ⓑ check up on: ~을 확인하다

02 '그 이야기들'을 가리킨다.

03 무서운 광대들에 관한 이야기들은 실제로 '주요 신문사나 TV 방송국'이 아닌 '10대들'이 지어냈다.

04 올바른 출처를 살펴보고, 무엇이 진짜이고 무엇이 가짜인지에 주의를 기울이는 것이 정말 중요하다고 생각하는 Garcia-Fuller의 학생들처럼, 많은 미국의 10대들은 '비판적으로' 생각하는 것을 배워 나가고 있다고 하는 것이 적절하다. ① 무비판적으로, ② 순응하여, ③ 적응하여, 순응하여, ⑤ 무조건으로, 절대적으로

05 (A) 올바른 '출처'를 살펴보라고 해야 하므로 sources가 적절하다. source: 자료, 출처 resource: 자원, (B) Garcia-Fuller의 학생들'처럼'이라고 해야 하므로 Like가 적절하다. alike: [명사 앞에는 안 씀] (아주) 비슷한, like: ~와 비슷한, ~같은(전치사), (C) 누구나 '허위' 정보로 가득 찬 웹사이트를 만들어 낼 수 있기 때문에 이 기능이 최근 더 중요해지고 있다고 해야 하므로 false가 적절하다.

06 Patricia의 반 친구인 Ivy-Brooks는 많은 사람이 '단지 한 가지만을 보고' 그것이 사실이라고 믿는 것 같다고 했다.

07 appear는 수동태로 쓸 수 없기 때문에, is appeared를 appears로 고치는 것이 적절하다.

08 along with = together with: ~와 함께

09 누가 '나무 문어'에 대한 정보를 꾸며냈는지는 알 수 없다. ① Sometimes it can be very hard to be a smart news reader. ② No. ③ Information on an animal called a tree octopus. ④ Information on the animal called a tree octopus, along with a few unclear photos of octopuses in trees.

10 ⓐ와 ①, ④ tell(know/distinguish) A from B: A와 B를 구분하다

11 ⓑ와 ②, ⑤: 주격 관계대명사, ① so ... that ~: 너무 …해서 ~하다(접속사), ③ 동격의 접속사, ④ 목적어를 이끄는 접속사

12 이 글은 'Garcia-Fuller가 자신의 학생들에게 가짜 뉴스를 진짜 뉴스로부터 구분하는 방법과 뉴스에서 사실을 의견과 구분하는 방법에 대해서 가르치는' 내용의 글이므로, 주제로는 ③번 '가짜 뉴스와 진짜 뉴스를, 그리고 뉴스에서 사실을 의견과 구분하는 방법'이 적절하다.

13 주격 관계대명사 which[that]와 be동사인 is가 생략되어 있다.

14 '사람들이 왜 허위 정보로 가득 찬 웹사이트를 만드는지'는 대답

할 수 없다. ① They just look at one thing. ② They are learning to think critically about information they're seeing in the news and on the Internet. ③ They're seeing it in the news and on the Internet. ④ Yes.

15 주격 관계대명사 'that'이 선행사 'any evidence'를 수식하도록 하고, 선행사를 포함한 관계대명사 'what'이 이끄는 명사절이 동사 'supports'의 목적어가 되도록 쓰는 것이 적절하다.

16 '의견들'을 가리킨다.

17 주어진 문장의 they에 주목한다. ②번 앞 문장의 Some people을 받고 있으므로 ②번이 적절하다.

18 ⓐ와 ①, ③: 동격절을 이끄는 접속사, ② 목적절을 이끄는 접속사, ④ 주절을 이끄는 접속사, ⑤ 보어절을 이끄는 접속사

19 이 글은 '몇몇 사람들은 명백한 증거를 하나도 제공하지 못한 완벽한 거짓말로 드러난 무서운 광대들에 관한 이야기를 누가 말하고 있는지 전혀 확인하지도 않고 단지 소셜 미디어에 올라온 것만을 보고 무서워했지만, Danina Garcia-Fuller의 학생들은 조금도 그 이야기들을 믿지 않았다'는 내용의 글이므로, 제목으로는 ③번 '이봐, 소셜 미디어에 올라온 것들을 믿을 때는 신중해야 해!'가 적절하다.

20 '나무 문어'라고 불리는 동물이라고 해야 하므로 과거분사 called로 쓰는 것이 적절하다.

21 ⓑ와 ②: 교훈, ①, ④, ⑤: 수업[교습/교육] (시간), ③ (교과서의) 과(課)

서술형 시험대비 p.148~149

01 student → students　　02 not, but
03 It turned out that the story was a complete lie.
04 (A) on social media　(B) a complete lie
05 to think critically about information they're seeing in the news and on the Internet
06 filled with
07 It is really important to look at the right sources and to pay attention to what is real and what is fake.
08 (A) I am　(B) my
09 (A) is　(B) too good　(C) supports
10 they should
11 (A) slow down　(B) stop　(C) any evidence
12 a tree octopus　　13 what
14 (A) once more carefully　(B) question everything

01 one+of+소유격+복수명사: ~ 중의 하나
02 B, not A = not A but B: A가 아니라 B
03 the story를 that절의 주어로 바꾸고, to be를 was로 바꾸는

것이 적절하다.

04 몇몇 사람들은 그들이 '소셜 미디어에 올라온' 것들을 봤기 때문에 무서운 광대들에 관한 이야기를 무서워했지만 그들은 누가 그 이야기를 말하고 있는지를 전혀 확인하지 않았는데, 그 이야기는 결국 완벽한 거짓말인 것으로 드러났다.

05 '뉴스에서 그리고 인터넷상에서 보고 있는 정보에 관해 비판적으로 생각하는 것'을 가리킨다.

06 be full of = be filled with: ~로 가득 차 있다. full of 앞에 which[that] is가 생략되어 있다.

07 올바른 출처를 살펴보고, 무엇이 진짜이고 무엇이 가짜인지에 주의를 기울이는 것이 정말 중요하다.

08 직접화법으로 고치면 'she was'를 'I am'으로, 'her' students를 'my' students로 고치는 것이 적절하다.

09 (A) 주어가 One이므로 is가 적절하다. (B) '만약 어떤 이야기나 어떤 사진이 진짜라고 하기엔 너무 좋아 보인다면'이라고 해야 하므로 too good이 적절하다. too+형용사/부사+to부정사: '너무 …해서 ~할 수 없다', 형용사/부사+enough to부정사: ~할 만큼 충분히 …한, (C) 글쓴이가 말하고 있는 것을 '뒷받침하는' 어떠한 증거라도 있는가라고 해야 하므로 supports가 적절하다. deny: (무엇이) 사실이 아니라고 말하다, 부인[부정]하다

10 의문사+to부정사 = 의문사+주어+should+동사원형

11 첫 단계 중 하나는 '속도를 늦추는 것'이다. 만약 어떤 이야기나 어떤 사진이 진짜라고 하기엔 너무 좋아 보일 때, '멈춰서' 글쓴이의 말을 뒷받침하는 '어떠한 증거'라도 있는지와 이 정보의 출처에 대해 생각해야 한다.

12 '나무 문어'를 가리킨다.

13 선행사를 포함하는 관계대명사 'what'으로 바꿔 쓸 수 있다.

14 Garcia-Fuller가 그녀의 학생들에게 말하는 교훈은 당신이 보고 있는 정보를 '한 번 더 신중하게' 확인해 보라는 것과 '모든 것', 심지어 그녀가 말하는 것에도 '의문을 가져 보라'는 것이다.

영역별 핵심문제 p.151~155

01 attack	02 ③	03 ④	04 ④
05 ①	06 fake	07 comfortable	
08 ③	09 ⑤	10 ④	11 ②
12 ④	13 ②	14 ①that → if[whether]	
15 ④	16 ④	17 ③	

18 (1) He said to her, "What are you doing here?"
(2) She said to him, "I met my sister yesterday."
(3) She said, "I am very happy now."
19 ②　　　20 무서운 광대들에 관한 이야기
21 They offered no hard evidence that clowns really were trying to attack students.

22 ④	23 ②	24 ③
25 invented	26 ⑤	27 ④

01 반의어 관계다. 지루한-흥미로운 : 방어하다-공격하다

02 (a) 이 책은 실화에 바탕을 둔다. '~에 근거하다'는 'be based on'을 사용한다. (b) 분홍 말에 관한 이야기는 꾸며낸 것이었다. '꾸며낸'은 'made up'을 사용한다.

03 ④번의 'complete'는 형용사로 '완전한'의 의미이다. 'complete'가 '완료하다'라는 의미의 동사로 사용되려면 'wasn't completed'의 수동형이 되는 것이 적절하다.

04 '당신이 어떤 것이 사실이라고 믿도록 만드는 어떤 것'의 의미로 'evidence(증거)'가 적절하다.

05 '불찬성을 표현하는 방식으로'의 의미로 'critically(비판적으로)'가 적절하다.

06 '진짜가 아니지만 진짜처럼 보이도록 만들어진'의 의미로 4글자 단어인 'fake(가짜의)'가 적절하다.

07 look의 보어로 comfort의 형용사형이 와야 한다.

08 G가 그것이 가짜라고 한 말에 대해 동의하지 않는다고 말하고 있고, TV에서 저런 종류의 원숭이를 봤다고 했으므로 빈칸에는 'real'이 적절하다.

09 ⑤번은 '이 광고에 대해 어떻게 생각해?'라는 A의 물음에 대해 B가 '훌륭하다고 생각해.'라고 말한 다음 '우리는 모든 광고를 다 믿으면 안 된다'고 말하는 것은 어색하다.

10 '문어가 나무에서 산다고 Mr. Big Mouth가 말했어.'라는 Alex의 말에 대해 Somi는 '말도 안 돼.'라고 말하는 것이 자연스럽다. 'It doesn't make sense.'로 바꾸어야 한다.

11 위 대화는 Big Mouth's Show에서 보여준 사진이 사실인지 아닌지에 대한 대화이다.

12 Alex는 나무를 오르는 문어 사진이 사실이라고 생각하고 있다.

13 주어진 문장은 동사 'tells'의 목적절로 '~인지 아닌지'이다. ② '~인지 아닌지' ①, ③, ④, ⑤ 조건절. '만일 ~라면'

14 동사 'don't know'와 어울리는 접속사는 의문을 의미하는 'if'이다.

15 의문사가 주어이므로 문장의 어순은 바뀌지 않는다. 전달동사가 과거이므로 의문문의 과거동사는 과거완료로, 지시형용사 this는 that으로 바꾼다. 해석: 그는 나에게 누가 저 도마뱀붙이를 집으로 가져왔는지 물었다. *gecko: 도마뱀붙이

16 a. Do you know if it will be rainy tomorrow? b. I am not sure if he can finish his project. d. Tell me if[whether] you have the time. e. He asked me if I wanted something to eat.

17 전달동사가 과거이므로, 시제의 일치 법칙에 맞게 따옴표(" ") 안의 현재동사를 과거시제로 바꾸고 부사 tomorrow는 의미상 적절하게 the following day로 바꾼다. 또한 따옴표 속 'I'는 문장의 주어로 바꾸고 따옴표 속 'you'는 듣는 이로 바꾼다.

18 (1) 따옴표 안에서 의문문의 형태인 '의문사+동사+주어'의 어순이어야 한다. (2) 간접화법에서 과거완료시제이고, 전달동사는 과거이므로 따옴표 안에서 과거시제로 써야 한다. (3) 간접화법에서 then은 직접화법에서 내용이 현재시제이므로 now로 쓰는 것이 적절하다.

19 그 이야기들은 10대들이 지어낸 것이고 광대들이 정말로 학생들을 공격하려고 한다는 명백한 증거를 하나도 제공하지 않았다고 했으므로, 그 이야기는 결국 '완벽한 거짓말'인 것으로 드러났다고 하는 것이 적절하다. ① 근거 있는 소문, ③ valid: 타당한, ⑤ suspicious: 의심스러운, column: 칼럼

20 'the story about scary clowns'를 가리킨다.

21 동격의 접속사 'that' 이하가 'evidence'와 동격을 이루도록 쓰는 것이 적절하다.

22 ⓐ와 ④: 이유를 나타내는 접속사, ① ~하는 대로(접속사), ② ~하다시피[~이듯이](접속사), ③ [비례] ~함에 따라, ~할수록(접속사), ⑤ ~하고 있을 때(접속사)

23 이 글은 '이야기들은 아주 빠른 속도로 퍼져 나갈 수 있고 누구나 허위 정보로 가득 찬 웹사이트를 만들어 낼 수 있기 때문에, 뉴스에서 그리고 인터넷상에서 보고 있는 정보에 관해 비판적으로 생각하는 것이 최근 더 중요해지고 있다'는 내용의 글이므로, 주제로는 ②번 뉴스에서 그리고 인터넷상에서 보고 있는 정보에 관해 비판적으로 생각하는 것의 중요성'이 적절하다.

24 많은 미국의 10대들은 '뉴스에서 그리고 인터넷상에서' 보고 있는 정보에 관해 비판적으로 생각하는 것을 배워 나가고 있다.

25 make up: (특히 남을 속이거나 즐겁게 하기 위해 이야기 등을) 지어[만들어] 내다, be made up: ~로 꾸며지다, invent: (사실이 아닌 것을) 지어내다[날소아나]

26 이 글은 'Garcia-Fuller가 또한 때때로 현명한 뉴스 독자가 되는 것이 아주 어려울 수도 있다고 말하면서 그녀의 학생들에게 당신이 보고 있는 정보를 한 번만 더 신중하게 확인해 보고 모든 것, 심지어 그녀가 말하는 것에도 의문을 가져 보라는 교훈을 말하는' 내용의 글이므로, 제목으로는 ⑤번 '정보를 신중하게 확인하고 모든 것에 의문을 가져라'가 적절하다.

27 앞에 나오는 내용과 상반되는 내용이 뒤에 이어지므로 However가 적절하다. ② 게다가, ③ 다시 말해서, ⑤ 그러므로

28 이어동사의 목적어가 인칭대명사일 때는 목적어를 동사와 부사 사이에 쓰는 것이 적절하다.

단원별 예상문제 p.156~159

01 preform   02 ⑤

03 They were made out of a police officer's uniform., This police officer made them for the kids.

04 Is there anything special about them?

05 ②   06 ④   07 ③   08 ②, ⑤

09 (1) the answer of that question

(2) had been in trouble

(3) my new house now

(4) said to

(5) Are you hungry now

10 (1) Don't go out during class

(2) told[asked, ordered] students not to go out during class

11 I wonder if[whether] they will show us the fan dance.

12 (1) I am so tired now   (2) I was right

13 ④   14 proved

15 They were made by teenagers.   16 ②

17 many teenagers in America   18 ①

19 ②, ③, ⑤   20 ④   21 while → during

22 ①, ④   23 best

---

01 '명사-동사'의 관계이다. 정보 - 알리다 : 공연 - 공연하다

02 '매우 중요하고 진지한'의 의미로 'major(주된, 주요한)'가 적절하다.

03 대화에서 'Teddy Bears'에 관해 알 수 있는 'Fact'는 '한 경찰관의 제복으로 만들어졌다.'는 것과 '이 경찰이 아이들을 위해 그것들을 만들어 줬다'는 두 가지다.

04 '~가 있니?'라는 의문문으로 'Is there+주어 ~?'로 시작하고, anything은 형용사가 뒤에서 수식해야 하므로 anything special로 쓴다.

05 '그것이 가짜라고 생각해.'라는 G의 말에 B가 '저런 종류의 원숭이를 TV에서 본 적이 있어.'라고 말하고 있으므로 G의 말에 동의하지 않는다는 것을 알 수 있다.

06 요새 여자아이들은 짧은 머리를 더 좋아한다는 말에 대해 '그것에 동의하지 않아.'라는 말을 한 다음 주어진 문장이 들어가는 것이 자연스럽다.

07 (a) '매우 예쁘다고 생각해.'라는 말 다음에 머리를 왜 잘랐는지 화제를 바꾸어 말하고 있으므로 'By the way'가 적절하다. (b) '여기 이 아이는 여자아이가 아니야.'라는 말 다음에 '강조, 첨가'하는 표현으로 '사실'의 의미를 가지는 'In fact'가 적절하다.

08 debate의 목적절이고 의문의 내용이므로 빈칸에 접속사 if 또는 whether를 쓴다. 해석: 팀 A와 팀 B는 십대들이 파트타임을 해야 할지에 관해 토론할 것이다.

09 (1) 직접화법에서 this는 간접화법에서 that으로 쓴다. (2) 전달동사가 과거이고 직접화법의 시제가 과거이면 간접화법에서 과거완료시제로 쓴다. (3) 간접화법에서 that절의 주어와 주절의 주어가 같다면 직접화법에서 일인칭으로 쓰고, then은 now로 쓴다. (4) 간접화법에서 전달동사 tell은 듣는 이가 있다면 직접화법에서 say to로 쓴다. (5) 간접화법에서의 듣는 이와 종속절의 주어가 같다면, 직접화법에서 you로 쓰고, 전달동사의 시제와 종속절의 시제가 과거로 같다면 직접화법에서 따옴표 안에서 현재시제로 쓴다. 부사 then은 now로 바꾸어 쓴다.

10 (1) 부정의 명령문 'Don't+동사원형'의 형태로 문장을 쓴다.

---

(2) 명령문으로 간접화법을 쓸 때, 전달동사는 의미에 따라 tell, ask, order 등을 쓸 수 있고, 부정의 명령문은 not to로 바꾸어 쓴다.

11 동사 wonder의 목적어 자리에 의미상 의문문을 넣어야 하므로, 명사절의 접속사 if 또는 whether를 넣어 목적절을 완성한다.

12 (1) that절의 주어와 주절의 주어가 같으면 따옴표 속에서 'I'로 쓰고, that절과 주절의 시제가 과거로 같으므로 따옴표 속에서 현재시제로 쓴다. 부사 then은 따옴표 속에서 now로 쓴다. (2) 직접화법을 간접화법으로 바꿀 때 전달동사가 과거라면 따옴표 속 현재시제는 과거로 바꾸고, 'you'는 듣는 이로 바꾼다.

13 ⓐ와 ④: 명백한(형용사), ① 단단한, 굳은(형용사), ② 열심히, 힘껏(부사), ③ (이해하거나 답하기) 어려운(형용사), ⑤ 열심히 하는(형용사)

14 turn out = prove: ~로 드러나다

15 무서운 광대들에 관한 이야기는 '10대들에 의해 지어졌다.'

16 ⓐ와 ②, ⑤: 명사적 용법, ①, ④: 부사적 용법, ③: 형용사적 용법

17 '많은 미국의 10대들'을 가리킨다.

18 주어진 문장의 the first steps에 주목한다. ①번 앞 문장의 '가짜 뉴스를 진짜 뉴스로부터 구분하는 방법'의 첫 단계를 말하는 것이므로 ①번이 적절하다.

19 ⓐ와 ①, ④: 부사적 용법, ②: 형용사적 용법, ③, ⑤: 명사적 용법

20 "의견들은 '읽을 만한' 가치가 있다."라고 15살인 McKenzie Campbell이 말했다.

21 during+기간을 나타내는 명사, while+주어+동사

22 ⓑ와 ①, ④: '~인지 아닌지'라는 뜻의 명사절을 이끄는 접속사, = whether, ②, ③, ⑤: '만약 ~한다면'이라는 조건의 의미를 지니는 부사절을 이끄는 접속사

23 비교급+than+any+other+단수명사: 최상급의 뜻

서술형 실전문제
p.160~161

01 Because an octopus can't live out of the sea.

02 (1) if these shoes fit his feet

(2) that the baby is crying now

(3) Whether this kid is a girl or a boy

03 (1) she liked Tony

(2) he wanted some water

(3) his sister looked happy

04 (1) I was living then

(2) if I liked to study in that library

05 he had seen the cat the day before[the previous day], if she had an owner

06 about information they're seeing in the news and on the Internet

07 fake

08 (A) the right sources   (B) what is real

09 so, that, can't   10 that → if[whether]

11 We have to check if[whether] they are based on facts.

01 질문: 왜 소미는 그것이 가짜 사진이라 말했는가?

02 (1) 동사 wonder의 목적절로 접속사 if절이 적절하다. (2) 확신하는 내용이므로 목적절로 접속사 that절이 적절하다. (3) 의문의 내용이고 주절이 필요하므로 접속사 whether절이 적절하다.

03 (1), (2), (3) 직접화법을 간접화법으로 바꿀 때 따옴표 속 'I'는 문장의 주어로 바꾼다. 또한 전달동사가 과거라면, 시제의 일치 법칙에 맞게 따옴표(" ") 안의 동사가 현재시제라면 과거시제로 바꾼다.

04 의문문을 직접화법에서 간접화법으로 바꿀 때, 간접의문문의 형태로 바꾸고, 따옴표 속 'I'는 문장의 주어로, 따옴표 속 'you'는 듣는 이로 바꾼다. 전달동사가 과거라면, 시제의 일치 법칙에 맞게 따옴표(" ") 안의 동사가 현재시제라면 과거시제로 바꾼다. 지시대명사와 부사를 전달자의 입장에 맞게 바꾼다. now는 then으로, this는 that으로 바꾼다.

05 전달동사가 과거이므로 그림 속 대화의 현재는 과거시제, 과거는 과거완료시제로 바꾸고, 질문은 간접의문문으로 바꾼다. 이때, 부사를 적절히 바꾼다. (yesterday → the day before 또는 the previous day)

06 'information'과 'they're' 사이에는 목적격 관계대명사 'that[which]'이 생략되어 있다.

07 fake: 가짜의, 거짓된, 진짜가 아닌; 진짜인 물건의 모조품인

08 Patricia의 반 친구인 Ivy-Brooks에 따르면, '올바른 출처들'을 살펴보고, '무엇이 진짜이고' 무엇이 가짜인지에 주의를 기울이는 것이 정말 중요하다.

09 too ~ to = so ~ that ... can't

10 접속사 'if'는 명사절을 이끌어 '~인지 아닌지'라는 뜻이다. 'whether'로 교체할 수 있다.

11 그것들이 사실에 기반을 둔 것인지를 확인해 보아야 한다.

[모범답안]

01 (1) A: How do you feel about persimmons?
      B: I like them.

(2) A: How do you feel about cucumbers?
      B: I hate them.

(3) A: How do you feel about pears?
      B: I don't like them.

02 (1) if he could tell her about his day

(2) he always gets up at 6 and goes to the

stadium at 7

(3) how long his training hours had been that day

(4) it had taken 5 hours and had been really hard

(5) what he would do in his spare time that day

(6) after that interview, he would go swimming or watch a movie

02 직접화법을 간접화법으로 바꿀 때 따옴표 속 'I'는 문장의 주어로 바꾸고, 따옴표 속 'you'는 듣는 이로 바꾼다. 전달동사가 과거일 때, 시제의 일치 법칙에 맞게 따옴표(" ") 안의 동사가 현재시제라면 과거시제로, 과거시제라면 과거완료시제로 바꾼다. 단, 그 내용이 변하지 않는 사실 혹은 규칙적인 행위인 경우는 전달동사에 상관없이 항상 현재시제로 쓴다. this는 that으로, today는 that day로 바꾼다.

01 ②   02 (p)rovide   03 ⑤   04 ④

05 ③   06 it doesn't seem real, it's a little boring

07 ③   08 Look at those shoes the girl is wearing.

09 (1) fact   (2) uniform   (3) if[whether]

10 It is climbing a tree.   11 ②   12 ①

13 Mr. Kim asked his daughter if[whether] he could ask her a few questions.

14 (1) He says to her, "Where do you work now?"

(2) She told me that she hadn't been at school the day before.

15 ③

16 (1) I wonder if she will like my present.

(2) Do you know if she is married?

17 (A) scary   (B) scared   (C) offered

18 stories about scary clowns

19 ③   20 ⑤

21 opinion in the news → real news
   또는 fake news → fact

22 ① 글쓴이가 말하고 있는 것을 뒷받침하는 어떠한 증거라도 있는가?
   ② 이 정보가 어디서 온 것인가?

23 ③   24 ④

01 ②번은 '무엇에 관하여 생각하거나 믿고 있는 것'의 의미로 'opinion(의견)'에 관한 설명이다. 'fact'는 'something that is known to have happened or to exist, especially something for which proof exists, or about which there is information'으로 '어떤 일이 일어났거나 존재한다고 알려진 것, 특히 증거가 존재하거나 정보가 있는 것'이다.

02 유의어 관계이다. 찾다, 조사하다 : 제공하다

03 '한 도시, 국가 또는 세계의 특정 부분'의 의미로 'area(지역)'가

적절하다.

04 상대방의 의견을 묻는 질문에 '나는 동의하지 않아.'라고 말하는 것은 어색하다.

05 빈칸 뒤에서 '소년이 그의 여동생을 구하기 위해 자신의 생명을 포기했잖아.'라고 하고 있으므로 '감동적이라고 생각한다'는 말이 적절하다.

06 질문: 여학생은 왜 그것이 좋은 드라마가 아니라고 생각하는가?

07 요즘 여자아이들은 짧은 머리를 더 좋아한다는 B의 의견에 대해 '대부분의 여자아이는 짧은 머리보다 긴 머리를 좋아해.'라고 말하고 있으므로 (3)은 'I don't agree with that.'이 되어야 한다.

08 명령문이므로 동사원형으로 문장을 시작한다. '저 여자애가 신고 있는'에 해당하는 말이 'shoes'를 수식하는 역할을 한다.

09 (1) 경찰관이 아이들에게 곰 인형을 사주었다는 말 다음에 'However'가 이어지므로, 앞 문장에 대한 역접의 의미가 온다는 것을 알 수 있다. (2) 경찰관 제복으로 인형을 만들어 주었다. (3) 기자가 그들을 직접 만났는지 어떤지 궁금하다는 의미로 접속사 'if나 whether'가 적절하다.

10 질문: 사진 속의 문어는 무엇을 하고 있는가?

11 보기와 ② 'that'은 형용사를 수식하는 '지시부사'다. ① 지시형용사, ③ 접속사, ④ It ~ that ... 강조구문에 사용된 접속사, ⑤ 지시대명사

12 ① 동사 discuss의 목적절로 '~인지 아닌지'의 의미이다. ②~⑤ 조건의 접속사로 '만일 ~라면'의 의미이다.

13 의문문을 간접화법으로 전환할 때 전달동사 said to를 asked로 바꾸고 접속사 if 또는 whether를 쓴다. 전달동사가 과거이므로, 시제의 일치 법칙에 맞게 따옴표(" ") 안의 현재동사를 과거시제로 바꾼다. 또한 따옴표 속 'I'는 문장의 주어로 바꾸고 따옴표 속 'you'는 듣는 이로 바꾼다.

14 (1) 듣는 이가 있을 때 직접화법의 전달동사는 say to를 쓴다. (2) 전달동사가 과거이므로 that절의 시제는 과거 또는 과거완료시제를 쓴다. 내용상 전달하기 이전의 내용이므로 과거완료시제로 쓰는 것이 적절하다.

15 의문사가 없는 의문문을 명사절로 바꿀 때 접속사 if는 사용할 수 없고, whether를 쓴다.

16 (1) 동사 wonder의 목적절로 if절을 쓴다. 이때 명사절인 if절에서는 will을 사용하는 것이 가능하다. (2) 의문문 'Do you know'의 목적절로 if절을 쓴다. 결혼한 상태를 나타내는 표현은 be married이다.

17 (A) '무서운 광대들'이라고 해야 하므로 scary가 적절하다. scary: 무서운, scared: 무서워하는, (B) '무서워했다'고 해야 하므로 scared가 적절하다. (C) They가 '그 이야기들'을 가리키고 있고, '그 이야기들은 증거를 하나도 제공하지 않았다'고 해야 하므로 능동태인 offered가 적절하다.

18 '무서운 광대들에 관한 이야기'를 가리킨다.

19 ⓐ pay attention to: ~에 주목하다, 유의하다, ⓑ on the Internet: 인터넷상에서

20 (A)와 ⑤: ~처럼(전치사), ① 비슷한(형용사), ② (예를 들어) ~과 같은(= such as)(전치사), ③ ~을 좋아하다(동사), ④ 비

숫한 것(명사)

21 Garcia-Fuller는 자신의 학생들에게 가짜 뉴스를 '진짜 뉴스'로부터 구분하는 방법과 또한 뉴스에서 '사실'을 의견과 구분하는 방법을 가르치고 있다

22 ① Is there any evidence that supports what the writer says? ② Where is this coming from?

23 주어진 문장의 The site에 주목한다. ③번 앞 문장의 a website를 받고 있으므로 ③번이 적절하다.

24 무서운 광대들의 이야기와 마찬가지로 '나무 문어'에 대한 정보는 완전히 꾸며진 것이다.

교과서 파헤치기

Lesson 5

01 근사한, 멋진, 엄청난, 어마어마한　02 전쟁, 전투
03 땅, 지면　04 ~을 향하여　05 교통
06 굴뚝　07 광고　08 강한, 강력한
09 가까이, 근접하여　10 번역하다, 해석하다
11 준비하다　12 호기심이 많은, 궁금한
13 다소, 약간　14 답장　15 남편
16 죽은, 쓸모없는　17 치다, 두드리다　18 발견하다
19 숨은, 숨겨진　20 포옹; 포옹하다　21 오해
22 진지하게, 심각하게
23 큰 소리로, 시끄럽게　24 ~처럼 보이다
25 적군, 적대자　26 좌석, 의석　27 군인
28 정확하게　29 투표하다, 선출하다
30 국경, 경계　31 점자　32 표현
33 고용하다　34 상품, 제품
35 이겨내다, 극복하다　36 ~을 돌보다
37 ~로 덮다　38 ~의 가격으로　39 ~을 제외하고
40 ~에 (찬성하는) 투표를 하다　41 ~에 조심하다
42 즉시, 당장　43 ~ 대신에

01 traffic　02 awesome　03 letter
04 battle　05 translate　06 dead
07 enemy　08 discover　09 light
10 loudly　11 exactly　12 curious
13 expression　14 husband　15 toward
16 chimney　17 seriously　18 rather
19 prepare　20 hidden　21 soldier
22 border　23 product　24 sign language
25 hire　26 misunderstanding
27 hug　28 knock　29 seat
30 pond　31 foreign　32 gesture
33 pull　34 vote　35 instead of
36 except for　37 look after　38 be careful with
39 step back　40 right away
41 be covered with　42 at a price of
43 get over

1 dead, 죽은　2 toward, ~을 향하여　3 reply, 답장
4 foreign, 외국의　5 ground, 땅, 지면　6 hire, 고용하다
7 husband, 남편　8 ill, 아픈, 병든　9 prepare, 준비하다
10 seat, 의석　11 vote, 투표하다, 선출하다　12 oil, 기름
13 ring, 반지　14 translate, 번역하다, 해석하다
15 discover, 발견하다　16 hug, 포옹

Get Ready 2

(1) curious about, is it standing / a kind of, tells, batteries, powerful
(2) m curious about / traffic sign, means, enter
(3) dots for, m curious about / Braille, blind / guess what, mean
(4) curious, balloon, hanging / ad, product, powerful

Start Off – Listen & Talk A

1. soldiers, with, chimneys / messages, by using, chimneys / m curious about, system / smoking chimneys / What, mean / saw enemy
2. enemy, smoke at all, do / Smoke, chimney, enemy / rising, What does, mean / It means, close, border

Start Off B

is crossing, border, dark, soldiers going to do, messages, curious about / light, chimneys / light, chimneys / It means, battle, started

Start Off – Speak Up

m curious about, language / Let, show, expression / What, mean / It means

Step Up – Real-life Scene

hidden secrets / curious about, secrets / Find, yourself / Let's see, letters / one, means, Latin / awesome, Any other secrets / tells, rich / understand / spend lots of, to buy, kind at that time / the rich, that kind, right / Exactly, speak a thousand

Express Yourself A

1. gesture, curious about / it means, into, pond / Why, think so / lots of bees, pointing, pond
2. So, gesture mean / It means, chicken / should bring, to get, right / I think so
3. What, gesture mean, curious about / Turn it off / What makes, so / The other hunter, close / see

33

p.07~08

Get Ready 2

(1) G: I'm curious about that robot. Why is it standing there?

B: It's a kind of ad. It tells people their batteries are very powerful.

(2) G: What's this? I'm curious about it.

B: It's a traffic sign. It means "Do not enter."

G: Oh, I see.

(3) G: What are these dots for? I'm curious about them.

B: Oh, they are Braille. They are for blind people.

G: I see. Now I can guess what they mean.

(4) G: I'm curious about that balloon. Why is it hanging there?

B: Oh, that. It's an ad. It says the product is very powerful.

Start Off – Listen & Talk A

1. B: What are the soldiers doing with the five chimneys on TV?

G: They are sending messages to the king by using the chimneys.

B: Really? I'm curious about the system. Can you tell me more?

G: Well, do you see the two smoking chimneys?

B: Yes. What do they mean?

G: They mean they just saw an enemy.

2. B: If there's no enemy, they don't smoke at all, do they?

G: Yes, they do. Smoke from one chimney means "No enemy."

B: Now smoke is rising from three chimneys. What does that mean?

G: It means an enemy is coming close to the border.

Start Off B

B: Now the enemy is crossing the border in the dark. What are the soldiers going to do to send messages? I'm curious about that.

G: They will light four chimneys.

B: When they light all five of the chimneys, what does that mean?

G: It means the battle has started.

Start Off – Speak Up

B: I'm curious about sign language.

G: Are you? Let me show you one expression. Look.

B: What does it mean?

G: It means "Hello."

Step Up – Real-life Scene

B: This painting has some hidden secrets in it.

G: Really? I'm curious about them. Where are the secrets?

B: Find one yourself.

G: Let's see. ... Oh, I see some letters here.

B: You found one! It means "Jan van Eyck was here. 1434." It's Latin.

G: That's awesome! Any other secrets?

B: Okay. This dog tells us the man here was very rich.

G: I don't understand.

B: They had to spend lots of money to buy a dog of that kind at that time.

G: I see. Only the rich could have that kind of dog, right?

B: Exactly. Pictures speak a thousand words, you know.

Express Yourself A

1. W: What does this woman's gesture mean? I'm curious about it.

M: I think it means "Jump into the pond."

W: Why do you think so?

M: The boy has lots of bees on his head. And the woman is pointing at the pond.

2. W: This woman doesn't want a dollar. So what does her gesture mean?

M: It means she wants a chicken.

W: Then the boy should bring a chicken to get the fruit, right?

M: I think so.

3. W: What does this man's gesture mean? I'm curious about it.

M: It means "Turn it off."

W: Really? What makes you think so?

M: The other hunter there is coming close to an animal.

W: Oh, I see.

p.09~10

01 Picture Letter from, of

02 Speaking, foreign, rather, simple

03 before, days, that easy

04 sent, waited for, reply

05 lot harder, couldn't, write

06 how, got over, difficulties

07 by, whose, far away

08 island, while, worked in

09 more than, one of

10 was discovered by, writer

11 how, translated, into words

12 miss, reach, out toward 13 in, expect for, little

14 little sick, not seriously 15 sent, there, reply so

16 got, from, would be 17 fell ill, going, with

18 with, while, looks, youngest

19 had, prepare, plant seeds

20 voted for 21 so, that, almost seems

22 whether, other wins, same

23 Nothing changes, poor

24 worked, will work again 25 picked lots, from, this

26 hired, whose, workers

27 knocked, down, picking, up

28 paid, for, work 29 spent, for, press

30 enough, to fill, pot 31 sell, at, price, lire

32 heart, of, as, coming 33 would be, if, were

34 all miss, so 35 sending, big hug, little

36 dear love 37 heart, yours, joined, as

28 paid, for 29 spent, for, press

30 enough, to fill, one 31 at a price of

32 as 33 would be, were with

34 miss 35 a big hug, little kids

36 dear love 37 joined, as

01 A Picture Letter

02 Opeaking, foregin country is rather, simple

03 before, that easy

04 sent, waited for, for weeks

05 a lot harder, couldn't read or write

06 got over

07 was written in, whose, far away

08 while, worked in Germany

09 more than 5%, one of them

10 was discovered by, writer

11 how, translated, into

12 miss, reach, out toward

13 all in good health except for, one

14 a little, not seriously

15 already, there was no reply

16 got, would be 17 fell ill, with

18 while, looks after, youngest

19 had, prepare, plant seeds

20 voted for 21 so, that

22 whether one or the other, the same

23 Nothing changes 24 will work again

25 picked, from 26 hired, whose, workers

27 knocked, down, picking, up from

1 세 아이의 엄마가 보낸 그림 편지

2 오늘날 외국에 있는 가족이나 친구와 대화하는 것은 다소 쉽고 간단하다.

3 하지만 전화와 인터넷 시대 이전에는 그것이 그렇게 쉽지 않았다.

4 사람들은 단지 편지를 보내고 답장을 몇 주 동안 기다렸다.

5 그리고 그들이 읽거나 쓸 수 없었다면 그건 훨씬 더 힘들었다.

6 이 편지는 사람들이 이런 어려움을 어떻게 극복했는지 보여준다.

7 그것은 남편이 멀리 떨어져 살았던 한 여자에 의해 1973년에 쓰여졌다.

8 그녀의 남편은 독일에서 일한 반면, 그녀는 이탈리아의 섬인 시실리에서 살았다.

9 그 당시에는 5% 이상의 이탈리아 사람들이 읽거나 쓸 수 없었고, 그녀도 그들 중 한 명이었다.

10 이 편지는 시실리의 작가 Gesualdo Bufalino가 발견하였다.

11 그가 그림들을 어떻게 글로 번역했는지는 다음과 같다.

12 사랑하는 여보, 난 당신이 정말 그립고, 우리 세 아이와 함께 당신을 향해 내 팔을 쭉 뻗고 있어요.

13 막내를 제외하고는 우리 모두 건강해요.

14 그 아이는 약간 아프지만 심각하진 않아요.

15 난 당신에게 이미 편지를 보냈지만, 답장이 없어서 그것 때문에 나는 슬퍼요.

16 당신에게서 편지를 받는다면, 나는 정말 행복할 거예요.

17 당신의 어머니께서는 병이 드셨고, 나는 약간의 돈과 음식을 가지고 병원에 있는 어머니를 방문할 예정이에요.

18 큰애가 막내를 돌보는 동안 둘째와 함께 그곳에 갈 거예요.

19 나는 150,000리라에 두 일꾼을 시켜 우리 밭을 준비하고 씨앗을 심게 했어요.

20 나는 DC에 투표했어요.

21 PCI는 매우 많은 의석을 잃어서 거의 죽은 것처럼 보여요.

22 하지만 이쪽이 이기건 저쪽이 이기건, 상황은 똑같아요.

23 우리 가난한 사람들에게는 아무 것도 바뀌지 않지요.

24 우리는 어제도 일했고, 내일도 다시 일할 거예요.

25 우리는 올해 올리브나무에서 올리브를 많이 땄어요.

26 나는 아들들이 훌륭한 일꾼인 한 남자를 고용했어요.

27 그가 올리브를 쳐서 떨어뜨리면 그의 두 아들이 땅에서 올리브를 주우면서 그를 도왔어요.

28 나는 그 일을 위해 그에게 27,000리라를 지급했어요.

29 올리브 압착을 위해 12,000리라를 더 썼어요.

30 나는 큰 항아리 하나와 작은 항아리 하나를 채울 만큼 충분한 기름을 얻었어요.

31 리터당 1,300리라의 가격으로 팔 수 있을 것 같아요.

32 여보, 크리스마스가 다가오면서 내 마음은 당신을 떠올려요.

33 당신이 나와 함께 있다면 난 정말 행복할 거예요.

34 우리는 모두 당신을 매우 많이 그리워해요.

35 나와 우리 세 아이의 큰 포옹을 보내요.

36 잘 있어요, 여보.

37 내 마음은 당신의 것이에요, 우리들의 두 반지처럼 당신과 연결된 채로요.

본문 TEST Step 4 - Step 5   p.15~18

1 A Picture Letter from a Mother of Three

2 Speaking to family members or friends in a foreign country is rather easy and simple today.

3 But before the days of phones and the Internet, it was not that easy.

4 People just sent a letter and waited for a reply for weeks.

5 And it was a lot harder if they couldn't read or write.

6 This letter shows how people got over these difficulties.

7 It was written in 1973 by a woman whose husband was far away.

8 She lived in Sicily, an Italian island, while her husband worked in Germany.

9 At the time, more than 5% of the people in Italy could not read or write, and she was one of them.

10 This letter was discovered by Sicilian writer Gesualdo Bufalino.

11 Here's how he translated the pictures into words.

12 My dear love, I miss you so much, and I reach my arms out toward you, together with our three kids.

13 We are all in good health except for the little one.

14 He's a little sick, but not seriously.

15 I already sent you a letter, but there was no reply, so I am sad about it.

16 If I got a letter from you, I would be very happy.

17 Your mother fell ill, and I'm going to visit her in the hospital with some money and food.

18 I'll go there with our middle son while the oldest looks after the youngest.

19 I had two workers prepare our field and plant

seeds for 150,000 lire.

20 I voted for the DC.

21 The PCI lost so many seats that it almost seems dead.

22 But whether one or the other wins, it's the same.

23 Nothing changes for us poor people.

24 We worked yesterday, and we will work again tomorrow.

25 We picked lots of olives from our olive trees this year.

26 I hired a man whose sons are good workers.

27 He knocked the olives down, and his two sons helped him, picking them up from the ground.

28 I paid him 27,000 lire for the work.

29 I spent 12,000 more for the olive press.

30 I got enough oil to fill a large pot and a small one.

31 I can sell it at a price of 1,300 lire a liter.

32 My love, my heart thinks of you as Christmas is coming.

33 I would be so happy if you were with me.

34 We all miss you so much.

35 I'm sending you a big hug from me and our three little kids.

36 Goodbye, dear love.

37 My heart is yours, joined to you as our two rings are.

구석구석지문 TEST Step 1   p.19

Express Yourself C1

1. whose, is covered with, doesn't understand

2. means, Jump into

3. were, would jump into, right away

Project Do It Yourself

1. Climb up

2. had, would so kites to send

3. would fly, whose, looks like, make the soldiers climb

Link to the World

1. was created by

2. At first, didn't want to use, writing system

3. However, tried hard to help, use

4. Thanks to, can express anything with

5. didn't know, could not express ourselves

Express Yourself C1

1. The boy whose head is covered with bees doesn't understand the woman's gesture.
2. I think it means "Jump into the pond."
3. If I were the boy, I would jump into the pond right away.

Project Do It Yourself

1. "Climb up the mountain."
2. If I had soldiers to lead, I would so kites to send my messages.
3. For example, I would fly a kite whose face looks like a mountain to make the soldiers climb up the mountain.

Link to the World

1. Hangeul was created by King Sejong.
2. At first, many people didn't want to use this new writing system.
3. However, King Sejong tried hard to help people use Hangeul.
4. Thanks to him, we can express anything with Hangeul now.
5. If we didn't know Hangeul, we could not express ourselves easily.

Lesson 6

01 생산하다, 산출하다	02 이용할 수 있는
03 ~을 거르다, 여과하다; 여과 장치	04 질병, 질환
05 얼굴의 06 예술품, 공예품	07 공공의, 공중의
08 도공, 옹기장이, 도예가	09 연결하다
10 출판업자, 출판사 11 예술적인	12 등록하다
13 사실, 실제로 14 (마음의) 긴장을 풀다	
15 3차원 인쇄를 하다 16 모으다	17 전통적인
18 제공하다 19 무게, 중량	20 화려한
21 회사 22 씨앗	23 길이
24 ~을 찢다, 뜯어내다	25 아주 작은
26 유쾌한, 기분 좋은 27 전시, 진열; 전시하다, 진열하다	
28 마실 수 있는 29 자랑으로 여기는	30 물리치다
31 (사람, 동물의) 상, 모양, 숫자	32 불가능한
33 필요한 34 물체	35 손으로
36 찢다 37 집어들다	38 목욕하다
39 알아내다 40 A와 B 둘 다	
41 남에게 주다, 나누어 주다	42 더 이상 ~ 않다
43 …을 ~으로 생각하다	

01 traditional	02 available	03 produce
04 artistic	05 beat	06 collect
07 tear	08 relax	09 colorful
10 proud	11 connect	12 disease
13 company	14 weight	15 provide
16 actually	17 cheerful	18 display
19 public	20 drinkable	21 figure
22 filter	23 facial	24 artwork
25 possible	26 pour	27 publisher
28 register	29 necessary	30 object
31 length	32 seed	33 3D print
34 tiny	35 find out	36 pick up
37 tear out	38 by hand	39 take a bath
40 think of ... as ~		41 both A and B
42 give away	43 not ~ anymore	

1 tiny, 아주 작은   2 bookstore, 서점

3 drinkable, 마실 수 있는   4 public, 공공의, 공중의

5 length, 길이   6 pour, 붓다, 따르다

7 tear, ~을 찢다, 뜯어내다 8 filter, ~을 거르다, 여과하다

9 publisher, 출판업자, 출판사 10 potter, 옹기장이, 도공

11 register, 등록하다 12 weight, 무게, 중량

13 leave, 남겨 두다 14 display, 전시하다

15 seed, 씨앗 16 print, 인쇄하다, 출판하다

대화문 TEST Step 1   p.24~25

Get Ready 2

(1) Which, better, cloth, artwork / better, Actually

(2) Which do you prefer, drawings, wood, figures / prefer, figures / Let's, some of them

(3) Which, prefer, folding, clothes / prefer folding paper, way to realx

Start Off – Listen & Talk A

1. Why don't we, pockets / What shall we / Which, board, holder / prefer, holder, to make, hate spending, making / Let's, together

2. Why don't we, with / What kind, to make / Which, prefer / Actually, hate holding, in / Let's make, together

Start Off - Listen & Talk B

with jeans / pencil case for / going to draw / Which do you prefer / prefer, lovely / draw, lovely / I can't wait for

Start Off – Speak Up

join / Sure, Which, prefer, or / prefer, making / Let, introduce, to

Start Off - Your Turn

Which, taking, taking / prefer taking the subway, hate taking

Step Up – Real-life Scene

just, away / proud that, collected, interesting, to give away / let's prepare, any / making bookmarks / Let's / Which, prefer, writing / Actually, writing / No problem, cheerful messages / sure, bookmarks

Express Yourself A

1. flying, flying drones / prefer flying / working, machines

2. Which, making, making / both, it, making, that, prefer / something delicious

대화문 TEST Step 2   p.26~27

Get Ready 2

(1) G: Which do you like better, cloth dolls or digital artwork?

B: I like digital artwork better. Actually, I don't like dolls much.

(2) G: Which do you prefer, paper drawings or wood block figures?

B: I prefer wood block figures.

G: Me, too. Let's go to look at some of them.

(3) G: Which do you prefer, folding paper or making clothes?

B: I prefer folding paper. It's fun and a great way to relax.

Start Off – Listen & Talk A

1. G: Why don't we make something with jean pockets?

B: Great! What shall we make?

G: Which do you prefer, a pocket board or a cell phone holder?

B: I prefer a cell phone holder. It'll be easier to make. And I hate spending too much time making things.

G: Okay. Let's make a cute cell phone holder together.

2. B: Why don't we make a bag with old jeans?

G: Great! What kind of bag are we going to make?

B: Which do you prefer, a shoulder bag or a hand bag?

G: I prefer a shoulder bag. Actually, I hate holding things in my hands.

B: Okay. Let's make a shoulder bag together.

Start Off - Listen & Talk B

G: Junha, what are you doing with jeans?

B: I'm making a pencil case for you.

G: That's great! What are you going to draw on it?

B: Which do you prefer, pandas or cats?

G: I prefer cats. They're lovely.

B: Okay. Let me draw a lovely cat on this pencil case.

G: Thanks! I can't wait for it!

Start Off – Speak Up

A: Can I join your book-making project?

B: Sure. Which do you prefer, paper books or digital books?

A: I prefer digital books. Actually, I hate making paper books.

B: Okay. Let me introduce you to the digital book team.

Start Off - Your Turn

A: Which do you prefer, taking the bus or taking the

subway?

B: I prefer taking the subway. Actually, I hate taking the bus.

Step Up – Real-life Scene

Minji: Seho, the book club day is just one week away.

Seho: Right, Minji. I'm proud that we've collected so many interesting books to give away.

Minji: Now, let's prepare some gifts for visitors. Do you have any good ideas?

Seho: How about making bookmarks?

Minji: Great idea! Let's write cheerful messages on them, too.

Seho: Okay. Which do you prefer, making the bookmarks or writing the messages?

Minji: Actually, I hate writing. I'd like to make the bookmarks.

Seho: No problem. I'll write the cheerful messages.

Minji: I'm sure they will love our bookmarks.

Express Yourself A

1. G: Which do you prefer, flying kites or flying drones?

   B: I prefer flying kites.

   G: Why is that?

   B: I hate working with machines.

2. B: Which do you prefer, making masks or making food art?

   G: I like both, but it is making food art that I prefer.

   B: Why is that?

   G: I love making something delicious.

본문 TEST Step 1 p.28~30

01 This, Amazing
02 think, traditional, books, read
03 However, there, unique, around
04 Let's learn, a few   05 Books Travel
06 found, old, on   07 note, read, Free
08 Take me home
09 Actually, had, was registered
10 out, traveled, number, different
11 How, that possible
12 There, book-sharing project
13 register, online, get
14 leave, public place
15 reader, reports back, check
16 way, whole, become, library

17 more, share, the, learn   18 Drinkable Book
19 tiny, important, in, town
20 provides both, information, tools
21 is called, Drinkable   22 actually, use, as, filter
23 tear out, pour, on
24 As, through, changes into
25 It, filtered, that, drink
26 possible because, made, special
27 amazing, saves, from diseases
28 Tree-Book-Tree Project
29 most amazing, have, seen
30 finish reading, plant, water
31 see new leaves growing
32 some, copy, producing, leaves
33 secret, has seeds, each
34 tiny seeds, change, into
35 made by, children's, publisher
36 not, anymore, think, from
37 just a few, unique
38 What other unique books
39 would, like to do
40 bigger, imagination, more wonderful

본문 TEST Step 2 p.31~33

01 This, Amazing
02 think of, as traditional paper books
03 are, unique, around   04 Let's, a few
05 Travel   06 found, old book
07 note, read, Free   08 Take me home
09 Actually, ID number, was registered
10 found out, had traveled, had read
11 How, possible   12 book-sharing project
13 register, get   14 leave it, public place
15 reports back, where your book is
16 whole world, a big library
17 The more books, the more
18 Drinkable   19 This tiny book
20 both the information and the tools necessary to make
21 is called, Drinkable   22 as a filter
23 tear out, pour, on
24 As, goes through, changes into
25 It is, that
26 is made of special filter paper
27 amazing, saves, from diseases, come from
28 Tree-Book-Tree Project
29 the most amazing book, seen

30 reading, plant, water

31 see new leaves growing

32 a copy of, producing new leaves

33 has seeds

34 these tiny seeds, change, into

35 was made by, publisher

36 Though, not, anymore, makes, think

37 just a few, unique books

38 What other unique books

39 would, like to do with

40 The bigger, imagination, the more wonderful

본문 TEST Step 3   p.34~36

1 이 책은 놀라워요!

2 대부분의 사람은 책을 읽기 위한 전통적인 종이책으로 생각합니다.

3 하지만, 여러분 주변에는 독특한 책이 많이 있습니다.

4 이러한 책 중 몇 가지에 대해 배워 봅시다.

5 책이 여행합니다!

6 저는 어제 공원 벤치에서 이 낡은 책을 발견했습니다.

7 표지 위의 쪽지에 "공짜 책이에요!

8 저를 집으로 데려가서 읽어 주세요!"라고 쓰여 있었습니다.

9 사실, 이 책은 ID 번호가 있고 웹사이트에 등록되어 있었어요.

10 제가 온라인으로 그 번호를 입력했을 때, 저는 그 책이 많은 나라를 여행하고 다른 나라의 많은 독자가 저보다 앞서 이 책을 읽었다는 것을 알아냈습니다.

11 그게 어떻게 가능했을까요?

12 책을 공유하는 프로젝트가 있습니다.

13 우선, 온라인에 여러분의 책을 등록하고 ID 번호를 얻으세요.

14 그다음, 그것을 공공장소에 놓아두세요.

15 다음 독자가 여러분의 책을 발견해서 그 웹사이트에 다시 알릴 때, 여러분은 책이 어디 있는지 확인할 수 있습니다.

16 이런 식으로, 전 세계가 하나의 큰 도서관이 될 수 있습니다.

17 우리가 더 많은 책을 공유할수록, 우리는 더 많이 배웁니다.

18 마실 수 있는 책

19 이 작은 책은 우리 마을 사람들에게는 정말로 중요합니다.

20 그것은 깨끗한 마실 물을 만드는 데 필요한 정보와 도구 둘 다를 제공합니다.

21 그것은 '마실 수 있는 책'이라고 불립니다.

22 여러분은 실제로 그 책을 마실 수는 없지만, 그것을 필터로 사용할 수 있습니다.

23 그냥 한 페이지를 떼어 내서 그 위에 더러운 물을 부으세요.

24 물이 그 페이지를 통과하면서, 깨끗한 마실 물로 바뀝니다.

25 여러분이 마실 수 있는 것은 이 여과된 물입니다.

26 책이 특별한 여과지로 만들어졌기 때문에 이것이 가능합니다.

27 이 놀라운 책은 더러운 물로 생기는 질병으로부터 많은 어린이의 생명을 구합니다.

---

28 나무-책-나무 프로젝트

29 이것은 제가 지금까지 본 것 중에서 가장 놀라운 책입니다.

30 여러분이 이 책을 다 읽은 후에, 그것을 심고 물을 주세요.

31 여러분은 책에서 새잎이 자라는 것을 보게 될 거예요.

32 우리 마을의 몇몇 서점에서, 여러분은 이 책 한 권이 새잎을 내는 것을 볼 수 있습니다.

33 비밀은 책이 각 페이지 안에 씨앗을 갖고 있다는 것입니다.

34 책을 나무로 변화시키는 것은 이 아주 작은 씨앗들이에요.

35 이 책은 아르헨티나에 있는 한 작은 아동 도서 출판사에 의해 만들어졌습니다.

36 그 회사가 더는 이 책을 발행하지는 않지만, 이 특별한 프로젝트는 우리에게 책이 어디에서 오는지에 대해 생각하게 해 줍니다.

37 이것들은 여러분이 찾을 수 있는 독특한 책 중의 단지 몇 가지입니다.

38 여러분은 어떤 다른 독특한 책을 만들기 원하나요?

39 여러분은 책으로 어떤 특별한 프로젝트를 하고 싶나요?

40 여러분의 상상이 크면 클수록, 여러분의 책은 더 훌륭해질 것입니다.

본문 TEST Step 4-Step 5   p.37~42

1 This Book Is Amazing!

2 Most people think of books as traditional paper books to read.

3 However, there are many unique books around you.

4 Let's learn about a few of these books.

5 Books Travel!

6 I found this old book on a park bench yesterday.

7 A note on the cover read, "Free Book!

8 Take me home and read me!"

9 Actually, this book had an ID number and was registered on a website.

10 When I entered the number online, I found out that the book had traveled to many countries and that a number of readers in different countries had read it before me.

11 How was that possible?

12 There is a book-sharing project.

13 First, register your book online and get an ID number.

14 Next, leave it in a public place.

15 When the next reader finds your book and reports back to the website, you can check where your book is.

16 This way, the whole world can become a big

library.

17 The more books we share, the more we learn.

18 The Drinkable Book

19 This tiny book is really important to people in my town.

20 It provides both the information and the tools necessary to make clean drinking water.

21 It is called the Drinkable Book.

22 You cannot actually drink the book, but you can use it as a filter.

23 Simply tear out a page and pour dirty water on it.

24 As the water goes through the page, it changes into clean drinking water.

25 It is this filtered water that you can drink.

26 This is possible because the book is made of special filter paper.

27 This amazing book saves the lives of many children from diseases that come from dirty water.

28 The Tree-Book-Tree Project

29 This is the most amazing book that I have ever seen.

30 After you finish reading this book, plant it and water it.

31 You will see new leaves growing on the book.

32 In some bookstores in my town, you can see a copy of this book producing new leaves.

33 The secret is that the book has seeds in each page.

34 It is these tiny seeds that change the book into a tree.

35 This book was made by a small children's book publisher in Argentina.

36 Though the company does not print this book anymore, this special project makes us think about where books come from.

37 These are just a few of the unique books you can find.

38 What other unique books do you want to make?

39 What special project would you like to do with the books?

40 The bigger your imagination is, the more wonderful your books will become.

구석구석지문 TEST Step 1   p.43

Express Yourself C

1. making, flying, its weight

2. light drone, long battery life

3. The lighter, the longer

Link to the World

1. is called, because, looks like a full moon

2. it, impossible to make, by hand

3. The larger, the more difficult

4. It, a potter that

5. put, to make this moon jar

Learning Diary – Listen & Speak 2

1. Which, prefer, or

2. prefer going camping, hate going swimming

3. prefer going swimming

구석구석지문 TEST Step 2   p.44

Express Yourself C

1. In making and flying a drone, its weight is important.

2. It is a light drone that has a long battery life.

3. The lighter the drone is, the longer it flies.

Link to the World

1. This is called Dalhang-ari, a moon jar, because it looks like a full moon.

2. In the past, it was impossible to make this large round jar by hand.

3. The larger a jar was, the more difficult it was to make.

4. It was a potter that solved this problem.

5. A smart potter put two large bowls together to make this moon jar.

Learning Diary – Listen & Speak 2

1. A: Which do you prefer, going camping or going swimming?

2. B: I prefer going camping. Actually, I hate going swimming. How about you?

3. A: Well, I prefer going swimming.

단어 TEST Step 1 p.45

01 제공하다	02 최근에	03 건강한
04 찾다, 검색하다	05 증거	06 거짓의, 잘못된
07 근원, 출처	08 실제로, 사실	09 예술 작품
10 지지하다, 후원하다		11 ~인 것 같다
12 전적으로	13 가라앉다	14 비판적으로
15 우스운	16 가벼운	17 주요한, 주된
18 문어	19 감동적인	20 장소
21 공격하다	22 광대	23 제공하다
24 독특한	25 편안한	26 사실이 아닌
27 세제, 청소기	28 완벽한	29 공연, 수행
30 퍼진; 퍼지다	31 불확실한	32 완전한
33 뱀	34 선호하다	35 판명되다
36 포기하다	37 A와 B를 구별하다	
38 의미가 통하다	39 ~에 바탕을 두다	
40 돌아가시다	41 ~에 주의를 기울이다	
42 꾸며낸, 지어낸	43 큰 소리로 웃다	

단어 TEST Step 2 p.46

01 save	02 perfect	03 sink
04 prefer	05 cleaner	06 critically
07 attack	08 recently	09 false
10 performance	11 comfortable	12 actually
13 totally	14 source	15 evidence
16 support	17 complete	18 provide
19 scary	20 site	21 clown
22 spread	23 healthy	24 cheer
25 untrue	26 light	27 major
28 touching	29 octopus	30 artwork
31 unique	32 wear	33 boring
34 search	35 give up	36 pass away
37 be based on	38 make sense	39 laugh out loud
40 be made out of		41 turn out
42 pay attention to		43 tell A from B

단어 TEST Step 3 p.47

1 totally, 전적으로 2 lie, 거짓말 3 touching, 감동적인
4 major, 주된, 주요한 5 false, 거짓의, 잘못된
6 cheer, 환호하다 7 opinion, 의견 8 provide, 제공하다
9 critically, 비판적으로 10 sink, 가라앉다
11 octopus, 문어 12 evidence, 증거

13 spread, 퍼지다 14 attack, 공격하다
15 support, 지지하다 16 clown, 광대

대화문 TEST Step 1 p.48~49

Get Ready 2
(1) like, I think, fake / agree, kind, real
(2) sharp teeth. What do you think of, real / let's search, check
(3) What, think of / look like, strange / too
(4) This, real / Let's, fact sites, check, together

Start Off – Listen & Talk A
1. How do you feel about / light, comfortable / to buy, school field trip
2. is wearing, warm, light / agree with, Actually, much heavier / believe

Start Off - Listen & Talk B
How, feel / touching, gave up, to save, the best drama / don't agree / Why, think so / seem real, a little boring

Start Off – Speak Up
How, about, ad / shows / should not believe

Step Up – Real-life Scene
cool, How do you feel about / that / makes, laugh out loud / everything, says / octopus / make sense / when, climbing, lying / agree with, fake, out of

Express Yourself A
1. How, feel about / get along, with / these two, enjoying, together
2. How, feel / By the way / guess / prefer / with, better than, In fact / to help
3. feel about / anything special / were made out, uniform / passed away recently / touching

대화문 TEST Step 2 p.50~51

Get Ready 2
(1) G: There's no monkey like this in the world. Its nose is too big. I think it's fake.
B: I don't agree. I saw that kind of monkey on TV. It's real.
(2) G: This animal has a long nose and two long, sharp teeth. What do you think of it? Is it real?
B: Well, let's search the Internet and check it together.
G: That's a good idea.

(3) B: What do you think of this animal?

G: It doesn't have legs, but it doesn't look like a snake. It's very strange.

B: I think so, too.

(4) B: This monkey is very small. Is it real?

G: I don't know. Let's visit some animal fact sites and check it together.

B: That's a good idea.

Start Off – Listen & Talk A

1. G: Look at those shoes the girl is wearing. I think they're great. How do you feel about them?

B: I think they look light and comfortable.

G: Right. I want to buy them for the school field trip.

2. G: I like the coat the boy is wearing. I think it's warm and light.

B: Well, I don't agree with you. Actually, I bought one last week. It's not so warm, and it's much heavier than it looks.

G: Really? I don't believe it.

Start Off - Listen & Talk B

G: How do you feel about this drama?

B: I think it's very touching. The boy gave up his life to save his sister. It's the best drama of this year.

G: I don't agree. It's not a good drama.

B: Come on. Why do you think so?

G: It doesn't seem real. And it's a little boring.

Start Off – Speak Up

A: How do you feel about this ad?

B: I think it's great. It shows the phone is strong.

A: I don't agree. We should not believe every ad.

Step Up – Real-life Scene

Alex: Big Mouth's show is really cool. How do you feel about it?

Somi: Well, I don't think it's that great.

Alex: Come on. I love Mr. Big Mouth. He always makes me laugh out loud.

Somi: He's funny, but don't believe everything he says.

Alex: All right. Oh, look at his photo of an octopus. He said it lives in a tree.

Somi: It doesn't make sense.

Alex: He took the photo when it was climbing the tree. I don't think he's lying. It's a great photo.

Somi: I don't agree with you. It's a fake photo. An octopus can't live out of the sea.

Express Yourself A

1. G: How do you feel about these animals?

B: They are very cute, but I think cats don't get along well with dogs.

G: I don't agree. And these two are good friends. They are enjoying the trip together.

2. G: How do you feel about this kid here?

B: I think she is very pretty. By the way, why did she cut her hair?

G: Can you guess?

B: Well, girls these days prefer short hair.

G: I don't agree with that. Most girls like long hair better than short hair. And this kid here is not a girl. In fact, he is a boy.

B: Really?

G: Yes. He grew his hair to help sick children.

3. G: How do you feel about the teddy bears?

B: They are cute. Is there anything special about them?

G: They were made out of a police officer's uniform.

B: Oh, I see.

G: This police officer made them for the kids. Their dad was a police officer, and he passed away recently.

B: That's very touching.

본문 TEST step 1 p.52~53

01 Smart News Reader

02 scary, shook, across, bit

03 getting scared, things, one

04 checked up on, saying

05 actually made by, stations

06 hard evidence, trying, attack

07 turned out, complete lie

08 lot, at, thing, true

09 right sources, real, fake

10 Like, teenagers, think critically

11 getting, spread, full, false

12 how to tell, from

13 One, steps, slow down   14 too, to, true, think

15 evidence, supports what, says

16 where, coming from

17 tell fact from opinion   18 check, based on facts

19 hard, smart news reader

20 appears, provide, called, octopus

21 site, full, along, unclear

22 scary clowns, made up

23 once, carefully, everything, even

01 How to, Smart News Reader

02 shook schools across, didn't believe, a bit

03 getting scared, one of

04 checked up on, was saying

05 were actually made by, major newspapers

06 no hard evidence, trying to attack

07 turned out to be, complete lie

08 just look at one thing

09 to look at the right sources, pay attention to what is real, what is fake

10 Like, to think critically, on the Internet

11 getting more important, spread, full of false information

12 how to tell, from real news

13 One of the first steps, slow down

14 too good to be true

15 evidence, what the writer says

16 coming from   17 how to tell, from

18 have to, if, are based on facts

19 a smart news reader   20 appears to provide

21 is full of, along with, unclear photos

22 like, scary clowns, made up

23 once more carefully, question everything

1 현명한 뉴스 독자가 되는 방법

2 2016년 10월, 무서운 광대들에 관한 이야기가 워싱턴 지역 전역의 학교에 충격을 안겼지만, Danina Garcia-Fuller의 학생들은 조금도 그 이야기들을 믿지 않았다.

3 "몇몇 사람들은 그들이 소셜 미디어에 올라온 것들을 봤기 때문에 무서워했어요."라고 Garcia-Fuller의 학생 중 한 명인 Patricia Visoso가 말했다.

4 "하지만 그들은 이것을 누가 말하고 있는지를 전혀 확인하지 않았어요."

5 그 이야기들은 실제로 주요 신문사나 TV 방송국이 아닌 10대들이 지어냈다.

6 그들은 광대들이 정말로 학생들을 공격하려고 한다는 명백한 증거를 하나도 제공하지 않았다.

7 그 이야기는 결국 완벽한 거짓말인 것으로 드러났다.

8 "많은 사람이 단지 한 가지만을 보고 그것이 사실이라고 믿는 것 같아요."라고 Patricia의 반 친구인 Ivy-Brooks가 말했다.

9 올바른 출처를 살펴보고, 무엇이 진짜이고 무엇이 가짜인지에 주의를 기울이는 것은 정말 중요해요."

10 Garcia-Fuller의 학생들처럼, 많은 미국의 10대들은 뉴스 속 그리고 인터넷상에서 보고 있는 정보에 관해 비판적으로

생각하는 것을 배워 나가고 있다.

11 이 기능은 최근 더 중요해지고 있는데, 이야기들은 아주 빠른 속도로 퍼져 나갈 수 있고 누구나 허위 정보로 가득 찬 웹사이트를 만들어 낼 수 있기 때문이다.

12 Garcia-Fuller는 그녀가 자신의 학생들에게 가짜 뉴스를 진짜 뉴스로부터 구분하는 방법을 가르치고 있다고 말했다.

13 "첫 단계 중 하나는 속도를 늦추는 것(천천히 생각하는 것) 입니다.

14 만약 어떤 이야기나 어떤 사진이 진짜라고 하기엔 너무 좋아 보인다면, 멈춰서 생각해 보세요.

15 글쓴이가 말하고 있는 것을 뒷받침하는 어떠한 증거라도 있나요?

16 그리고 이 정보가 어디서 온 것인가요?"

17 Garcia-Fuller의 학생들은 또한 뉴스에서 사실을 의견과 구분하는 방법에 대해서도 배운다.

18 "의견들은 읽을 만한 가치가 있습니다."라고 15살인 McKenzie Campbell이 말했다. "하지만 여러분은 그것들이 사실에 기반을 둔 것인지를 확인해 보아야 합니다."

19 Garcia-Fuller는 또한 때때로 현명한 뉴스 독자가 되는 것이 아주 어려울 수도 있다고 말했다.

20 그녀는 자신의 학생들을 '나무 문어'라는 이름의 동물에 대한 정보를 제공하는 것처럼 보이는 웹사이트로 시험한다.

21 그 사이트는 나무 위에 있는 문어들의 몇몇 불확실한 사진과 함께, 이 동물에 대한 정보로 가득 차 있다.

22 하지만 무서운 광대들의 이야기와 마찬가지로, 그것은 완전히 꾸며진 것이다.

23 Garcia-Fuller가 그녀의 학생들에게 말하는 교훈은 '당신이 보고 있는 정보를 한 번만 더 신중하게 확인해 보라'는 것과 '모든 것, 심지어 내가 말하는 것에도 의문을 가져 보라'는 것이다.

1 How to Be a Smart News Reader

2 In October 2016, stories about scary clowns shook schools across the Washington area, but Danina Garcia-Fuller's students didn't believe them a bit.

3 "Some people were getting scared because they saw things on social media," said Patricia Visoso, one of Garcia-Fuller's students.

4 "But they never checked up on who was saying this."

5 The stories were actually made by teenagers, not by major newspapers or TV stations.

6 They offered no hard evidence that clowns really were trying to attack students.

7 The story turned out to be a complete lie.

8 "I think a lot of people just look at one thing and

believe it's true," Patricia's classmate Ivy-Brooks said.

9 "It's really important to look at the right sources and to pay attention to what is real and what is fake."

10 Like Garcia-Fuller's students, many teenagers in America are learning to think critically about information they're seeing in the news and on the Internet.

11 This skill is getting more important these days as stories can spread very fast, and anyone can make a website full of false information.

12 Garcia-Fuller said she was teaching her students how to tell fake news from real news.

13 "One of the first steps is to slow down.

14 If a story or a photo seems too good to be true, stop and think.

15 Is there any evidence that supports what the writer says?

16 And where is this coming from?"

17 Garcia-Fuller's students also learn how to tell fact from opinion in the news.

18 "Opinions are good to read," said 15-year-old McKenzie Campbell, "but you also have to check if they are based on facts."

19 Garcia-Fuller also said sometimes it can be very hard to be a smart news reader.

20 She tests her students with a website that appears to provide information on an animal called a tree octopus.

21 The site is full of information on this animal, along with a few unclear photos of octopuses in trees.

22 But like the story of scary clowns, it's totally made up.

23 The lesson, Garcia-Fuller tells her students, is to "check the information you're seeing once more carefully" and to "question everything, even things that I say."

구석구석지문 TEST Step 1   p.62

After You Read A

1. shook, across the Washington area
2. how to tell fact from opinion
3. is full of, along with, unclear photos of octopuses

Do It Yourself

1. danced on the stage during

2. wondered if, would like their dancing
3. much better than any other
4. stood up, cheered loudly
5. the performance of the year

Link to the World

1. one of Picasso's works
2. drew, with, against a white background
3. if, brave, looks very tired, hungry
4. needs some food, water
5. artwork shows the most interesting part

구석구석지문 TEST Step 2   p.63

After You Read A

1. In October 2016, stories about scary clowns shook schools across the Washington area.
2. Garcia-Fuller's students also learn how to tell fact from opinion in the news.
3. The site is full of information on this animal, along with a few unclear photos of octopuses in trees.

Do It Yourself

1. Team NW danced on the stage during the school festival.
2. They wondered if the students and teachers would like their dancing.
3. But they performed much better than any other team.
4. A lot of students stood up and cheered loudly when the team danced.
5. Ms. Yu, the P.E. teacher, said it was the performance of the year.

Link to the World

1. This drawing, *Don Quixote*, is one of Picasso's works.
2. Picasso drew it in 1955 with black lines against a white background.
3. I don't know if the man on the horse is brave, but he looks very tired and hungry.
4. I think he needs some food and water.
5. I think this artwork shows the most interesting part of Cervantes' novel *Don Quixote*.

MEMO

MEMO

MEMO

적중100

영어 기출 문제집

정답 및 해설

천재 | 정사열